About Pearson

Pearson is the world's learning company, with presence across 70 countries worldwide. Our unique insights and world-class expertise come from a long history of working closely with renowned teachers, authors and thought leaders, as a result of which, we have emerged as the preferred choice for millions of teachers and learners across the world.

We believe learning opens up opportunities, creates fulfilling careers and hence better lives. We hence collaborate with the best of minds to deliver you class-leading products, spread across the Higher Education and Test Preparation spectrum.

Superior learning experience and improved outcomes are at the heart of everything we do. This product is the result of one such effort.

Your feedback plays a critical role in the evolution of our products and you can contact us at reachus@pearson.com. We look forward to it.

NVision

FOUNDATION BIOLOGY

CLASS 9

Second Edition

Pearson

Photo Credit

Chapter Opener Image: Leonid Zarubin / 123RF

ISBN 978-93-671-3422-1

First Impression

Published by Pearson India Education Services Pvt. Ltd, CIN: U72200TN2005PTC057128.

Head Office: 1st Floor, Berger Tower, Plot No. C-001A/2, Sector 16B, Noida - 201 301, Uttar Pradesh, India.
Registered Office: Featherlite, 'The Address' 5th Floor, Survey No 203/10B, 200 Ft MMRD Road, Zamin Pallavaram, Chennai – 600 044.
Website: in.pearson.com, Email: companysecretary.india@pearson.com

Compositor: Satish Kumar Shrivastava
Printed in India by: Rahul Print O Pack

Contents

Preface

When you envision something, you are looking ahead. With this series, you are looking ahead anew; with a whole 'N'ew perspective backed by immense knowledge. This book is designed to help the students perform well in the class, as well as prepare for various competitive examinations like JEE, NEET, and Olympiads like NSO, IOM, IMO, NSTSE, IOS, etc. Let's see how to use the different components of the book.

- **Theory:** The theoretical portion of the book has been written to perfectly integrate text and important notes with solved examples. Theory-based exercises have been inserted at relevant checkpoints to enhance the reading experience of the students. Use of testing room, tables, and figures highly enrich the overall learning experience.
- **Assessment Level 1:** This exercise is a **Concept-Building Exercise (CBE)**. The questions in this exercise are clear and simple, and include match the following, true and false, fill in the blanks, assertion-reason based, comprehension-type, case-based, very short answer, short answer, and long answer questions. They focus on the application of freshly learnt theory discussed in the chapter. This aids the students assimilate the concepts included in the chapter (which justifies the name). The question patterns covered are in accordance with the patterns followed in school examinations. This gives the students an edge while preparing for school examinations. Case-based problems and comprehension-type problems follow the current structure of CBSE examinations. The important point to remember is that the homework for this exercise needs to be neatly maintained in a separate exercise book.
- **Assessment Level 2:** This exercise is a **Competitive Level Exercise (CLE)**. After completing the Concept-Building Exercise and absorbing the important concepts, students are prepared to apply their learning at a slightly higher level. These questions include MCQs and ones that focus on improving higher order thinking skills (HOTS) and are in line with the level being asked in the National Level Competitive Examinations as mentioned in the opening paragraph. These questions are imperative for all students looking to strengthen their concepts.
- **Archive Corner:** This exercise comprises questions from previous year papers of competitive examinations like NSO, IOM, IOS, NTSE, IMO, etc. It has been added for students to assess their current level of chapter proficiency in relation to the competitive examinations.

After reading the theory and completing the exercises, a student should have a solid conceptual understanding and problem-solving aptitude of that particular chapter. For best results, **all exercises should be solved in a fair notebook and all the solutions should be kept so that this notebook proves handy while revising.**

Parents are requested to regularly check their children's homework. It is not necessary to check everything, just make sure that the answers to all the questions are being meticulously maintained. This simple observation serves a dual purpose. First, the child believes that his or her education is important to the parent. Second, he or she regularly completes the assigned homework. I am hoping that by combining the efforts of the student, the parents, and the teacher, we can get the most and the best out of this book.

Prashant Jain
B. Tech (CSE), IIT Bombay
Lead Author, NVision Series

About the Authors

Prashant Jain (*Series Lead Author*)

Popularly known as PJ Sir, Mr. Jain is the team lead and main author of the NVision book series. He is an IIT-Bombay graduate (AIR 42-2008), an Indian National Chemistry Olympiad (INChO) Gold Medalist, has qualified Indian National Physics Olympiad (INPhO), and ranked #1 in Rajasthan PTET (2019). He has authored various books like *IOQM Mathematics and CUET* with Pearson. In addition to being a top educator, he is the National Outcomes Head and National Foundation Head in Unacademy, with a strong social media (YouTube, etc.) presence with more than 10+ million views on most of his videos and is behind the success of *1000 + learners* in IOQM in last 2 years.

Nisha Gautam (*Lead Author – Biology*)

Director and Head of Department, Biology, at Proton Tutorials since 2012, Mrs. Gautam has been previously associated with institutes like Allen Career Institute and Unacademy. She has published research paper in Indian Journal of Food Science and Technology and have taught and mentored 10000+ students till date.

Harshita Sharma *(Co-Author – Biology)*

Mrs. Sharma has a rich teaching experience in the Test Preparation section at Resonance, Kota and Surat and has also been associated with Resonance as Head of Department, Biology.

Chapter Insights

Learning Outcomes
These outline the targets the chapter aims to achieve. It gives the learner a to-do list to adhere to while going through the chapter.

Learning Outcomes

After reading this chapter, you would be able to:

- discuss the discovery of cell, cell types, shape, number of cells in different organisms.
- explain cell structure and organelles-cell wall, plasma membranes, cytoplasm, mitochondria, and golgi apparatus.
- describe endoplasmic reticulum, nucleus, lysosomes, ribosomes, plastids, vacuoles, ribosomes.
- explain osmosis, active and passive transport, endocytosis and

Geekspeak

- Cell
- Nucleus
- ER
- Plastids
- Chloroplast
- Cell wall
- Plasmalemma
- Lysosome
- Golgi apparatus
- Mitosis
- Bacteria
- Osmosis

Geekspeak
This introduces the learner to the keywords they shall learn from the chapter.

Introduction
This provides the learner with a basic summary of what to expect from the chapter.

i

Introduction

We know that everything starts with cells. Also, in some species, it ends in a cell. For others, however, cells come together to form tissues, tissues form organs, organs form organ systems, and organ systems combine to form organisms.

Prokaryotes are unicellular or colonial organisms that do not have a membrane-bound nucleus or organelles. In contrast, eukaryotic cells have membrane-bound organelles and a membrane-bound nucleus. In larger organisms, cells associate to form tissues. Tissues are groups of similar cells that perform similar or related functions. An organ is a collection of tissues that are grouped together and perform a common function. Organs are not only found in animals, but also in plants. An organ system is a higher level organization made up of functionally related organs. Mammals have many organ systems. For example, the circulatory system carries blood throughout the body and to and from the lungs. Includes organs such as the heart and blood vessels.

Organisms are individual living entities. For example, all trees in a forest are living things. Single-celled prokaryotes and single-celled eukaryotes are also considered organisms and are usually referred to as microorganisms.

H1
This outlines the first concept to be taught in the chapter.

Plant Tissue

On the basis of dividing capacity of the tissue, plant tissues are of two types:

1. Meristematic tissue (growing tissue)
2. Permanent tissue

Differences in meristematic and permanent tissue are discussed in Table 2.2.

Structure of Compound/Light Microscope

The microscope used in schools is called a compound microscope (Fig 1.3). A compound microscope ha

- **Base:** It is the basal, metallic, horseshoe-shaped structure. It bears the whole weight of the r
- **Handle:** It is the curved part to hold the microscope. It is also known as arm.
- **Stage:** A sturdy metal rectangular horizontal plate attached to a handle.
- **Stage Clamps:** Two clamps are attached to the stage to hold the slide in place.

H2
This builds on the first concept and outlines the second concept to be taught in the chapter.

H3
This builds on the first and second topics and outlines the third concept to be taught in the chapter.

Cuboidal Epithelium

They are cube like cells that fit closely, cells look like squares in section (as shown in Fig 2.13), but free surface appears hexagonal. It is found in kidney tubules, thyroid vesicles and in glands (salivary glands, sweat glands). It forms germinal epithelium of gonads (testes and ovaries). It is involved in absorption, excretion, and secretion. It also provides mechanical support.

Columnar Epithelium

Columnar means 'pillar-like' epithelium. It forms lining of stomach, small intestine and colon, forming mucous membranes. Border of microvilli is present at the free surface end of each cell which increases absorption efficiency in small intestine.

Ciliated Epithelium

In this type of epithelium, the cells may be cuboidal or columnar. On its free surface are present very fine hair-like protoplasmic outgrowths. It is found lining the body of nephrons, trachea, and fallopian tube.

Competition Corner

The functions of cilia and microvilli present on surface of epithelial tissue are:

Cilia show rhythmic beating movements in the respiratory tract. Thus, this beating of cilia helps particle from entering the lungs.

The microvilli are finger-like projections on the epithelial cells of intestine where they help in inc area for absorption.

Competition Corner
Attain competitive edge by learning some additional definitions to help with basic concept-learning.

Intext Questions
Learn while applying your concepts with these questions provided alongside concepts to enhance assimilation.

❖ INTEXT QUESTIONS

6. What are cisterns?

   Ans: Cisterns are flattened membrane-bound vesicles placed parallel to each otherin stacks that ar

7. Describe the structure and function of vacuoles?

   Ans:

   - Vacuoles are present in both animals and plants.
   - The plant vacuole contains cell sap and provides the cell with rigidity and turgidity.

Check Point 3

7. Write the types of lysosomes.
8. Differentiate between rough and smooth endoplasmic reticulum
9. Why mitochondria is called power house of cell.
10. Describe cell division.

Check Points
Self-analyse your learning by answering some questions based on recently learnt concepts.

Testing Room
Satisfy your scientific curiosity by performing fun little experiments and observing the results.

Testing Room 4

Rhoeo leaf under the microscope; compare the osmosis with its leaf boiled in water.

Observation and explanation:

Rhoeo is a common decorative plant found in our home and gardens. Its slides are easy to prepare, so we use them to study cell components and functions. Under the microscope, we see changes similar to eggs, raisins and dried apricots, i.e., swelling in water and shrinkage with saline or sugar solution. Boiling of leaf breaks the cell wall and other cellular components like cytoplasm. Osmosis in a leaf is a function of protoplasm. As a result, we do not see any change in shape or size in leaf cells whether in water or solution.

Conclusion: A cell is alive until its protoplasm is functioning. A living cell responds to changes in external osmotic pressure while a dead cell ceases to show response to osmotic pressure.

Keystone

The term tissue was coined by Nehemiah Grew. The study of tissues is known as histology.

Keystone
Enhance the knowledge of trivia with fun little tidbits about surrounding things.

Structural Outline
Quickly revise the concepts learnt by going through this simple flowchart that summarises the key ideas.

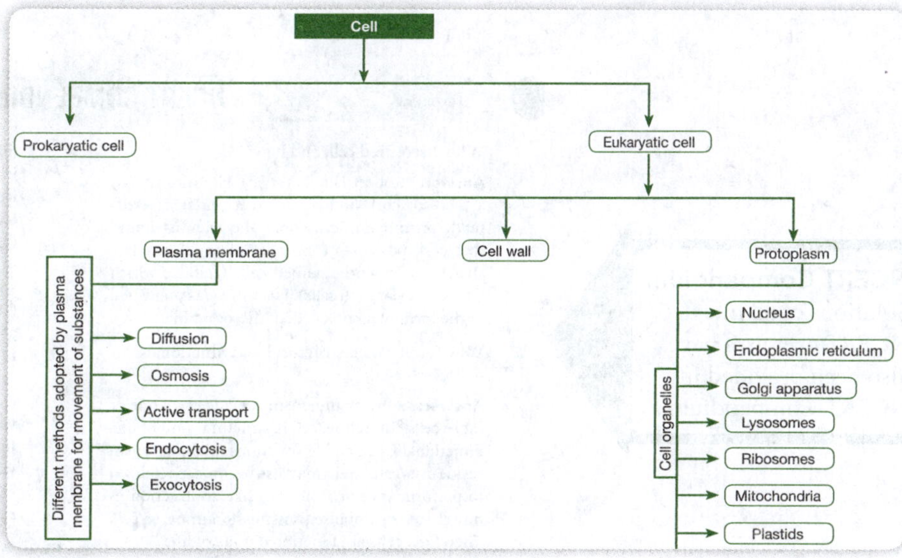

Abridgement
Make learning a smooth journey by availing these bridges that connect the learning between classes.

Abridgement

Class 11th

Anatomy of flowering plants

- Simple and permanent plant tissues
- Anatomy of dicot, monocot stem and root
- Secondary growth
- Vascular and cork cambium
- Annual rings

EXEMPLIFICATION

1. Name the basic packing tissue of plant.

   Ans. Parenchyma.

2. Which body cell provides resistance against infections?

   Ans. White blood cells (WBCs) provide resistance against infections.

3. List any four salient features of meristematic tissue.

   Ans. The salient features of meristematic tissue are:
   - This tissue consists of cells which continuously divide to produce new cells.
   - The cells of this tissue lack vacuoles.
   - The cells of this tissue have dense cytoplasm.
   - The cells of this tissue have thin cellulosic cell walls and prominent nuclei.

4. Write the functions of collenchyma in plants.

   Ans. Collenchyma allows easy bending in various parts of a plant (leaf, stem) without l mechanical support to plants like in the leaf stalks below the epidermis.

5. What are the two main components of blood? Why is blood considered a type of connect

   Ans. Blood is a special connective tissue consisting of a fluid matrix, plasma, and form

Exemplification
Enhance concept learning with examples that have been solved for your benefit.

NCERT Compendium
Solutions of all intext NCERT exercises have also been provided in NCERT Compendium.

NCERT COMPENDIUM

1. Who discovered cell, and how?

   Answer: Robert Hooke (1665). He thinly pared a piece of cork and observed it under his self-made primitive microscope. The scientist found that cork possesses a number of small box-like structures which he named cells (cellulae which later abbreviated to cells). His work was published in the form of a book called Micrographia.

2. Why is cell called structural and functional unit of life?

   Answer: A living organism is made up of one or more cells. Therefore, cell is structural unit of life. Functional Unit: all life functions of an organism reside in its cells. Cells may also become specialized to perform specific functions like contraction in muscle cell or impulse transmission in nerve cell. Therefore, cells are functional units of life.

(ii) In photosynthetic cell, CO_2 is being consumed in photosynthesis. Its intracellular concentration is lower than outside medium. Therefore, CO_2 diffuses from outside to inside of the cell. Osmosis: it is movement of water from the region of its higher concentration (pure water or dilute solution) to the region of its lower concentration (strong solution) when the two are separated by a semipermeable membrane. Plasma membrane functions as a semipermeable membrane. Cell sap functions as strong solution. Therefore, external water enters the cell (endosmosis) till wall pressure counter-balances this tendency. If the external medium has a very strong solution, water would pass out from the cell into the external medium. The phenomenon is called exosmosis.

4. Why is plasma membrane called selectively

Level 1

Fixed Response Type

Multiple Choice Questions

1. Double membrane is absent in:
   (A) Mitochondrion (B) Chloroplast
   (C) Nucleus (D) Lysosome
2. Animal cell is limited by:
   (A) Plasma membrane
   (B) Shell membrane

Level 1 MCQ
Learn to avoid confusions by confidently answering the questions asked in this exercise.

Fill in the Blanks
Fill in the gaps in your learning by finding answers to the blanks in the sentences.

Fill in the Blanks

1. Matrix of cartilage contains ___________ and of bone ___________ protein.
2. Cartilage cells are called ___________ and bone cells ___________.
3. Anormal human adult has about ___________ extracellular fluid.
4. Formation of RBC in liver, spleen and red bone marrow is called ___________.

True/False

1. Muscle fibres or cells are multinucleated and unbranched.
2. Cork tissue is permeable for water.
3. Meristematic tissues have large central vacuole.
4. Primary meristem usually add the diameter to the plant.
5. Matrix of bone is hard due to calcium phosphate, $CaCO_3$ (60-70%), etc., and a protein ossein.

True/False
Double-check your concepts by fact-checking your answers.

Match Type Questions
This exercise is like solving a puzzle. Find the best match so two halves of a sentence can fit together.

Match Type Questions

1.

Column - I	Column-II
(i) Pith	(a) Secondary meristem
(ii) Cork cambium	(b) Parenchyma
(iii) Cambium	(c) Primary meristem
(iv) Pits	(d) Xylem vessels

Assertion and Reason Type Questions

This exercise enhances learners' analytical skills by providing them with assertions that may or may not be justified by a list of accompanying reasons.

Assertion and Reason Type Questions

Directions: In the following questions, a statement of assertion (A) is followed by statement of reason (R). Mark the correct choice as:

(A) Both Assertion and Reason are correct, and reason is the correct explanation for assertion.
(B) Both Assertion and Reason are correct, and Reason is not the correct explanation for Assertion.
(C) Assertion is true but Reason is false.
(D) Assertion is false but Reason is true.
(E) Both assertion and reason are false

1. **Assertion:** All plants and animals are composed of cells.
   Reason: Plants and animals made up of DNA.
2. **Assertion:** Plasma membrane is also known as selectively permeable membrane.
   Reason: Plasma membrane allows or permits the entry and exit of some materials in and out of the cell.
3. **Assertion:** A cell swells up when present in a hypotonic solution.
   Reason: More water molecules enter the cell than they leave.

Comprehension Type Questions

This exercise tests concept learning by checking for a learner's level of understanding.

Comprehension Based Question

Comprehension-1

If you germinate a kidney bean seed in a Petri dish, then the reserve food material present in plant part undergoes oxidation to release energy. This energy is used in cell division and hence sprouting takes place. The two small plant parts that come out of the seed are plumule and radicle, respectively.

A. Plumule helps in the formation of:
(A) Fruit (B) Seed
(C) Flower (D) None of these

B. Root that helps in anchorage are specialized structures of:
(A) Plumule
(B) Radicle
(C) Embryo
(D) None of these

Very Short Answer Type Questions

Summarise your learning in a few words by answering these questions.

Free Response Type

Very Short Answer Type Questions

1. Name the plant tissue having dead cells.
2. Write any 2 functions of adipose tissues.
3. Which plant tissue remains in active metabolic state always?
4. Which meristematic tissue causes elongation of stem and root in primary growth of a plant?
5. What is the role of lateral meristem in plant?
6. Which type of tissue contains sieve tubes and companion cell?
7. Name the different elements of xylem and phloem.

Short Answer Type Questions

1. What are different of plastids? What are their functions?
2. Differentiate between rough and smooth endoplasmic reticulum. How is endoplasmic reticulum important for membrane biogenesis?
3. Draw a neat and labelled diagram of nucleus. State its main functions.
4. Draw a neat and well labelled diagram of a typical prokaryotic cell.
5. Differentiate between prokaryotic and eukaryotic cell.
6. Write comparison between plant and animal cell.

Short Answer Type Questions
Summarise your learning in a short sentence by answering these questions.

Long Answer Type Questions
Elaborate on concepts learnt by knowing exactly what to include in these long-answer type questions.

Long Answer Type Questions

1. Describe the structure and function of mitochondria with a labeled diagram.
2. Draw a well-labelled diagram of a eukaryotic nucleus. How is it different from nucleoid?
3. Write in detail the structure and function of endoplasmic reticulum.
4. Write the detail description on different kind of plastids.

Numerical Based Questions

1. Count natural fibre out of following option:
   Nylon, Rayon, Silk, Dacron, Cotton, PVC, Acrylic
2. Differentiate thermoplastics from following:
   PVC, Rayon, Dacron, Polystyrene, Polythene, Melamine
3. Select thermosetting plastics and polyesters from following:
   Bakelite, Dacron, Melamine, Nylon, Rayon, PVC, Teflon

Numerical Based Question
Play with numbers in this fun activity that checks for your understanding of mathematical concepts.

Case Based Questions
This exercise enhances learners' analytical skills by providing them with practical situations where they can apply the theories learnt.

Case Based Questions

Case-1: Identify the given two slides A and B as a parenchyma or sclerenchyma. Sclerenchyma can be identified by which characteristic?

Slide A

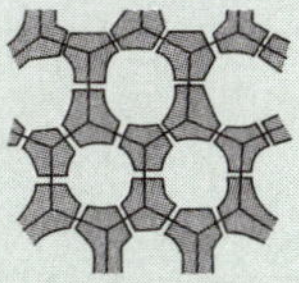
Slide B

Level 2

Multiple Choice Questions

1. Fluid part of blood after removal of corpuscles is:
   (A) plasma (B) lymph
   (C) serum (D) vaccine
2. Yellow muscle fibers are also known as:
   (A) bone (B) muscle
   (C) ligament (D) none of these

Level 2 MCQ
Learn to avoid confusions by confidently answering the questions asked in this exercise.

Higher Order Thinking Skills (HOTS)
Apply theories at a higher level by applying your learning and analysing these higher order thinking questions.

High Order Thinking Skills (HOTS)

1. What will happen if:
   (i) Apical meristem is damaged or cut?
   (ii) Cork is not formed in older stems and roots?
   (iii) Cells of epithelial tissue are not compactly packed?
   (iv) Lymph is not returned to blood?
2.
   (i) Identify figures: A, B, and C.
   (ii) Which one of them provides both mechanical strength as well as flexibility?
   (iii) Which one of them is commercially exploited to obtain hemp and jute?

ARCHIVE CORNER

1. Read the given paragraph and select the option that correctly fills the blanks.

   Vacuole is a space in the (i) of a cell which his enclosed by a (ii) membrane. Vacuole is filled with a liquid called (iii) which contains dissolved (iv) and (v).

	(i)	(ii)	(iii)	(iv)	(v)
(A)	Cytoplasm	Single	Cell sap	Sugars	Salts
(B)	Cytoplasm	Double	Leucoplast	Sugars	Salts
(C)	Nucleus	Single	Grana	Lipids	Sugars
(D)	Protoplasm	Double	Matrix	Lipids	Salts

2. Aradhya was asked b basic features that are and eukaryotic cells of the following opti Aradhya's correct ans
   (A) Endoplasmic retic
   (B) Cytoplasm, Plasm
   (C) Cell wall, Mitoch
   (D) Plasma membrane

Archive Corner
Reassess your learning by understanding and remembering questions you have already answered and concepts you have already learnt.

Answer Keys
Cross-check your answers by referring to this comprehensive list provided.

ANSWER KEY

Level 1

Fixed Response Type

Multiple Choice Questions

1. A	2. A	3. A	4. B	5. A	6. A	7. B	8. C
11. B	12. C	13. C	14. A	15. B	16. D	17. B	18. B
21. C	22. A	23. B	24. B	25. B	26. C	27. B	28. A

CHAPTER 2: TISSUES

Check Point 1

1. Tips of shoots and roots in all vascular plants.
2. Intercalary meristem.
3. Apical meristem is responsible for increase in length of the plant.
4. Lateral meristems.

Check Point 2

5. Sclerenchyma.
6. Sclerenchyma tissue.
7. Lignin
8. Sclerenchyma and Collenchyma.

Check Point 3

9. The nervous tissue, contains densely packed cells called nerve cells or neurons, is present in the
10. Well labelled diagram of cardiac muscles:

Hints and Explanations
Address any and all gaps in learning by referring to hints and explanations provided for better understanding of concepts and questions.

CHAPTER 1

The Fundamental Unit of Life

Learning Outcomes

After reading this chapter, you would be able to:

- discuss the discovery of cell, cell types, shape, number of cells in different organisms.
- explain cell structure and organelles-cell wall, plasma membranes, cytoplasm, mitochondria, and golgi apparatus.
- describe endoplasmic reticulum, nucleus, lysosomes, ribosomes, plastids, vacuoles, ribosomes.
- explain osmosis, active and passive transport, endocytosis and exocytosis.
- discuss cell division.

Geekspeak

- Cell
- Nucleus
- ER
- Plastids
- Chloroplast
- Cell wall
- Plasmalemma
- Lysosome
- Golgi apparatus
- Mitosis
- Bacteria
- Osmosis
- Diffusion

Introduction

All organisms are made up of one or more cells. Cells are the simplest units of life and are responsible for maintaining the life and functions of organisms. All living organisms are made up of structural and functional units of life called "cells".

The body of some organisms like bacteria, protozoans and some algae are made up of a single cell whereas the body of higher fungi, plants and animals are composed of many cells. The human body is made up of about 1 trillion cells. Cells differ in size and structure as they are specialized to perform different functions. However, the basic building blocks of cells are common to all living cells.

Many different organisms contain only one cell and are called unicellular or unicellular organisms.

Your single cell performs all the functions necessary to keep an organism alive. All types of bacteria and archaea are unicellular organisms. Large organisms like humans, on the other hand, are made up of trillions of cells that work together to keep the organism alive.

The most basic classification of organisms on Earth is determined by different types of cells. All cells can be divided into one of her two classifications: prokaryotic and eukaryotic. Prokaryotic cells are found in bacteria and archaea.

Eukaryotic cells are found in organisms from the domain Eukaryote which includes animals, plants, fungi and protists.

This introduction to cells describes the basic structure of cells, the differences between prokaryotic and eukaryotic cells, and introduces organelles.

A cell may be defined as the smallest unit of structure and functions of living organisms. The word cell is derived from latin word "cellula" meaning small room. Smallest "unit of structure" means the smallest structures by the union of which the body of an organism is constructed

Cytology: Cells and their structures are studied in the branch of biology called cytology.

Definition of cell- The structural and functional unit of living beings is called cell.

OR

A unit of biological activity surrounded by membranes of different permeability and capable of self-renewal.

History of Cell

Following are the important discoveries:

- Dutch spectacle maker **Zacharias Janssen** (born 1585) is credited with building one of the earliest compound microscopes (with two lenses) around 1600. Early microscopes could magnify objects to 20 or 30 times their normal size. (as shown in Fig 1.1).

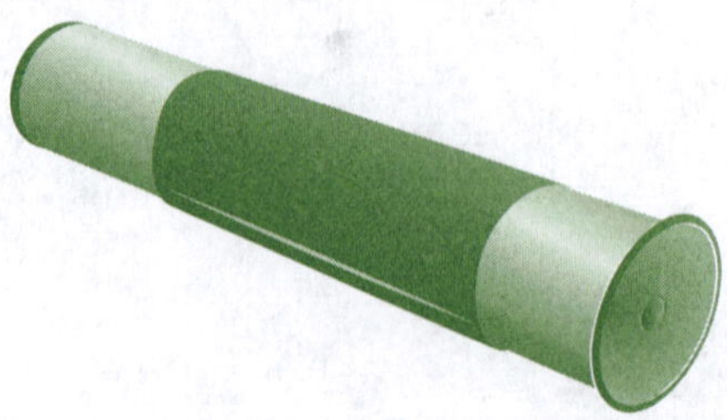

Figure 1.1 The first microscope

- **Robert Hooke** (1665), an English and first curator of the Royal Society of London, observed a thin section of tree bark under a self-designed microscope (as shown in Fig. 1.2). He noticed honeycomb-like compartments. He coined the term cell. He also wrote a book titled "Micrographia".

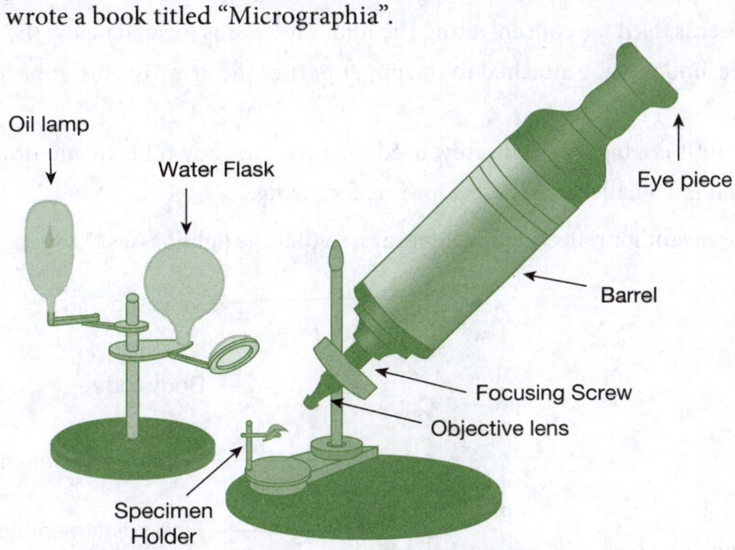

Figure 1.2 Robert Hooke's self-designed Microscope

- **Anton Van Leeuwenhoek** (1674): was the first to observe living cells like bacteria, algae (spirogyra cells) in pond water human RBC sperm cells, muscle cells. The called living cells "animalcules".
- **N. Grew** (1682): Proposed cell concept stating that the cell is the structural unit of living organisms.
- **Rudolf Virchow** (1858) proposed that new cells formed from the pre-existing cells.
- **Robert Brown** (1831): discovered the nucleus in the cell.
- **Purkinje** (1839)-coined the term 'protoplasm' for the fluid substance of the cell.
- **Schleiden** (1838) and **Schwann** (1839)-proposed cell theory, that all plants and animals are composed of cells and that the cell is the basic unit of life.
- **Knoll & Ruska** (1932) designed the electron microscope that was employed to study the ultra-structure of cell and various cell organelles. Protoplasm was discovered by "Felix Dujardin" and named as sarcode. The term cyto-plasm was coined by **Purkinje** in 1839 and in the 1940s by the cellular ultrastructure (microstructure) and various organelles.
- Cell Theory was proposed by **M.J. Schleiden** and **Theodore Schwann** (two German biologists). It was later modified by **Rudolf Virchow**.
  - According to it
    - All plants and animals are made up of cells.
    - Cells are the functional units of life.
    - All cells arise from pre—existing cell. [Rudolf Virchow Omnis cellula e cellula]

Keystone

Viruses are the exceptions of cell theory.

Microscope

An instrument used to inspect objects that cannot be seen with the naked eye or with the aid of handheld lenses. A microscope has more than one lens. The first compound microscope was the **F. Janssen and Zacharias Janssen** (1590).

Structure of Compound/Light Microscope

The microscope used in schools is called a compound microscope (Fig 1.3). A compound microscope has following parts :

- **Base:** It is the basal, metallic, horseshoe-shaped structure. It bears the whole weight of the microscope.
- **Handle:** It is the curved part to hold the microscope. It is also known as arm.

- **Stage:** A sturdy metal rectangular horizontal plate attached to a handle.
- **Stage Clamps:** Two clamps are attached to the stage to hold the slide in place.
- **Condenser:** A condenser is used for concentrating the light rays and is located below the stage.
- **Body Tube:** It is a wide, hollow tube attached to the upper part of the arm. To this, tube lenses are attached.
- **Adjustment Screw:**
  - **Coarse adjustment:** It is a bigger sized screw used to move the body tube up and down.
  - **Fine adjustment:** It is a smaller sized screw for fine focussing.
- **Reflecting Mirror:** It is meant for reflecting the light rays, so that the light passes through the object that is to be seen.

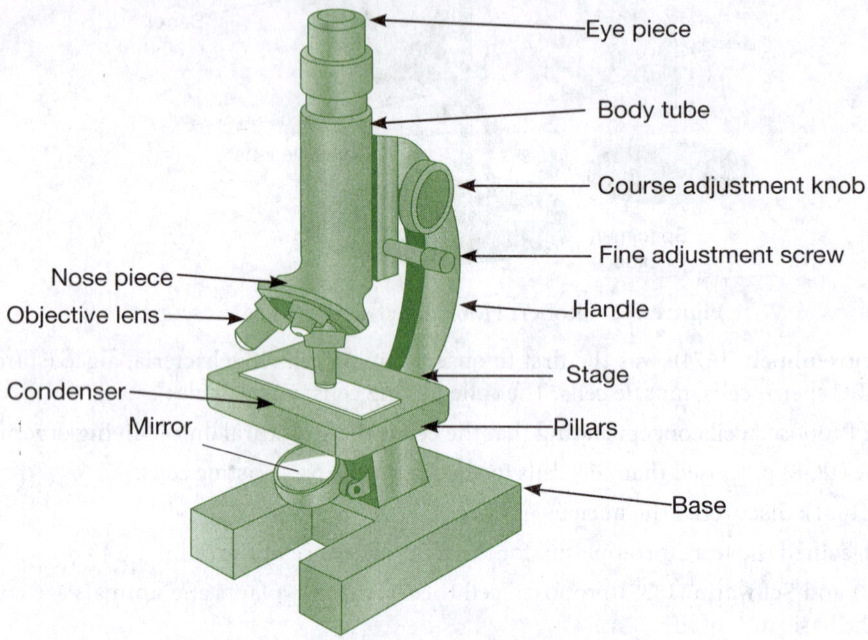

Figure 1.3. Compound Microscope

Preparation of Microscopic Slide

The object to be viewed under a microscope is called the specimen. A thin sheet of glass called a microscopic slide is used to hold a small sample of the specimen (Fig 1.4). A second, much thinner sheet of glass is placed over the sample, called a coverslip.

- Take a clean glass slide.
- With a dropper, put a drop of water in the middle of the slide.

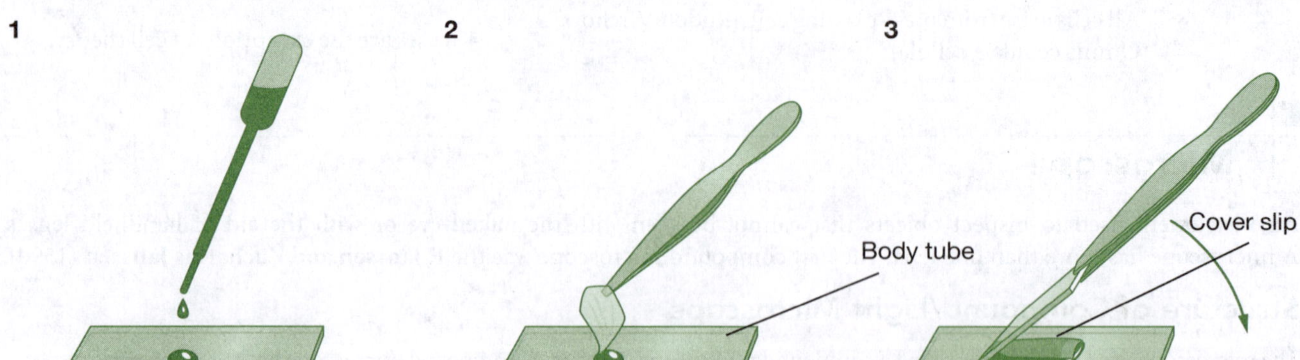

Figure 1.4. Slide Preparation

- Gently put the object to be observed in the drop of water on the slide with the help of a brush.
- Objects, if transparent, are first stained with a proper chemical.
- Hold the coverslip over the object in such a manner that it touches the edge of the drop of water. Gently lower the coverslip onto the water.
- Dry the extra water that may come out from under the coverslip with the help of a blotting paper. Take care that the slide thus prepared is clean and dry.

Testing Room 1

Aim: Prepare a Microscopic Slide from Cheek Cells.

Observation and Explanation: A thin layer of mucosal cells lines the inside of the cheek cells. These are easy to scrape off and observe under the microscope. Under high power microscope, we can see the cell membranes, outlines of various organelles like Golgi bodies, endoplasmic reticulum, nucleus, etc. Nucleus is the most important part of the cell. It coordinates functions of the cells by protein synthesis. In normal condition, it appears as a double-membraned structure with thick dense material inside, known as chromatin. When the cell is under the division process, the nucleus appears bigger with different chromosome visible.

Anatomy of an Animal Cell

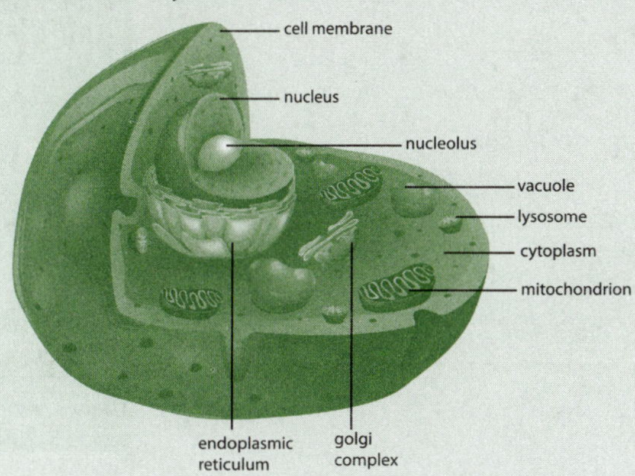

Working of Compound Microscope

The specimen or item to be examined is commonly mounted on a clear glass slide and placed between the condenser and objective lenses on the specimen stage. A condenser lens concentrates a beam of visible light from the base on the specimen.The objective lens collects the light emitted by the specimen and magnifies it inside the body tube to form a primary image. The ocular lens or eyepiece enlarges this image once more. When a higher magnification is necessary, the nose piece of the compound microscope is turned after low power focusing to align the higher magnification objective (usually 45X) with the lit section of the slide. It was sometimes necessary to use extremely high magnification (e.g., for observing bacterial cells). An oil immersion objective lens (often 100X) is used in this situation.

Competition Corner

Electron Microscope

It is a type of microscope in which instead of light beam, a beam of electrons is used to form a large image of very small object. These microscopes are widely used in the field of engineering and medicine.

Principle: A stream of electrons is passed through the object and the electron that carries the information about the object is focused by electric and magnetic fields.

Parts of Electron Microscope: Electron microscope is in the form of a tall vacuum column that is vertically mounted. It has the following components:

- Electron gun: The electron gun is a heated tungsten filament, which generates electrons.
- Electromagnetic lenses: The condenser lens focuses the electron beam on the specimen. A second condenser lens aligns the electrons into a thin tight beam. The electron beam coming out of the specimen passes down to the objective lens, which has high power and forms the intermediate magnified image. The third set of magnetic lenses called projector (ocular) lenses produce the final further magnified image. Each of these lenses acts as an image magnifier all the while maintaining an incredible level of detail and resolution.
- Specimen holder: The specimen holder is an extremely thin film of carbon or collodion held by a metal grid.
- Image viewing and recording system: The final image is projected on a fluorescent screen. A camera present below the fluorescent screen records the image.

The whole arrangement is kept inside a vacuum chamber to allow the passage of electron beam.

- Electron microscopes giving magnification more than 2,00,000 times are common in research laboratories.

There are two types of electron microscopes, with different operating styles:

1. **Transmission Electron Microscope (TEM)**
2. **Scanning Electron Microscope (SEM)**

Types of Cells

Cells are fundamental unit of life, cells can be of many type based on different factors, such as the organization, differentiation size of the cell, shape number etc.

On the Basis of Organization

Cells are of two types based on the organization, like prokaryotic cell and eukaryotic cell.

Prokaryotic Cells:

These are primitive and incomplete cells. They have less developed nucleus without nuclear membrane and nucleolus. Example, bacteria (as shown in Fig 1.5).

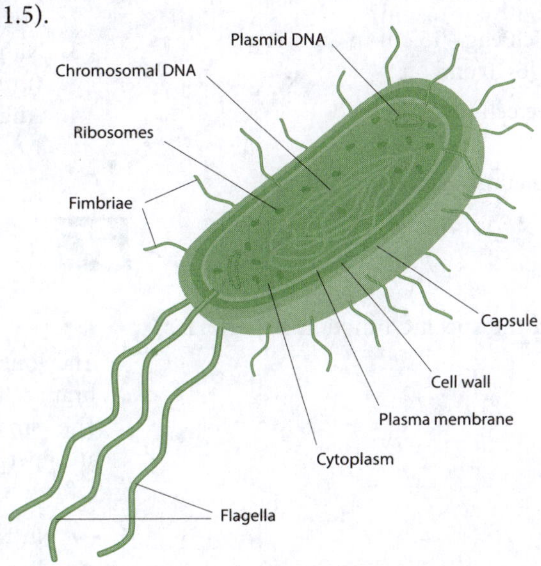

Figure 1.5 A typical prokaryotic cell–Bacteria

Eukaryotic Cells:

These are well developed cells. They have advanced nucleus with nuclear membrane (as shown in Fig 1.6).

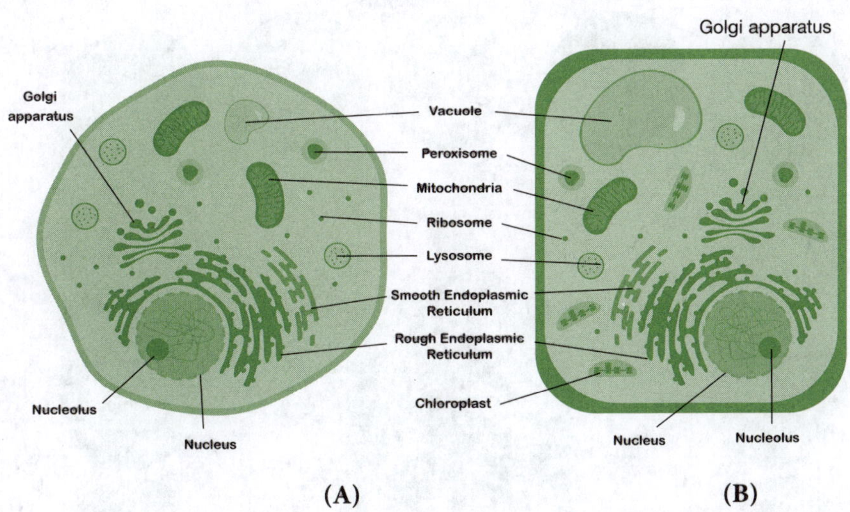

Figure 1.6. A typical structure of (A) animal cell (B) plant cell

On the Basis of Differentiation

- **Undifferentiated:** These are unspecialized cells which by mitotic divisions give rise to new cells for the formation and maintenance of tissues.

- **Differentiated:** These are specialized cells formed from the unspecialized cells by change in structure and function during development and growth of an organism.
- **Dedifferentiated:** De differentiated cells can regain its capacity for cell division under certain conditions. Example- formation of interfascicular cambium and cork cambium from fully differentiated parenchyma cells.

On the Basis of Cell Size

Size of cell is variable depending upon the type of organism. Some are microscopic while some are visible with naked eyes. Their size may vary from 0.2 μm to 18 cm. Size of a typical cell in a multicellular organism range from 20 to 30 μm.

Normal size in human: 20 μm to 30 μm in diameter.

- **Largest cell:** In animals – Ostrich egg [15 cm in diameter]
  In plants – Acetabularia [6-10 cm]
- **Longest cell:** In animals – Nerve cell [up to 1 mt]
  In plants – Hemp fibre.
- **Smallest cell:** PPLO – Pleuro pneumonia like organism (Mycoplasma – 0.1 to 0.5 μm.)

On the Basis of Cell Shape

Shape of cell mainly depends upon the specific function it performs (as shown in Fig 1.7).

- Elongated – Nerve cell
- Discoidal/saucer – RBC
- Spindal – Muscle cell
- Spherical – Eggs
- Branched – Pigment of the skin
- Sipper shaped – Paramecium
- Cuboidal – Germ cells of gonads
- Polygonal – Liver cells

Keystone

Measurement of cells

1. Millimetre (mm) 1 mm = 1000 μ
2. Micrometre (μm) or micron (μ)
3. Nanometer (nm) or millimicron (mμ) 1μ = 1000 mμ
4. Angstrom (Å)
   $1 \text{ Å} = 10^{-1} \text{ m}\mu = 10^{-4} \mu = 10^{-7} \text{ mm}$

Keystone

The longest living cell in the body are brain cells that can live an entire lifetime. The smaller cells have more surface area per unit volume. It ensures more diffusion of:

- Nutrients into the cells.
- Respiratory gases, i.e., O_2 into the cells and CO_2 out of the cells.
- Waste products out of the cells.

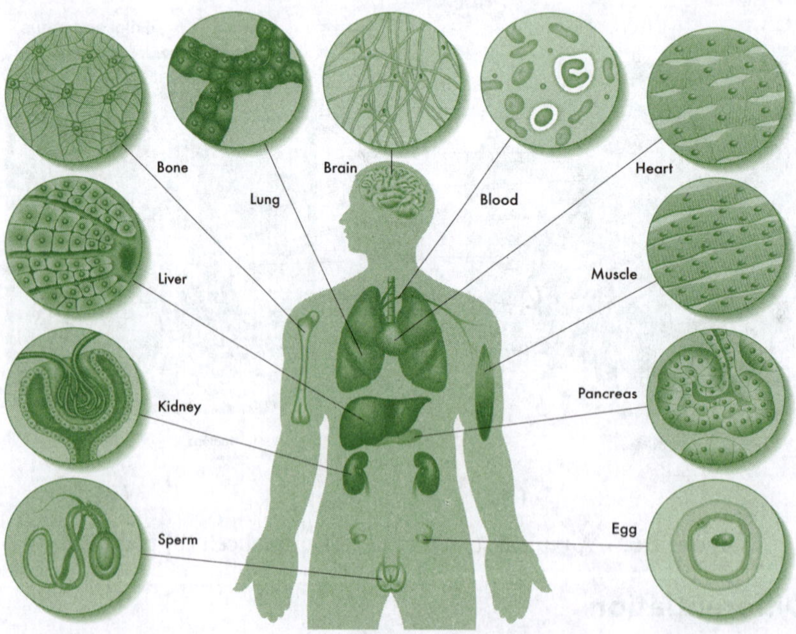

Figure 1.7 Cells of various shapes

Testing Room 2

Aim: Preparing temporary mounts of leaf peels, tip of roots of onion, or even peels of onions of different Sizes

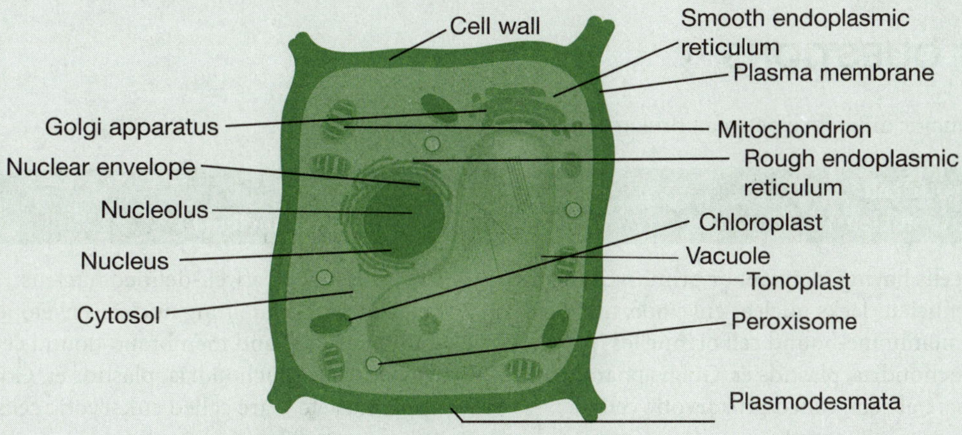

Procedure: Let us take a small piece from an onion bulb. With the help of a pair of forceps, we can peel off the skin (called the epidermis) from the concave side of the onion. This layer can be put immediately in a watch glass containing water. This will prevent the peel from getting folded or getting dry.

Let us take a glass slide, put a drop of water on it, and transfer a small piece of the peel from the watch glass to the slide. Make sure that the peel is perfectly flat on the slide. A thin camel-hair paintbrush might be necessary to help transfer the peel. Now we put a drop of safranin solution on this piece followed by a cover slip. Take care to avoid air bubbles while putting the coverslip with the help of a mounting needle. We have prepared a temporary mount of onion peel. We can observe this slide under low power followed by high powers of a compound microscope.

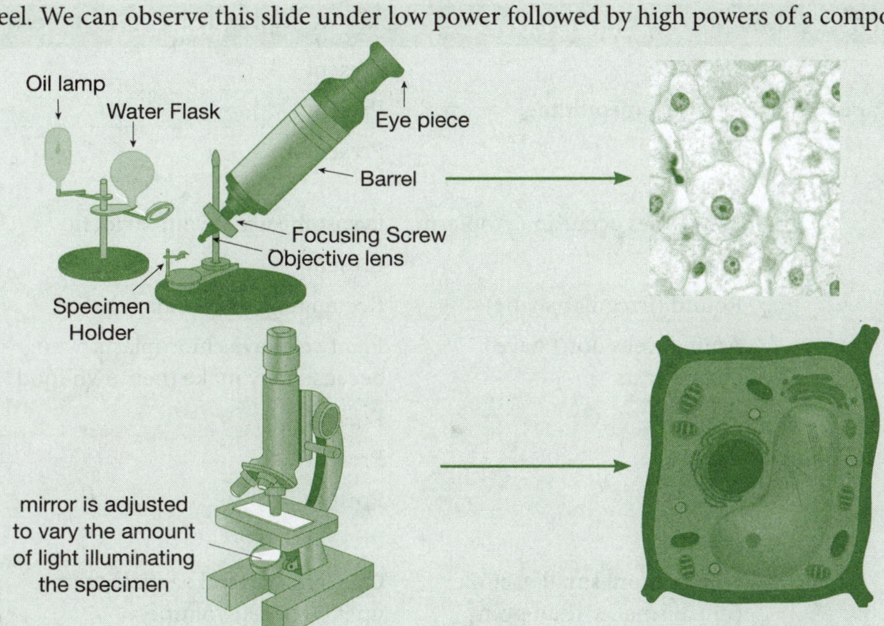

Observation: When we put the prepared slide under a low-power microscope, we can see large numbers of blocks (cells) side by side. We can see these cells are different in shape and size but they look alike in structure. All cells are bound by a thick cell wall and inner plasma membrane, they possess cytoplasm, nucleus, vacuole, and other cell organelles when this slide is seen under a powered microscope.

Conclusion: Cells are fundamental structural units of living beings. They are different in size and shape according to their functions but they have a similar structure.

On the Basis of Number of Cells

On the basis of number of cells, the organisms can be categorized as:

- **Unicellular** – Single celled, e.g., Amoeba, Paramecium, Euglena, Plasmodium – Malarial Parasite, *Ulothrix*, *Chlamydomonas*.
- **Multicellular** – Numerous cells, e.g., higher plants and animals.

❖ INTEXT QUESTIONS

1. Write the major difference between prokaryotic and eukaryotic cells.

Prokaryotic cell (primitive nucleus)	Eukaryotic cell (well-developed nucleus)
1. The cells having incipient or primitive nucleus (i.e., nucleus lacks nuclear envelope, nucleolus) and membrane-bound cell organelles (mitochondria, plastids er. Golgi apparatus, etc.) are absent, called prokaryotic cells.	1. The cells having a well-defined nucleus (i.e., nucleus containing nuclear envelope and nucleolus) and membrane-bound cell organelles (mitochondria, plastids er. Golgi apparatus etc.) are called eukaryotic cells
2. Ribosome – 70s type	2. Ribosome – 80s type
3. Normal size – 1 to 10 μm	3. Normal size – 5 to 100 μm
4. DNA – circular and lack histone protein	4 DNA – linear and having histone protein
5. Respiration by plasma membrane	5. Respiration by mitochondria
E.g., Bacteria, mycoplasma, blue green algae	E.g., - protists, fungi, plantae, and animalia

2. Write the major comparison between plant and animal cell.

Characters	Animals Cell	Plant Cell
Cell wall	Absent	Present
Plasma membrane	Only cell membrane	Present
Microtubules Microfilaments	Present	Present
Lysosomes	Lysosomes occur in cytoplasm	Lysosome usually not evident
Nucleus	Present	Present
Shape	Round (irregular shape)	Rectangular (fixed shape)
Chloroplast	Animal cells don't have chloroplasts	Plant cell have chloroplasts because they make their own food
Cytoplasm	Present	Present
Endoplasmic Reticulum	Present	Present
Ribosomes	Present	Present
Mitochondria	Present	Present
Vacuole	One or more small vacuoles (much smaller than point cells)	One large central vacuole taking up 90% of cell volume.
Centrioles	Present in all animal cell	Only present in lower plant forms
Golgi Apparatus	Present	Present

Check Point 1

1. What is cell?
2. What are three basic criteria (cell theory) for defining a cell?
3. Give any 3-3 examples of unicellular and multicellular organisms.

Component of A Cell

There is an occurrence of division of labour within a cell as they all have certain specific components called "cell organelles". Each cell organelle performs a specific function.

The three basic components of all the cells are:

(a) Cell coat, (b) Nucleus, (c) Cytoplasm

Cell Coat

Cell coat contains cell wall, and cell membrane.

Cell Wall

It is the outermost covering of the plant cells. It is absent in animal cells. Cell wall is a rigid, strong, thick, porous, and dead structure. It is made up of cellulose and hemicellulose. Cell walls of two adjacent cells are joined by a layer called middle lamellae. It is made up of calcium and magnesium pectate.

Composition of Different Kinds of Cell Wall

(i) Cellulose + Hemicellulose – in plants
(ii) Chitin – in fungi
(iii) Peptidoglycan – in bacteria and mycoplasma.
(iv) Plant protistans (diatoms)- Silica
(v) Cork tissues of some plants- Suberin

Keystone

Fibers of cotton, jute and coconut which are of great economic value are the cell walls of dead cell.

Functions of Cell Wall

- It provides and maintains the shape of a cell.
- It provides strength and plant can bear stress and strain because of cell wall.
- It is permeable and allows entry of molecules of different sizes.

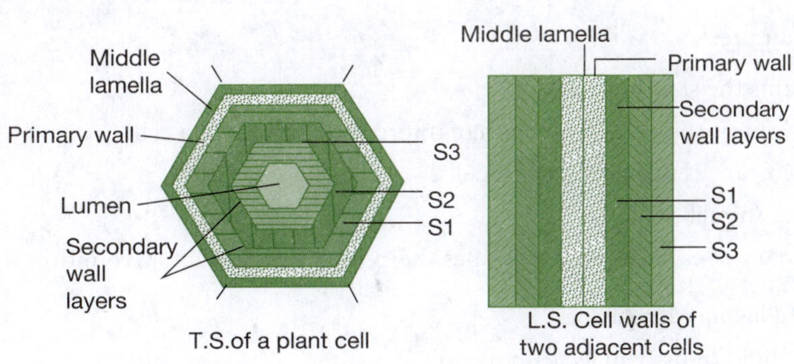

Figure 1.8 T.S. of Plant Cell

Cell Membrane

Cell membrane is also known as plasma membrane or plasmalemma. The name Plasma membrane was given by **Nageli.** It is found in both plant as well as animal cells. It is the outer most covering of a cell in case of animals and lies below the cell wall in case of plants. It is made up of proteins and lipids where proteins are sandwiched between bilayer of lipids. Viruses lack any membrane and hence do not show characteristics of life until they enter a living body and use its machinery to multiply.

The most accepted structural modal of plasma membranes is Fluid Mosaic Model (Fig 1.9). It was proposed by **S.J. Singer** and **G. Nicolson**. According to him, it consists of a protein layer sandwiched between two layers of lipids. It is 75 Å thick. It is flexible and can be folded, broken, and reunited. Plasma membrane is selectively permeable in nature. It allows or permits the entry and exit of some selective materials only.

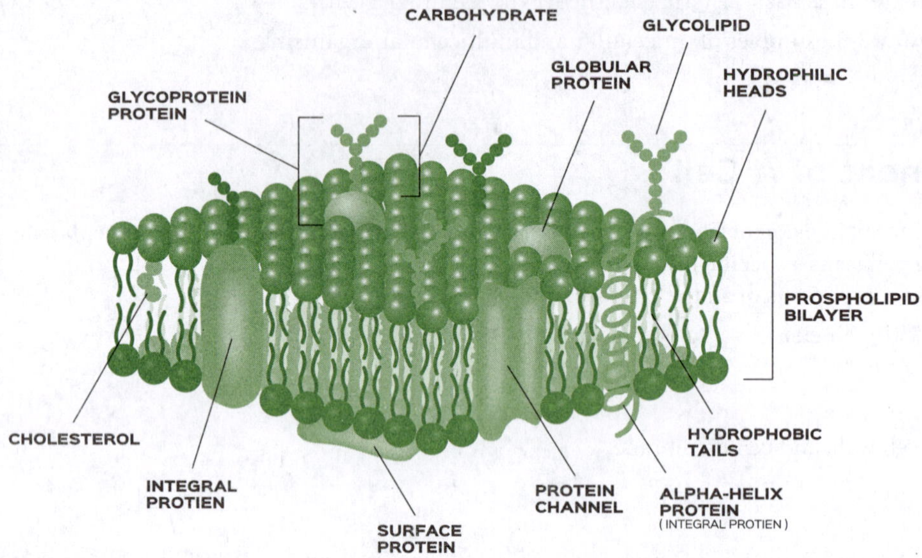

Figure 1.9 Fluid mosaic model of cell membrane

- Proteins are present in plasma membranes are of two types:
  - **Integral or intrinsic protein** – These proteins are tightly bound with phospholipid. Thus, they cannot be easily separated from the membrane. Some intrinsic proteins traverse the complete thickness of membrane. These types of protein are called as tunnel proteins that passage water-soluble material across the membrane.
  - **Peripheral or extrinsic protein** – These are superficially arranged on the outer side and can be separated easily. These proteins have enzymatic activity. Extrinsic proteins are loosely bound to the plasma membrane.

Keystone

This protein moves as icebergs in a bilayer of phospholipids that acts as a sea.

Functions of Plasma Membrane:

- It provides and maintains the shape of cell.
- It provides mechanical support for the protection of internal structures of a cell.
- It allows only useful substances to enter into the cells.
- It provides specificity to the cells.
- It is the limiting boundary of each cell that separates the cytoplasm from its surroundings.

Chemical Composition of Plasma Membrane

- Lipid: 30-40% phospholipid (mostly in lecithin form)
- Proteins: 40-60% in the form of intrinsic and extrinsic protein. It is the backbone of plasma membrane
- Carbohydrates: 1-6%

Transportation of molecules across the plasma membrane: This can be done by the following ways:

- **Diffusion:** Movement of molecules or ions from higher concentration to lower concentration is called as diffusion.

- **Significance of Diffusion**
  - Diffusion is important to cells because it allows them to gain the useful substances they require to obtain energy and grow, and lets them get rid of waste products.
  - Exchange of gases like CO_2 and O_2 move across the membrane.

Keystone

Both diffusion and osmosis do not require energy so they are known as **passive transport**.

- **Osmosis:** The movement of solvent or water from lower concentration of solution to higher concentration of solution through a semipermeable membrane is called osmosis. Osmosis can also be called as "diffusion of solvents". In other words, The net movement of water from a region of high-water concentration to a region of low water concentration through a selectively permeable membrane (as shown in Fig 1.10).

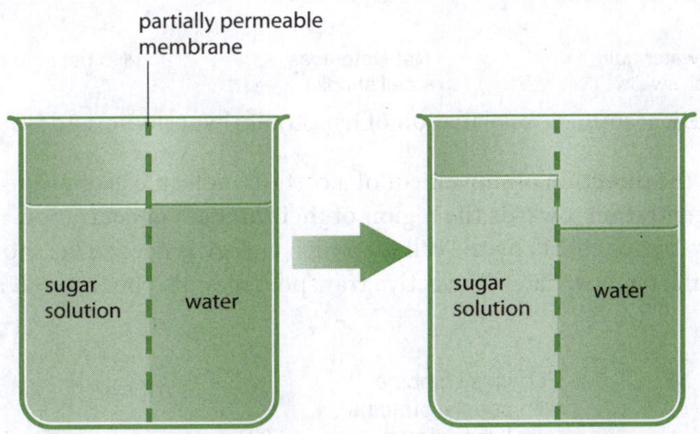

Figure 1.10 Omosis

Difference between diffusion and osmosis is discussed in Table 1.1.

Table 1.1 Differences between diffusion and osmosis

Diffusion	Osmosis
Diffusion can occur in any medium	In occurs only in liquid medium
The diffusing molecules may be solids, liquids, or gases	It involves movement of solvent molecules only
Semipermeable membrane is not required	Semipermeable membrane is required
It is dependent upon the free energy of the molecules of diffusing substance only; presence of other substance in the system is of no importance	Though it is the diffusion of solvent molecules only, yet influenced by the presence of other substance (solutes) in the system

- **Endosmosis:** Movement of solvent into the cell is called Endosmosis.
- **Exosmosis:** Movement of solvent outside the cell is called Exosmosis.

- **Facilitated or mediated diffusion:** This type diffusion occurs according to concentration gradient but it involves carriers like permeases, translocases, etc. Expenditure of metabolic energy or ATP is not involved in diffusion.

Type of solutions on the basis of concentration (as shown in Fig 1.11).

- **Isotonic solution:** When the concentration of the solution outside the cell is equal to the concentration of solution inside the cell, it is a isotonic solution (no effect on size of cell).
- **Hypertonic solution:** When the concentration of the solution outside the cell is more than that of inside the cell, it is a hypertonic solution. (cell becomes plasmolyzed).
- **Hypotonic solution:** When the concentration of the solution outside cell is lower than the inside of the cell, it is a hypotonic solution (cell swelled up).

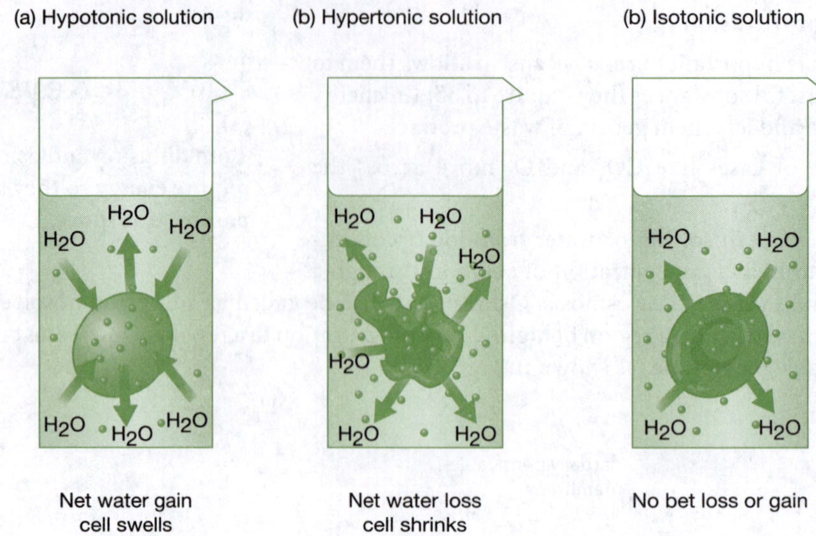

Figure 1.11 Diagrammatic explanation of hypotonic, hypertonic, and isotonic solutions

- **Active Transport:** When the direction of movement of a certain molecule is opposite to that of diffusion, i.e., from region of their lower concentration towards the region of their higher concentration across a semipermeable membrane, it would require an "active effort" by the cell for which energy is needed (as shown in Fig 1.12). This energy is provided by ATP (adenosine triphosphate). The active transport may also be through a carrier molecule.

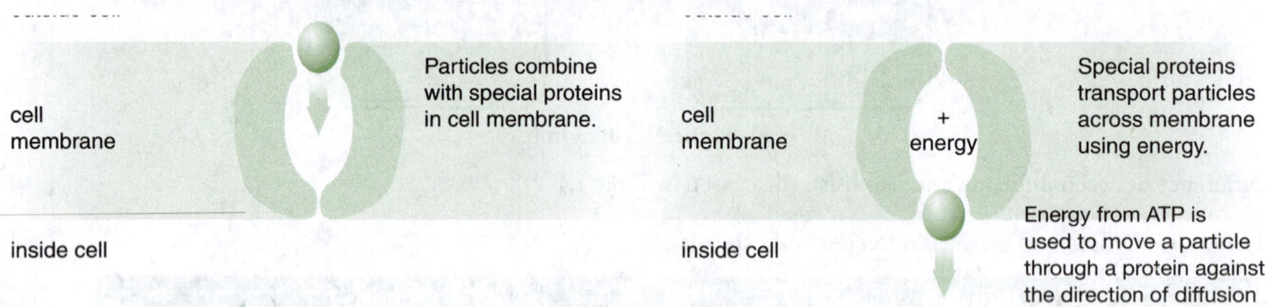

Figure 1.12 Active transport

Testing Room 3

Aim: Show osmosis with an egg cell.

Procedure: Remove the shell of an egg by dissolving it in dilute hydrochloric acid. The shell is mostly calcium carbonate, and a thin outer skin now encloses the egg. Put the egg in pure water and observe after 5 minutes. What do we observe? Place a similar de-shelled egg in concentrated salt solution and observe for 5 minutes. The egg shrinks why?

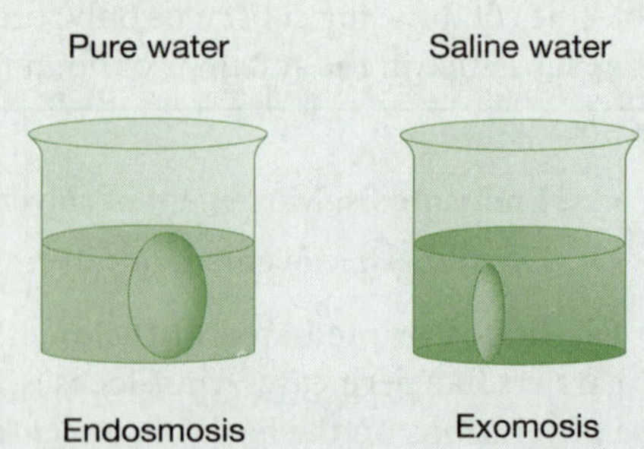

Observation: When the peeled egg is kept in pure water, it swells and in saline water, it shrinks.

Explanation: The shell of the egg is made up of calcium carbonate, when it reacts with dilute hydrochloric acid, the shell washes away. The cell membrane beneath the shell is permeable to some substances while impermeable to others. When the egg is kept in pure water, it absorbs water and swells. This phenomenon is called endosmosis. When the egg is kept in saline water (salt solution), water passes out of the egg into the salt solution, this phenomenon is called exosmosis.

Conclusion: This activity shows the phenomenon of endosmosis and exosmosis.

Testing Room 4

Aim: Compare the osmosis with Rhoeo leaf boiled in water.

Observation and explanation:

Rhoeo is a common decorative plant found in our home and gardens. Its slides are easy to prepare, so we use them to study cell components and functions. Under the microscope, we see changes similar to eggs, raisins and dried apricots, i.e., swelling in water and shrinkage with saline or sugar solution. Boiling of leaf breaks the cell wall and other cellular components like cytoplasm. Osmosis in a leaf is a function of protoplasm. As a result, we do not see any change in shape or size in leaf cells whether in water or solution.

Conclusion: A cell is alive until its protoplasm is functioning. A living cell responds to changes in external osmotic pressure while a dead cell ceases to show response to osmotic pressure.

- **Bulk Transport:** Bulk transport is a type of transport that involves the transport of large amount of substance like lipid droplets and solid food particles across plasma membrane by utilizing energy. It involves 2 processes - endocytosis and exocytosis.
  - **Endocytosis**- The process of taking in a bulk of materials from external environment into the cell is known as endocytosis (as shown in Fig 1.13). It is of two types–phagocytosis (cell eating) and pinocytosis (cell drinking). Phagocytosis + Pinocytosis → Endocytosis.
    - **Phagocytosis:** Cell eating–Ingestion of solid complex materials by plasmalemma in the form of vesicles (phagosome) is called phagocytosis. Examples, Amoeba, sponge, and WBC (leucocytes-engulf waste products and harmful bacteria and viruses).
    - **Pinocytosis:** Cell drinking–Ingestion of liquid material by plasmalemma in the form of vesicles or bag like structure (Pinosome) is called pinocytosis.

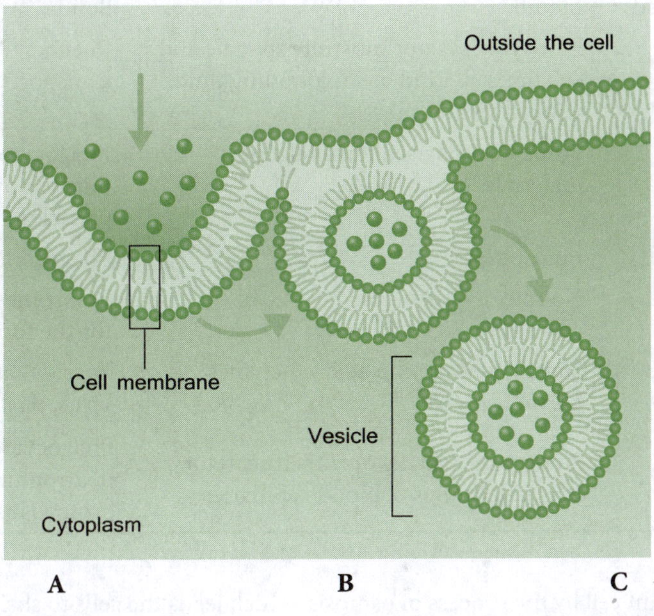

Figure 1.13 Endocytosis-showing (A) phagocytosis, (B) pinocytosis, and (C) receptor-mediated endocytosis.

- **Exocytosis/ Cell vomiting/Ephagy:** Egestion of waste material from all through plasma membrane through exocytic vesicles (as shown in Fig 1.14).

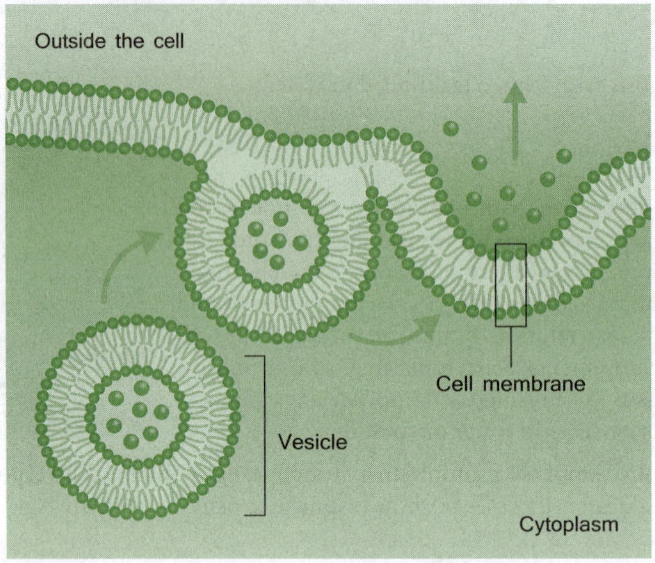

Figure 1.14 Exocytosis by a cell

❖ INTEXT QUESTION

3. Differentiate between phagocytosis and pinocytosis.

Ans:

Basis for Comparison	Pinocytosis	Phagocytosis
Meaning	Pinocytosis is called cell drinking; substance is directly ingested as it is in dissolved form and ready for cellular absorption.	Phagocytosis is called cell eating, in which particles are broken down into simpler substance with the help of enzymes for absorption.
Process of engulfing	By invagination	By pseudopodia (false feet).
Kind of particles ingested	Liquid.	Solid.
Substrate specific	Pinocytosis is not substrate specific and cell takes all kind of surrounding fluids with all solutes present.	Phagocytosis is specific in substrate it transports
Purpose	Pinocytosis is used for intake of materials.	Phagocytosis is used for defensive purpose by engulfing the foreign particles
Vesicles formed	Pinosomes	Phagosomes
Role of lysosomes	No role of lysosomes.	Lysosomes combine with phagosomes for the formation of food vacuole.
Types of particles intake	Sugars, ions, amino acids, enzymes, hormones, etc.	Foreign particles, harmful bacteria and virus, dust, etc.
Where it happens	Pinocytosis usually occurs in secretory cells, cell linings of blood capillaries	Phagocytosis is performed by neutrophils, macrophages and protozoans

4. What is plasmolysis?

Ans: Water loses in a plant cell by the process of osmosis, which leads the cells to shrink is called plasmolysis.

5. Differentiate between diffusion and osmosis. Write any two examples where a living organism uses osmosis to absorb water.

   Ans: Diffusion – The movement of a substance from a region of its high concentration to the region of its low concentration is called diffusion.

   Osmosis – The spontaneous movement of water molecules from a region of its high concentration to the region of its low concentration through a selectively permeable membrane is called osmosis.

   Examples where a living organism uses osmosis to absorb water are:
   - Roots of plants absorb water by osmosis.
   - Unicellular organisms like Amoeba absorb water by osmosis.

Check Point 2

4. Write the composition of plant cell wall.
5. Describe about the fluid mosaic modal of plasma membrane.
6. What do you understand by active and bulk transport.

Nucleus

Nucleus is considered as controller or director of cell.

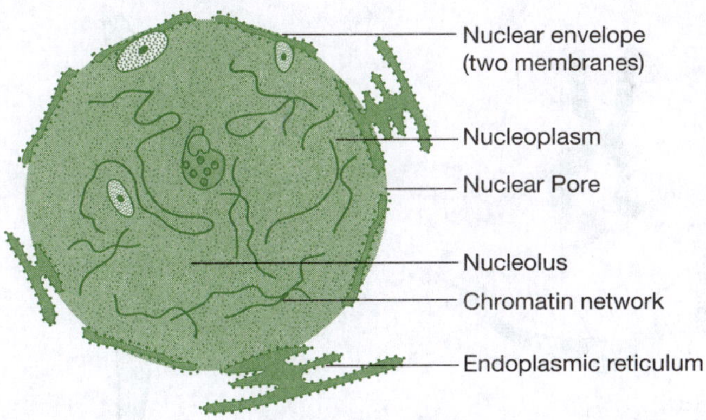

Figure 1.15 Nucleus

Nucleus-Headquarter of the cell.
Discovered by – Robert Brown (1831).
"Nucleus is double membrane bound dense protoplasmic body, which controls all cellular metabolism and encloses the genetic information of cell".

Structure

It is made up of following four contents:

- **Nuclear envelope:** Nucleus is surrounded by two membranes, that separates nucleoplasm from cytoplasm. The nuclear membrane has minute pores. These are called nucleo-pores (as shown in Fig 1.15).
- **Nucleoplasm:** The part of protoplasm that is enclosed by nuclear membrane is called nucleoplasm. It contains chromatin threads and nucleolus.
- **Nucleolus:** Discovered by Fontana. Usually, one nucleolus is present in each nucleus but sometimes more than one nucleoli are present. It is a store house of RNA.
- **Chromatin threads:** A darkly stained network of long fine threads called chromatin threads. Chromatin threads are intermingled with one another forming a network.

Keystone

Nucleopore takes part in exchange of different substance between nucleoplasm and cytoplasm.

Chromosomes are chemically made up of DNA and histone proteins. DNA carries all genetic information which is pass ed on to next generation. The functional segment OF DNA is called genes.

Functions of Nucleus

- The nucleus performs following functions:
    - It controls all the metabolic activities of the cell.
    - It brings about growth of the cell by directing the synthesis of structural proteins.
    - It takes part in the formation of ribosomes.
    - It regulates cell cycle.
    - It contains genetic information and is concerned with the transmission of hereditary traits from one generation to another.

Competition Corner

The structure in the nucleus of cells that carries the hereditary characteristics is called the chromosome. It is made up mainly of nucleic acids and proteins.

Chromosomes are chemically made up of DNA and histone proteins. DNA carries all genetic information which is passed on to next generation. The functional segment of DNA is called genes.

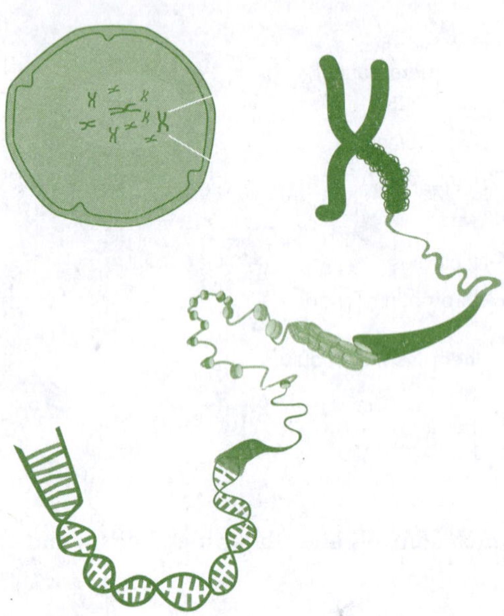

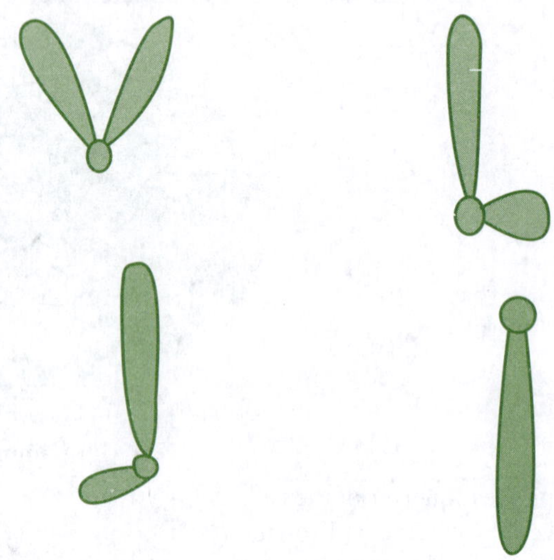

Depending upon the position of the centromere, there are four types of chromosomes.

(a) **Metacentric:** The centromere is exactly at the mid-point in this chromosome, and therefore, it looks like the English letter 'V'. The arms of this chromosome are equal in length.

(b) **Sub-metacentric:** The centromere is somewhere near the mid-point in this chromosome which, therefore, looks like the English letter 'U. One arm is slightly shorter than the other.

(c) **Acrocentric:** The centromere is near one end of the chromosome. One arm is much smaller than the other.

(d) **Telocentric:** The centromere is right at the end of this chromosome making the chromosome look like the English letter 'i'. This chromosome consists of only one arm.

Table 1.2 Comparative Study of Plant and Animal Cells

Characters	Animals Cell	Plant Cell
Cell wall	Absent	Present
Plasma membrane	Only cell membrane	Present
Microtubules Microfilaments	Present	Present
Lysosomes	Lysosomes occur in cytoplasm	Lysosome usually not evident
Nucleus	Present	Present
Shape	Round (Irregular shape)	Rectangular (Fixed shape)
Chloroplast	Animal cell don't have chloroplast	Plant cell have chloroplasts because they make their own food
Cytoplasm	Present	Present
Endoplasmic Reticulum	Present	Present
Ribosomes	Present	Present
Mitochondria	Present	Present
Vacuole	One or more small vacuoles (much smaller than point cells)	One large central vacuole taking up 90% of cell volume.
Centrioles	Present in all animal cell	Only present in lower plant forms
Golgi Apparatus	Present	Present

Competition Corner

Protoplasm: The entire matter found inner to the cell membrane is celled as protoplasm.

Protoplasm term is given by **Purkinje**

Huxley called it Physical basis of life

It can be divided into 2 parts:

(a) Cytoplasm (b) Nucleus

Cytoplasm: the substance present between cell membrane and nucleus is called cytoplasm.

Hyalopasm: Cytoplasm has a clear structureless fluid substance called cytoplasm.

Metaplasm/cytoplasmic inclusions: The non–living found in hyaloplasm are collectively termed as metaplast.

Cell organelles/Cytoplasmic organs: The living structures present in cytoplasm are called cell organelles. Examples, Golgi body, Endoplasmic reticulum, Mitochondria, Ribosome, Lysosome, Plastids Centrosome, Vacuole, Peroxisome.

Trophoplasm: Cell organelles and metaplest are collectively called as trophoplast.

Cytoplasm

Cytoplasm was discovered by **Kolliker** in 1862. It is the site of both biosynthetic and catabolic pathways. It can be divided into two parts:

- **Cytosol:** Aqueous soluble part contains various fibrous proteins forming cytoskeleton.
- **Cytoplasmic Inclusion:** In the cell cytoplasm, there are present numerous living and non-living structures, collectively called cytoplasmic inclusions. The living cytoplasmic inclusions are called cell organelles and the non-living structures are called Deutoplasmic or ergastic bodies.

Role of Cytoplasm:

- Participates in intracellular distribution of nutrients, metabolites, and enzymes.
- Helps in exchange of materials between cell organelle.
- Acts as a site of chemical reactions like glycolysis (step of respiration), synthesis of fatty acids.

Cell Organelles

These are living sub-cellular structures of the cytoplasm and are also called protoplasmic bodies or organoids. These include:

- Double membranous: Plastid and Mitochondria.
- Single membranous: Endoplasmic reticulum, Golgi apparatus, Lysosomes, peroxisomes, Glyoxysomes, etc.
- Non-membranous: Ribosomes, etc.

Double Membranous

Plastids, chloroplast and mitochondria are double membranous organelles. These topics are discussed below.

Plastid

Plants and some protists have several types of double membrane bound organelles called plastids, which harvest solar energy, manufacture nutrient molecules and store materials. Plastid term was coined by Ernst Haeckel. Plastids generally contain pigments and may synthesize and accumulate various substances.

Different type of pigments present in plastids, are discussed in Table 1.3.

> **Keystone**
>
> During ripening of fruits, the colour changes from green to yellow or reddish because of the degeneration of chlorophyll and the masked carotene pigments take over.

Table 1.3 Difference between Leucoplast, Chromoplast and Chloroplast

Leucoplast	Chromoplast	Chloroplast
Non-Pigmented White In Colour	Coloured Pigments All Colours Except Gree Phaeoplast – Brown Rhodoplast – Red	Green pigment chlorophyll is found in them.
Generally found in underground parts Important fro food storage. E.g., Aleuroplast (Protein). Elaioplast (Oil), Amyloplast (Starch)	Found in flowers, Fruits, leaves, etc.	Found in aerial parts of plant which are green in colour

Competition Corner

Different Shapes of Plastids:

- Discoidal or oval – Higher plants
- Girdle shaped – *Ulothrix*
- Spiral shaped – *Spirogyra*
- Cup shaped – *Chlamydomonas*

Chloroplast

Chloroplast is a double membranous discoidal structure, found only in plant cells (as shown in Fig 1.16).

Chloroplast was discovered by Anton van Leeuwenhoek and named by Schimper.

Besides being discoidal or rhombic in plant cells they occur in variable shapes like in algae they can be 'U' shaped, spiral, coiled, ribbon shaped etc.

Each chloroplast consists of two parts:

A. **Grana:** It constitutes the lamellar system. These are found layered on top of each other, these stacks are called as Grana. Each granum of the chloroplast is formed by superimposed closed compartments called Thylakoids. In each thylakoid, Quantasomes are present which are called as Photosynthetic units. Each quantasome possesses 230 chlorophyll molecules.

   Functions: Grana are the sites of light reaction of photosynthesis as they contain photosynthetic pigment chlorophyll. Different grana are connected with the help of tubular connections, called stroma lamellae or Fret channels or intergranum.

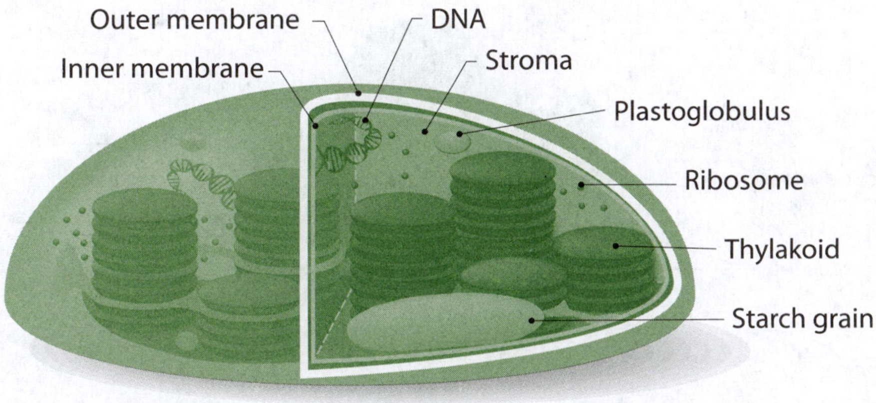

Figure 1.16 Internal structure of chloroplast

B. **Stroma:** It is a granular transparent substance also called as matrix. Grana is embedded in it. Besides grana they also contain lipid droplets, starch grains, ribosomes etc. It contains enzymes of calvin cycle or dark reaction. Rubisco is the most abundant enzyme on the earth. It made 16% protein of the chloroplast.

- Chloroplasts has their own genetic system and complete protein synthesis machinery (ds-DNA, RNA, 70S type of Ribosome enzymes, Amino Acids), thus chloroplasts are called as semi-autonomous organelle of the cell.

Function: This is the site of dark reaction of photosynthesis.

> **Keystone**
>
> DNA of chloroplast is called **plastidome.**

Mitochondria

Mitochondria is a rod-shaped structure found in cytoplasm of all eukaryotic cells except mammalian RBCs (as shown in Fig 1.17).

These are also absent in prokaryotes. Maximum mitochondria are found in metabolically active cells.

It is also called as "Power House of the Cell" or the "Storage Battery". It is double membranous structure where outer membrane has specific proteins while inner membrane is folded inside to form chambers called Cristae. "Cristae" are the infoldings of inner mitochondrial membrane that possess enzymes for respiratory cycles like Krebs Cycle. ATP synthesizing units are called Oxysomes or $F_0 - F_1$ Particles.

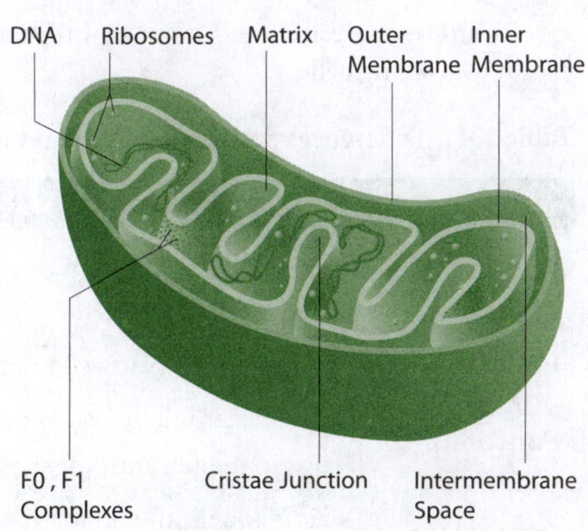

Figure 1.17 Mitochondria

Space between inner and outer mitochondrial membranes is called as peri-mitochondrial space. The fluid present in mitochondria is called as matrix.

Functions: Its main function is to produce and store the energy in the form of ATP.

It is the site of Krebs cycle of respiration, as it contains enzymes for Krebs cycle.

Oxysome contains enzymes for ATP production.

Keystone

Plastids and mitochondria are semi-autonomous cell organelles as they have ribosome DNA and enzymes that are useful in protein synthesis.

Single Membranous

Many Single Membranous organelles are discussed below.

Endoplasmic Reticulum

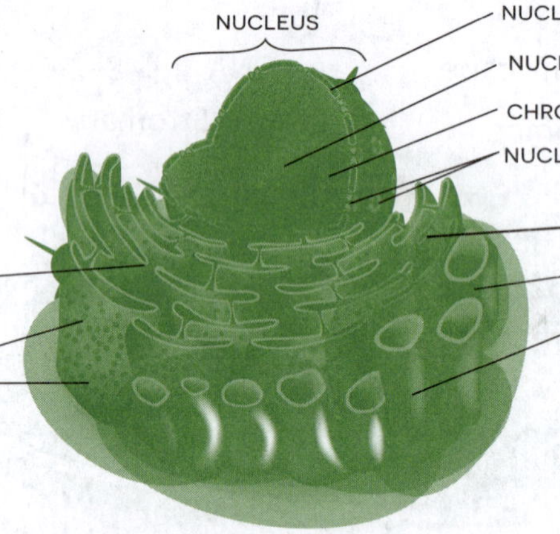

Figure 1.18 Endoplasmic reticulam

It is the network of membranes present in the cytoplasm. It was discovered by **Porter, Claude, and Fullan**. These are present in all cells except prokaryotes and mammalian erythrocytes.

Endoplasmic Reticulum is of two types, rough(granular) and smooth(agranular). Rough E.R. contains ribosomes and take part in protein synthesis. Smooth E.R. are devoid of ribosomes, they take part in glycogen and lipid metabolism. Many other differences between Rough and smooth E.R. are discussed in Table 1.4 They are made up of three components (as shown in Fig 1.18):

- **Cisternae:** These are long, flattened, parallel arranged, unbranched tubules. These form successive layers of nucleus. These are found in cells which are active in protein synthesis and are 40 – 50 μm in diameter.
- **Vesicles:** These are rounded or spherical, they are found in synthetically active cells.
- **Tubules:** These are small, smooth walled and have tubular spaces. These are found in non-secretory as well as steroid-synthesizing cells.

Table 1.4 Differences between Smooth and Rough Endoplasmic Reticulum

Character	SER	RER
Components	Made of tubules mainly.	Made of cisternae & vesicles.
Ribosomes	Absent	Present
Position	Mainly present near cell membrane	Mainly present near the nucleus
Functions	Helps in steroid, lipids & polysaccharide synthesis. Helps in membrane biogenesis	Helps in protein synthesis.
Occurrence	Mainly found in lipid forming cells like adipocytes (Fat cells)	Mainly found in protein forming cells like Nissl's granules of nerve cells.

Functions

- ER increases the surface area of the cytoplasm for various metabolic activities of the cell.
- It gives internal support to the colloidal matrix, i.e., cytoplasm.
- It functions as an intracellular transport system for various substances.
- Materials synthesized can be stored in different parts of ER.
- Protein synthesis occurs on the surface of rough ER by ribosomes. These proteins are either used within the cell or exported outside the cell.
- Synthesis of lipids in collaboration with Golgi complex occurs on the surface of the smooth ER. Smooth ER helps in the synthesis of sex hormones like testosterone in the testis and estrogens in ovary.

Keystone

Endoplasmic reticulum of striated muscles is called as sarcoplasmic reticulum.

Golgi Apparatus

Discovered by **Camillo Golgi** (1998) in nerve cell of an owl.

Position: It is located near the nucleus.

Golgi bodies are pleomorphic structures, because components of Golgi body are different in structure and shape in different cells (as shown in Fig 1.19). It contains a pile of flattened sacs named cisternae along with small vesicles and tubules.

Structure: It is formed of four types of contents:

- **Cisternae:** These are long flattened and unbranched saccules. 4 to 8 saccules are arranged in a stack. Convex surface of cisternae (towards the nucleus) is called cis-face or forming face. Concave surface of cisternae (towards the membrane) is called Trans-face or maturing face.
- **Tubules:** These are branched and irregular tube-like structures associated with cisternae.
- **Vacuoles:** Large spherical structures associated to tubules.
- **Vesicles:** Spherical structures arise by budding from tubules. Vesicles are filled with secretory materials. Golgi body is single membrane-bound cell organelle.

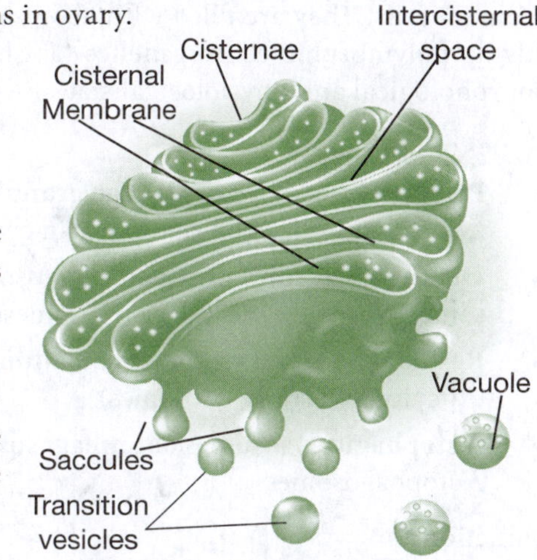

Figure 1.19 Golgi apparatus

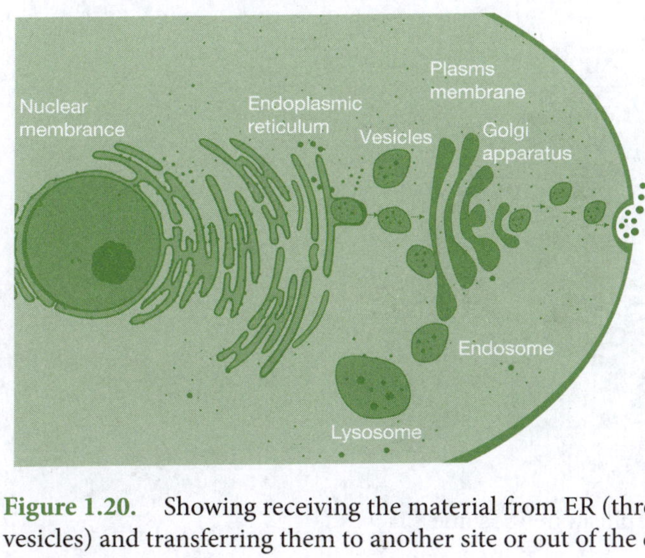

Figure 1.20. Showing receiving the material from ER (through vesicles) and transferring them to another site or out of the cell

Keystone

In plants, Golgi body is known as Dictyosomes.

It is absent in prokaryotes, mammalian RBCs, and sieve cells.

Acrosome is a bag-like structure filled with lytic enzymes that dissolve egg membrane at the time of fertilization.

Functions:

- It is involved in cell secretion and acts as storage, modification, and condensation or packaging membrane.
- They receive material from E.R. and transport them to other cells (as shown in Fig 1.20).
- It forms the acrosome of sperm.

- It forms lysosomes.
- Synthesis of cell wall material
- Formation of plasmalemma
- Cell plate formation (phragmoplast) during plant cell division formation.

Lysosomes:

(Discovery: **Christian de Duve**) (Lyso = digestive, soma = body)

It is a small vesicle or sac-like structure scattered in the cytoplasm. They do not have a definite shape or size. Lysosomes are spherical bag-like structures [0.1 – 0.8 μm] which are covered by single unit membrane. They are larger in size and number in phagocytes (WBC) – 0.8 to 2 μm. With the exception of mammalian RBCs, they are reported from all cells. They are filled with about 50 different types of digestive enzymes termed as acid hydrolases. They are highly polymorphic cell organelles (as shown in Fig 1.21). Because, during functioning, lysosomes have different morphological and physiological states.

Types of Lysosomes

- **Primary lysosomes or storage granules:** These lysosomes store enzyme acid hydrolases in the inactive form (enzymes synthesized on ribosomes in cytoplasm) these are newly formed lysosome.
- **Digestive vacuoles or Heterophagosomes:** These lysosome forms by the fusion of primary lysosomes and phagosomes. These are secondary lysosomes.
- **Residual bodies:** Lysosomes containing undigested material are called residual bodies. These may be eliminated by exocytosis (tertiary lysosomes).
- **Autophagic lysosomes/autophagosomes:** Lysosomes containing cell organelles to be digested are known as Autophagosomes.

Functions:

The main function of lysosomes is phagy = digestion (intra-cellular digestion):

- **Heterophagy:** It involve in digestion of foreign materials received in cell by phagocytosis and pinocytosis.
- **Autophagy:** Digestion of old or dead cell organelles. Autophagy also takes place during starvation of cell
- **Cellular digestion (Autolysis):** Sometimes all lysosomes of a cell burst to dissolve the cell completely. That's why lysosomes also known as suicidal bags.

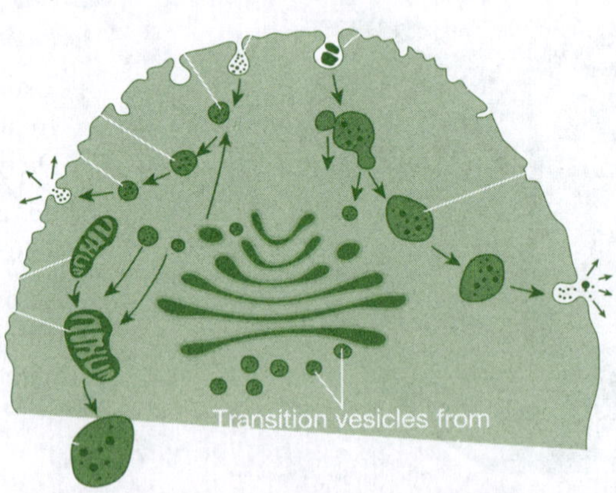

Figure 1.21 Polymorphism in lysosome

Peroxisomes/Uricosomes

- Discovered by **Rhodin & Tolbert.**
- Peroxisome term was first used by De Duve.

Peroxisomes are ovoid or granular structures, limited by a single unit membrane and have a diameter of 0.5-1.0mm.

In plants peroxisomes occur in calls of green tissues and concerned with photorespiration [Glycolate pathway]. It contains peroxide forming enzymes.

Functions:

- β-oxidation of fatty acids.
- Concerned with photorespiration.
- In animal cells peroxisomes concerned with peroxide (H_2O_2).

> **Keystone**
>
> Magnesium ion [Mg^{2+}] is essential for binding the ribosome subunits.

Membrane-less Organelle

Membrane less organelles are of following type.

Ribosomes

- First reported by **Claude** and named by **G.Palade**.
- They are small granular structures visible only under electron microscope.
- They are usually attached on the outer surface of endoplasmic reticulum as well as freely in the cytoplasm.
- They are the only organelles that are present in all types of cells.
- They help in protein synthesis and are known as "protein factories."
- Each ribosome consists of two unequal subunits, larger dome shaped and small ovoid.
- The size of ribosome is determined by sedimentation coefficient in the centrifuge.
- The cytoplasmic ribosomes of eukaryotes are 80S and 70S in prokaryotes.
- The two subunits of 80S ribosomes are 60S and 40S while 70S type ribosomes have 50S and 30S subunits (as shown in Fig. 1.22).

Function: Ribosomes are site of protein synthesis, so these are also called protein factories.

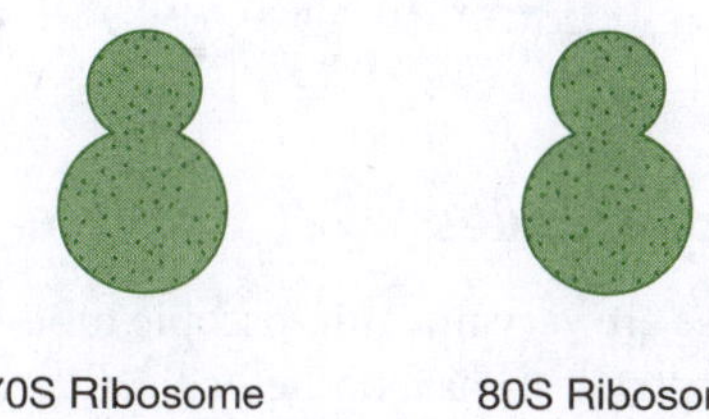

Figure 1.22 Types of ribosomes

Centrosome

Discovered by **Benden and Boveri** named as centrosome.

Centrosome is generally found in animal cells. Only few types of plant cells show its presence. It is situated near the nucleus of the cell and shaped like a star. It is differentiated into a clear, homogeneous mass of cytoplasm called centrosphere and one or a pair of microtubular centrioles.

Each centrosome has two centrioles. The two centrioles are placed perpendicular to each other.

- Centrioles are membrane less elongated structure which exhibit cart wheel structure (just like Basal body of cilia). Basel body is also a type of centriole. Centriole consist of 9 triple fibres of tubulin (9 +0 arrangement) (as shown in Fig. 1.23).

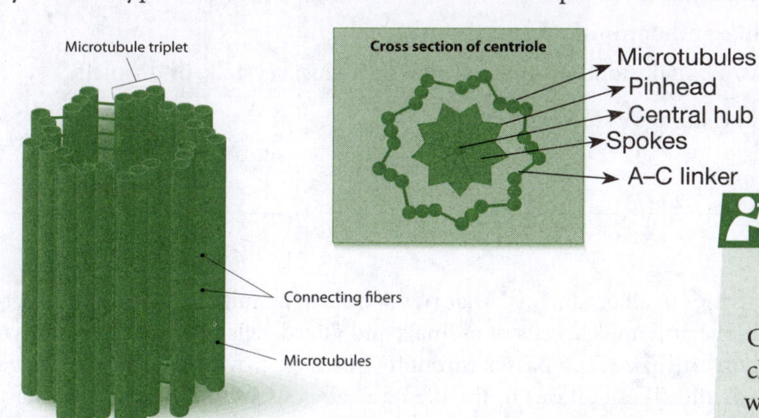

Figure 1.23 Showing (9 + 0) arrangement of centriole

> **Keystone**
>
> Cell organelles like mitochondria and chloroplast, they are 70S type. That's why mitochondria and chloroplast are called **semiautonomous organelle**.

Function: In animal cells, centrioles play important role in initiation of cell division by arranging spindle fibres between two poles of a cell. The location of centrioles during cell division decides the plant of division. It forms the basal granule of cilia and flagella in micro-organisms, zoo-spores, and motile gametes. It forms tail of sperm.

Competition Corner

Cilia and flagella (the organelles for motility)

- Some unicellular organisms like Paramecium and Euglena swim in water with the help of cilia and flagella, respectively.
- In multicellular organisms, some living tissues (epithelial tissues) have cilia. They beat and create a current in the fluid in order to move in a given direction. Example, in the wind pipe (trachea) to push out the mucus and dust particles.
- Cilia beat like tiny oars or pedals (as in a boat) and flagella bring about whiplash-like movement.
- Both are made up of contractile protein tubulin in the form of microtubules.
- The arrangement of the microtubules is termed as 9 + 2, that is, two central microtubules and nine duplet sets surrounding them.

Microtubules

These are very fine microscopic tube-like structures that may be present independently or as parts of some organelles such as centrioles, basal bodies, cilia, flagella, etc.

Fuctions of Microtubules: The microtubular structures provide strength and they also help in bringing about various movements inside the cell.

Ergastic Bodies

Ergastic bodies include non-living structures.

Vacuole: Vacuoles are non-living structures of cytoplasm. These are membrane bounded regions in the cytoplasm containing water and other substances. They are bounded by a single membrane called tonoplast. In animal cells, vacuoles are smaller in size and numerous while in plant cells a single large vacuole is found that occupies about 90% of the volume of cell.

Functions:

- It helps in maintaining osmotic pressure in a cell.
- It stores toxic metabolic products of plant cell.
- It contains various coloured pigments like anthocyanins.

Granules: These are also non-living cytoplasmic inclusions. These are small particles, crystals, or droplets.

Function: Starch grains, fat droplets help in the storage of food in cells.

Cell Division

Cell division is one of the most important activities in all organisms. Majority of cells in a multicellular organism grow and then can divide. However, the cells like the nerve and muscle cells of animals and guard cells of plants do not divide. The process of cell division is almost same in all organisms. A cell passes through phases of growth after which they are able to duplicate their chromosomes before they divide. These phases in the life of a cell constitute the cell cycle. Before each daughter cell undergoes division, it must grow to the same size as its mother cell.We can distinguish two main phases in the life of a cell.

Interphase/Non-dividing period (Growth phase)

The interval between two successive cell divisions is termed interphase (phase at which the cell is not dividing).It is the longest period in the cell cycle. The cell cycle consists of various stages (G1, S, G2, and M).The interphase is subdivided into three main periods - G1, S, and G2.

G1 (Gap-1) Phase

It is the first phase of growth. This is the longest phase. Lot of protein and RNA are synthesized during this phase.

S or synthetic Phase

It comes next. Lot of DNA is (synthesized). A chromosome contains a single double helical strand of DNA molecule. After S-phase, each chromosome becomes longitudinally double except at centromere, and thus, it has two molecules of DNA and two chromatids. Thus each chromatid contains one molecule of DNA. The two chromatids are joined by a centromere (which does not divide at this stage) to form a single chromosome.

G2 (GAP 2) phase

More protein including the histones are synthesized in this phase. Cytoplasmic organelles such as mitochondria and golgi bodies get duplicated. Centriole also divides into two centrioles contained in a single centrosome.

M-phase or dividing phase

Represented by the symbol M (mitosis or meiosis), mitosis occurs so that during this period the chromatids separate and form daughter chromosomes. The daughter chromosomes go to daughter nuclei and cytoplasm divides forming two identical daughter cells.

❖ INTEXT QUESTIONS

6. What are cisterns?

   Ans: Cisterns are flattened membrane-bound vesicles placed parallel to each otherin stacks that are called cisterns.

7. Describe the structure and function of vacuoles?

   Ans:

- Vacuoles are present in both animals and plants.
- The plant vacuole contains cell sap and provides the cell with rigidity and turgidity.
- The vacuoles are store house for amino acids, sugars, organic acids, etc.
- In animal cells, a number of small vacuoles are found. A special type of food vacuole is present in animal cells.

8. What are the two types of endoplasmic reticulum? State its functions.

   Ans: (a) The two types of ER are the rough endoplasmic reticulum (RER) and smooth endoplasmic reticulum (SER).

   (b) The rough endoplasmic reticulum is the site of protein synthesis.

   (c) The smooth endoplasmic reticulum is responsible for fat or lipid synthesis. It also helps in detoxification of poisons and drugs.

Check Point 3

7. Write the types of lysosomes.
8. Differentiate between rough and smooth endoplasmic reticulum
9. Why mitochondria is called power house of cell.
10. Describe cell division.

STRUCTURAL OUTLINE

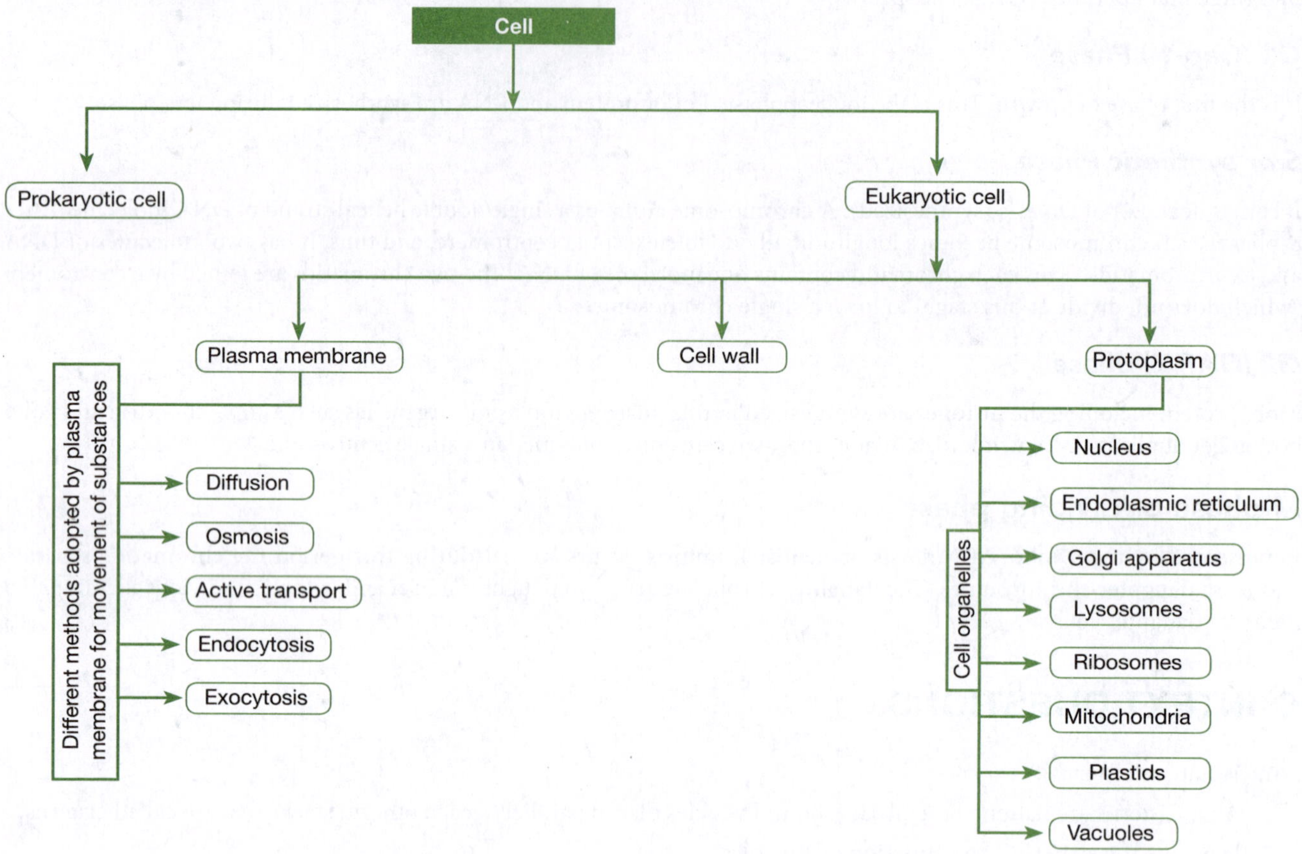

EXEMPLIFICATION

1. Differentiate between cell wall and cell membrane.

Ans.

Cell Wall	Cell Membrane
The cell wall is an additional, protective, rigid structure present outside the cell membrane.	The cell membrane is porous in nature and helps in the inward and outward movement of substances.
Cell wall is present only in plant cells.	Cell membrane is present in both animal and plant cells.
Plant cells do not move from one place to another and hence they require rigidity, which is provided by the cell wall.	The cell membrane is the outer boundary of the cell, which separates one cell from the other. It also separates the contents of the cell from its surrounding medium.

2. What will happen if we put a plant and animal cell in: (a) hypotonic solution, (b) hypertonic solution, (c) isotonic solution.

Ans. (a) **Hypotonic solution:** Plant cells swell up when kept in hypotonic solution because plant cells absorb large amounts of water. The vacuole gets completely filled with water and the cytoplasm presses against the cell wall. But it does not burst due to the presence of the cell wall. The cell wall can withstand dilute hypotonic media and thus it prevents bursting of cells. Therefore, plant cells withstand changes in environmental concentration much better than animal cells which burst in such conditions.

(b) **Hypertonic solution:** Both the animal and the plant cell will undergo plasmolysis. This means that water will move out of the cells and as a result they will shrink. The shrinking of the cell will result in the breaking down of plasma membrane.

(c) **Isotonic solution:** Both the animal and the plant cell will remain unaffected due to no net movement of water. This will occur because of balance of osmolarity in the cell and the solution.

3. Give the difference between nucleus and nucleoid.

Ans.

Nucleus	Nucleoid
Nucleus is the cell structure which is spherical or oval, usually located in the eukaryotic cell	Nucleoid is the part of a prokaryotic cell having undefined nuclear region
DNA with histone protein	DNA without histone
Nucleolus present	Nucleolus absent

4. In which form does the mitochondria release energy? Write its full form.

Ans. Mitochondria releases energy in the form of ATP (Adenosine triphosphate)

5. Write any 3 functions of vacoules.

Ans. It helps in maintaining osmotic pressure in a cell.'
It stores toxic metabolic products of plant cell.
It contains various coloured pigments like anthocyanins.

6. Which organisms are called as the (i) powerhouse of the cell, (ii) suicide bags of the cell, (iii) kitchen of the cell?

Ans. (i) Mitochondria
(ii) Lysosomes
(iii) Chloroplasts

7. What are chromoplasts and leucoplasts? Give an example of chromoplast that has green pigment.

Ans. The coloured plastids that have pigments of different colours are called chromoplasts. The colourless plastids that help to store starch, oils, or protein granules are called leucoplasts. The green-coloured plastid is called chloroplast and it contains a green-coloured pigment called chlorophyll.

8. How many membranes are present in mitochondria? Give the characteristic features of these membranes. What is the advantage of such features?

Ans. Mitochondrion is a double-membrane structure whose outer membrane is very porous while the inner membrane is deeply folded to form cristae. The porous membrane helps in getting oxygen and food. Cristae present on the inner membrane are the folds which create a large surface area for ATP-generating chemical reactions.

9. How do substances like carbon dioxide (CO_2) and water (H_2O) move in and out of the cell?

Ans. The movement of carbon dioxide occurs by the process of diffusion in and out of the cell, whereas the movement of water in and out of the cell occurs by the process of osmosis.

10. Which cell organelle controls most of the activities of the cell?

Ans. Nucleus is the control centre of the cell and controls most of the activities of the cell.

NCERT COMPENDIUM

1. Make a comparison to write down ways in which plant cells are different from animal cells.

Answer:

Plant Cell	Animal Cell
1. They are larger in size.	1. They are smaller in size.
2. Cell wall is present.	2. Cell wall is absent.
3. Lysosomes are absent or very few in number	3. Lysosomes are larger in number.
4. Plastids are present.	4. Plastids are absent.
5. Subunits of Golgi bodies known as dictyosomes are present.	5. Prominent Golgi bodies are present.
6. Vacuoles are larger in size.	6. Vacuoles are smaller in size.

2. How is prokaryotic cell different from eukaryotic cell?

Answer: The following are the differences between prokaryotic and eukaryotic cells.

Prokaryotic Cell	Eukaryotic Cell
Size: generally small (1-10 μm) 1 μm = 10^{-6} m	Size: generally large (5-100 μm)
The nuclear region is not well defined as and is referred to as the nucleoid the nuclear membrane is absent.	Nuclear region: well defined and girdled by a nuclear membrane
There is a single chromosome.	There are more than one chromosome.
Membrane-bound cell organelles absent	Membrane-bound cell organelles present.

3. What would happen if the plasma membrane ruptures or breaks down?

Answer: There will be spilling of cytoplasm and cell organelles, bursting of lysosomes and digestion of cellular contents.

4. What would happen to the life of a cell if there was no Golgi apparatus?

Answer: There would not be any lysosome for intracellular digestion and cleansing, no complexing of molecules, no excretion and no formation of new plasma membrane.

5. Which organelle is known as power house of the cell? Why?

Answer: Mitochondrion is known as power house of the cell because it produces most of the molecules of ATP (adenosine triphosphate) which are required for providing energy for synthesis of new chemicals, mechanical, and other cellular functions.

6. Where do the lipids and proteins constituting the cell membrane get synthesized?

Answer: Proteins are synthesized over ribosomes of RER while lipids are synthesized over SER.

7. How does Amoeba obtain food?

Answer: Plasma membrane of Amoeba is flexible. With its help, Amoeba engulfs food particle. The engulfed food particle passes into the body of Amoeba as a phagosome. Phagosome combines with lysosome to produce digestive or food vacuole. Digestion occurs in food vacuole. The digested food passes into surrounding cytoplasm. The undigested matter is thrown out of the cell in exocytosis.

8. What is osmosis?

Answer: Osmosis is diffusion of water from the region of its higher concentration (pure water or dilute solution) to the region of its lower concentration (strong solution) through a semipermeable membrane.

9. Carry out the following osmosis experiment.

Take four peeled potato halves and hollow each one out to make potato cups. One of these potato cups should be made from the boiled potato. Put each potato cup in the trough containing water. Now

(a) Keep cup A empty,
(b) Put one tea spoon sugar in cup B.
(c) Put one tea spoon of salt in cup C.
(d) Put one tea spoon sugar in boiled cup D.

Keep this set up for two hours. Then observe the four potato cups and answer the following :

(i) Explain why water gathers in the hollowed portion of B and C.

(ii) Why is potato A necessary for this experiment?
(iii) Explain why water does not gather in the hollowed out portion of A and D.

Answer: (i) Sugar and salt increases osmotic concentration which results in passage of water osmotically from the trough through the cells of potato B and C into its cavity.

(ii) Potato A functions as control experiment which indicates that the cavity of potato does not induce movement of water. Water does not gather in the hollowed-out portion of A because it does not have a higher osmotic concentration than the cells of potato tuber.

(iii) Potato tuber D does not have living cells. Osmosis does not occur in dead cells. Therefore, despite presence of sugar in the cavity of D, no water passes from trough through dead potato cells into cavity of the tuber.

10. Which type of cell division is required for growth and repair of body and which type is involved in formation of gametes?

Answer: Mitosis is required for growth and repair of body and meiosis is involved in formation of gametes.

ASSESSMENT CORNER

Level 1

Fixed Response Type

Multiple Choice Questions

1. Double membrane is absent in:
(A) Mitochondrion (B) Chloroplast
(C) Nucleus (D) Lysosome

2. The first person to observe a cell under microscope was-
(A) M. Schleiden
(B) T. Schwann
(C) Robert Hooke
(D) A.V. Leeuwnhoek

3. The network of endoplasmic reticulum is present in the:
(A) Nucleus (B) Nucleolus
(C) Cytoplasm (D) Chromosomes

4. Main difference between animal cell and plant cell is:
(A) Nutrition (B) Growth
(C) Movement (D) Respiration

5. Animal cell lacking nuclei would also lack in:
(A) Chromosome
(B) Ribosome
(C) Lysosome
(D) Endoplasmic reticulum

6. The radiant energy of sunlight is converted to chemical energy and stored as:
(A) AMP (B) ADP
(C) ATP (D) APP

7. Root hair absorbs water from soil through:
(A) Osmosis (B) Active transport
(C) Diffusion (D) Endocytosis

8. The barrier between the protoplasm and outer environment in a plant cell is:
(A) Cell membrane
(B) Nuclear membrane
(C) Cell wall
(D) Tonoplast

9. An animal cell differs from a plant cell in respect of:
(A) ER (B) Cell wall
(C) Ribosomes (D) Cell membrane.

10. If the nucleus is a cell's "control Centre" and chloroplasts its "solar collectors". Which of the following might be called the cell's combination "food processor" and "garbage disposer"?
(A) Lysosome (B) Ribosome
(C) Golgi apparatus (D) Nucleolus

11. The longest cell in human body is:
(A) WBC (B) RBC
(C) Platelets (D) Nerve cells

12. Identify human cell which lack nucleus:
(A) WBC (B) RBC
(C) Platelets (D) Nerve cells

13. The energy currency of a cell is:
(A) ADP (B) AMP
(C) ATP (D) CTP

14. The word cell was coined by -
(A) Robert Hooke
(B) Weismann
(C) Cuvier
(D) Darwin.

15. The term "protoplasm" to the living substance present inside the cell, was given by:
(A) Robert Hooks (B) Robert Brown
(C) J.E. Purkinje (D) W. Flaming

16. Ribosomes are the Centre for:
(A) Respiration (B) Photosynthesis
(C) Protein synthesis (D) Fat synthesis.

17. Lysosomes are the reservoirs for:
(A) Fat
(B) RNA
(C) Secretory glycoproteins
(D) Hydrolytic enzymes.

18. The membrane surrounding the vacuole of a plant cell is celled:
(A) Tonoplast
(B) Plasma membrane
(C) Nuclear membrane
(D) Cell wall

19. Centriole is associated with:
(A) DNA synthesis (B) Reproduction
(C) Spindle formation (D) Respiration

20. The cell organelle associated with cell secretion is:
(A) Plastids (B) Mitochondria
(C) Golgi apparatus (D) Nucleolus

21. Which of the following is an inclusion?
(A) Mitochondrion (B) Lysosome
(C) Golgi complex (D) Starch grain

22. Which of the following would not be considered part of a cell's cytoplasm?
(A) Ribosome (B) Nucleus
(C) Mitochondrion (D) Microtubule

23. Which one is present in bacteria?
(A) Nucleus (B) Golgi apparatus
(C) Mitochondria (D) Ribosomes

24. Which one is not a part of nucleus?
(A) Chromatin (B) Nucleolus
(C) Centrosome (D) Nucleoplasm

25. The common feature amongst nucleus, chloroplast and mitochondrion is:
(A) DNA (B) Lamellae
(C) Cristae (D) All of these

26. Nucleus is separated from surrounding cytoplasm by a nuclear envelope which is:
(A) Single and porous
(B) Double and porous
(C) Single and nonporous
(D) Double and nonporous

27. Nuclear membrane disappears during mitosis at:
(A) Telophase
(B) Late prophase
(C) Anaphase
(D) Early prophase.

28. Microtubules are present in:
(A) Bacteria (B) Viruses
(C) Eukaryotes (D) Mycoplasma

29. Nucleolus is continuous with cytoplasm through:
(A) Centriole
(B) Golgi apparatus
(C) Nuclear pores
(D) Endoplasmic reticulum

30. Nucleolus was discovered by:
(A) Fontana (B) Schleiden
(C) Altmann (D) Robert Brown

Fill in the Blanks

1. During cell division chromatin condensed into thick cord-like structures called ____________
2. The cells having well organized nucleus are called ____________
3. Transporting channel of the cell is ____________.
4. The cellular organelles often referred as suicide bags are ____________
5. Cell wall is found in ____________
6. Chromosomes are made up of ____________ and ____________.
7. The basic building units of an onion bulb, are called ____________.
8. Membrane-bound cell organelles are not found in ____________ cells.
9. ____________ are sites of protein synthesis
10. The infolding of mitochondria is known as ____________.

True/False

1. Lysosomes are called as "suicide bags" of a cell.
2. The folds of inner membrane of mitochondria increase the area for ATP generating chemical reactions.
3. Lysosomes are produced by endoplasmic reticulum.
4. Centriole consists of 10 triple fibres of tubulin.
5. Unicellular organisms have one-celled body.
6. Rubisco is the most abundant enzyme on the earth.
7. Muscle cells are branched.
8. Amoeba has irregular shape.
9. The entire matter found inner to the cell membrane is celled as cytoplasm.
10. Egestion of waste material from all through plasma membrane through exocytic vesicles.

Match Type Questions

1. Match the following A and B.

Column A		Column B	
(i)	Hypertonic solution	(a)	Nucleoid
(ii)	Selectively permeable	(b)	Functional unit
(iii)	Cell `	(c)	Cork
(iv)	Robert Brown	(d)	Plasmolysis
(v)	Suberin	(e)	Plasma membrane
(vi)	prokaryotic cell	(f)	Nucleus

2. Match the following A and B.

Column A		Column B	
(i)	Ribosome	(a)	Respiration
(ii)	Nucleolus	(b)	Protein
(iii)	Fluid-Mosaic Model	(c)	Fluid Droplets
(iv)	Mitochondria	(d)	Fontana
(v)	Pinocytosis	(e)	Nicholson and Singer

3. Match the following A and B

Column A		Column B	
(i)	Amoeba	(a)	Smooth endoplasmic reticulum
(ii)	Nucleus	(b)	Lysosome
(iii)	Bacteria	(c)	Nucleoid
(iv)	Detoxification	(d)	histone absent
(v)	Suicidal bag	(e)	Chromatin material and nucleolus

Assertion and Reason Type Questions

Directions: In the following questions, a statement of assertion (A) is followed by statement of reason (R). Mark the correct choice as:

(A) Both Assertion and Reason are correct, and reason is the correct explanation for assertion.
(B) Both Assertion and Reason are correct, and Reason is not the correct explanation for Assertion.
(C) Assertion is true but Reason is false.
(D) Assertion is false but Reason is true.
(E) Both assertion and reason are false

1. **Assertion:** All plants and animals are composed of cells.
   Reason: Plants and animals made up of DNA.
2. **Assertion:** Plasma membrane is also known as selectively permeable membrane.
   Reason: Plasma membrane allows or permits the entry and exit of some materials in and out of the cell.
3. **Assertion:** A cell swells up when present in a hypotonic solution.
   Reason: More water molecules enter the cell than they leave.
4. **Assertion:** Plant cells have very large vacuoles.
   Reason: In plant cells, vacuoles are full of cell sap.
5. **Assertion:** Mitochondria are called 'powerhouses' of the cell.
   Reason: Mitochondria produce cellular energy in the form of ATP.
6. **Assertion:** All plants and animals are composed of cells.
   Reason: Cell is the basic unit of life.
7. **Assertion:** A plant cell bursts if placed in water.
   Reason: High turgor pressure causes bursting of plant cells.
8. **Assertion:** Mitochondria and chloroplasts are semiautonomous organelles.
   Reason: They contain DNA but lack protein-synthesizing machinery.
9. **Assertion:** DNA is the heredity material.
   Reason: They transfer characters from one generation to next.
10. **Assertion:** Carbon dioxide and oxygen move across the cell membrane by diffusion process.
    Reason: Plasma membrane a permit the entry and exit of selective materials in and out of the cell.

Comprehension Type Questions

Passage 1: Cell theory was proposed by M.J. Schleiden and Theodore Schwann [Two German biologists]. It was later expanded by Rudolf Virchow –All plants and animals are composed of cells. Cell is the functional unit of life. All cells arise from pre-existing cell. [Rudolf Virchow – omnis cellula – e – cellulae.]

1. Who proposed cell theory?
2. Who modified cell theory?
3. "omnis cellula – e – cellulae" statement given by……….
4. What is cell theory?

Passage 2: Plasma membrane is also called selectively permeable membrane because it allows the entry and exit of selected materials in and out of the cell while it also prevents the movement of some other materials. Movement of solutes ion from higher concentration to lower concentration is called diffusion. Osmosis is passive movement. It is the movement of solvent water from its higher concentration to lower concentration through semi-permeable membrane is called osmosis. Movement of solvent of water into the cell is called endosmosis. While movement of solvent of water outside the cell is called exosmosis.

5. Why plasma membrane is called selective permeable?
6. Define diffusion.
7. Define osmosis.
8. Differentiate between endo and exo-osmosis.

Passage 3: The entire matter found inner to the cell membrane is celled as protoplasm. Huxley called it Physical basis of life. It can be divided into Cytoplasm and Nucleus. The substance present between cell membrane and nucleus is called cytoplasm. Cytoplasm has a clear structure-less fluid substance called cytoplasm. The non – living found in hyaloplasm are collectively termed as metaplast.

9. Define protoplasm.
10. Protoplasm is the combination of .... and ....
11. What is the physical basis of life?
12. Define the term cytoplasm.

Free Response Type

Very Short Answer Type Questions

1. Name any cell organelle which is non membranous.
2. Define protoplast.
3. Why is endocytosis found in animals only?
4. What is osmosis?
5. Why plasma membrane is called as selectively permeable membrane?
6. State any two functions of Golgi body.
7. Which is smallest cell?
8. Why are mitochondria called the power house of the cell?
9. What are lysosomes celled scavenger?
10. Why are lysosomes known as 'suicide-bags' of a cell?

Short Answer Type Questions

1. What are different of plastids? What are their functions?
2. Differentiate between rough and smooth endoplasmic reticulum. How is endoplasmic reticulum important for membrane biogenesis?
3. What is osmosis?
4. Draw a neat and well labelled diagram of a typical prokaryotic cell.
5. Differentiate between prokaryotic and eukaryotic cell.
6. Write comparison between plant and animal cell.
7. Draw a neat and labelled diagram of chloroplast with functions.
8. Write short note on ribosome with its functions.
9. Describe cell division?
10. Write any 4 functions of centrosome.

Long Answer Type Questions

1. Describe the structure and function of mitochondria with a labeled diagram.
2. Draw a well-labelled diagram of a eukaryotic nucleus. How is it different from nucleoid?
3. Write in detail the structure and function of endoplasmic reticulum.
4. What are the consequences of the following condition?
   (a) A cell containing higher water concentration than the surrounding medium
   (b) A cell having low water concentration than the surrounding medium.
   (c) A cell having equal water concentration to its surrounding medium.
5. Write the structure and working of compound microscope.

Case Based Questions

Case 1: The endoplasmic reticulum is a large network of membrane-bound tubes and sheets. It looks like long tubules or round or oblong bags (vesicles). It is discovered by Porter and Thompson. The ER membrane is similar in structure to the plasma membrane. There are two types of ER - rough endoplasmic reticulum (RER) and smooth endoplasmic reticulum (SER). RER looks rough under a microscope because it has particles called ribosomes attached to its surface. The ribosomes, which are present in all active cells, are the sites of protein manufacture. The manufactured proteins are then sent to various places in the cell depending on need, using the ER. The SER helps in the manufacture of fat molecules, or lipids, important for cell function. Some of these proteins and lipids help in building the cell membrane. This process is known as membrane biogenesis. Some other proteins and lipids function as enzymes and hormones. Although the ER varies greatly in appearance in different cells, it always forms a network system.

1. Who discovered endoplasmic reticulum?
   (A) Porter and Thompson
   (B) Robert Brown
   (C) Robert Hooke
   (D) Koshland
2. Which are the components of endoplasmic reticulum?
   (A) Cisternae, tubules, and vesicles.
   (B) Cisternae, chromatids, and vacuoles

(C) Both (A) and (B)
(D) None of the above

3. Endoplasmic reticulum membrane which is associated with ribosomes is called________
(A) ER lumen
(B) Smooth endoplasmic reticulum
(C) Rough endoplasmic reticulum
(D) Endosome

4. Enlist the types of Endoplasmic Reticulum.

5. Define membrane biogenesis.

Case 2: Study the given diagram of bacterial cell and answer any four questions from (i) to (v).

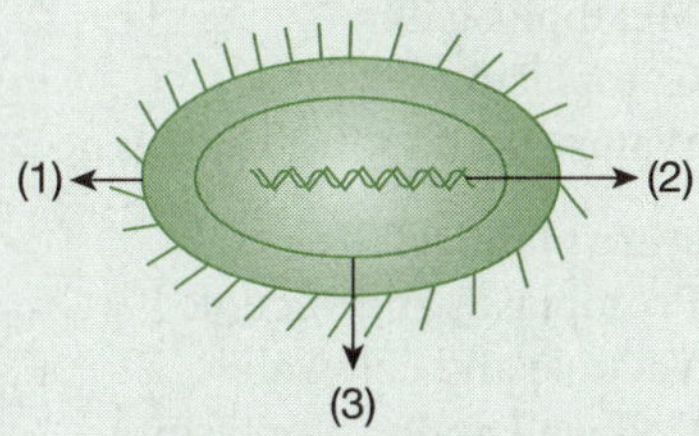

1. Label the parts marked 1, 2, and 3.
(A) 1-Nucleus, 2-Cell wall, 3-Plasma membrane.
(B) 1-Cell wall, 2-Nucleoid, 3-Plasma membrane.
(C) 1-Cytoplasm, 2-Nucleus, 3-Cell wall.
(D) 1-Nucleus, 2-Cytoplasm, 3-Cell wall.

2. Which structure present in the region 2 of a living cell bear gene?
(A) Chromosome
(B) Plasma membrane
(C) Cytoplasm
(D) Cell wall

3. How nuclear region of a bacterial cell and nuclear region of an animal cell is different from each other?
(A) Nuclear region of bacterial cell is well defined but lacks any covering while nuclear region of an animal cell is poorly defined and membrane bound.
(B) Nuclear region of bacterial cell is poorly defined and has a covering while nuclear region of an animal cell is poorly defined and membrane bound.
(C) Nuclear region of bacterial cell is poorly defined and lacks any covering while nuclear region of an animal cell is well defined and membrane bound.
(D) Nuclear region of bacterial cell is poorly defined and lack any covering while nuclear region of an animal cell is well defined and membrane bound.

4. Which of the following statement is correct?
(A) A single cell cannot perform all the life processes independently.
(B) A single cell can perform all the life processes independently.
(C) A single bacterial cell always needs another cell to carry out the life processes.
(D) A bacterium is a multicellular organism.

5. An example of single celled organism is:
(A) Bird (B) Fish
(C) Snake (D) Amoeba

Case 3: Every cell has a membrane around it to keep its own contents separate from the external environment. Large and complex cells, including cells from multicellular organisms, need a lot of chemical activities to support their complicated structure and function. To keep these activities of different kinds, separate from each other, these cells use membrane-bound little structures within themselves. The cytoplasm is the jelly-like fluid content inside the plasma membrane which contains many specialised cell organelles. Such as Endoplasmic Reticulum, Golgi apparatus, Lysosomes, Ribosomes, Nucleus, Chloroplast, Mitochondria and Plastids. Each of these organelles performs a specific function for the cell. Some of these organelles are visible only with an electron microscope. They are important because they carry out some very crucial functions in cells.

1. Identify the statement which is true for cells.
Statement 1: Some cell organelles are visible only with an electron microscope.
Statement 2: Cytoplasm is jelly like fluid present inside the cell.
Statement 3: Cell organelles perform all the functions in cell.
Statement 4: Every cell has a membrane around it to keep its own contents separate from the external environment.
(A) Statement 1 & 3
(B) Statement 2 & 4
(C) Statement 1 & 4
(D) All statements are true.

2. A suitable term for the various components of cells is:
(A) Tissue (B) Cell organelles
(C) Chromosomes (D) Genes

3. The jelly-like fluid substance present in cells is called
(A) Protoplasm (B) Chromosome
(C) Chloroplast (D) Cytoplasm

4. What are cell organelles?

5. Enlist the any five cell organelles.

ASSESSMENT CORNER

ASSESSMENT CORNER

Level 2

Multiple Choice Questions

1. Nucleolus is mainly formed of:
(A) DNA and RNA
(B) DNA, RNA and protein
(C) RNA and proteins
(D) RNA

2. Cell organelle which differentiates plant cell from animal cell is –
(A) Cell membrane
(B) Plastids
(C) Nucleolus
(D) Vacuoles

3. Which of the following phenomena is commonly referred as 'cell drinking'?
(A) Exocytosis (B) Pinocytosis
(C) Endocytosis (D) Phagocytosis

4. The cell organelle taking part in photorespiration is:
(A) Glyoxysome
(B) Dictyosome
(C) Peroxisome
(D) Endoplasmic reticulum

5. Endoplasmic reticulum sometime contains:
(A) Ribosomes (B) Lysosomes
(C) Golgi bodies (D) None of these

6. Which of the following help in synthesis of ribosomes?
(A) m - RNA (B) r - RNA
(C) t - RNA (D) DNA

7. Example of cell organelle which do not have a unit membrane is
(A) Mitochondria (B) Lysosome
(C) Ribosome (D) Plastid

8. In chloroplasts, chlorophyll is present in the:
(A) Stroma
(B) Tthylakoids
(C) Outer membrane
(D) Inner membrane

9. The sedimentation coefficient of complete ribosome in bacterial cell is:
(A) 70S (B) 80S
(C) 78S (D) 60S

10. Which cell organelles is absent in human sperm?
(A) ER (B) Nucleus
(C) Centrioles (D) Mitochondria

11. Mitochondria and chloroplasts are similar because.
(A) Both have nuclei
(B) Both have 80s ribosomes
(C) Both have DNA
(D) Both have single membrane envelope

12. Which of the following is a nonliving cell inclusion?
(A) Vacuoles (B) Ribosomes
(C) Centrosomes (D) Golgi complex

13. Cell vacuole contains:
(A) Water
(B) Metabolic gases
(C) Cytoplasm
(D) Water and dissolved substances

14. A mature plant cell has:
(A) Protoplasm and vacuole
(B) Vacuole and cell wall
(C) Cell wall and protoplasm
(D) Protoplasm, cell wall and vacuole

15. Which of the following is a non – membranous cell organelle?
(A) Chloroplast (B) Nucleus
(C) Mitochondria (D) Centriole

16. The function of centrosome is:
(A) Formation of RNA
(B) Duplication of DNA
(C) Movement of chromosomes
(D) Duplication of chromosomes

17. Centriole takes part in:
(A) Cell plate formation
(B) Spindle formation
(C) Nucleolus formation
(D) Start of cell division.

18. Which of the following is called 'an organelle within an organelle?
(A) Plastid (B) Ribosome
(C) Lysosome (D) Microsome

19. Mitosis
(A) Leads to recombinant daughter cells
(B) is a reduction division
(C) Leads to formation of parental type of daughter cells
(D) Occurs in gametes

20. Which is the largest cell in human body?
(A) Liver cell (B) Nerve cell
(C) Muscle cell (D) Kidney cell

Higher Order Thinking Skills (HOTS)

1.

(A) Identify the above figure.

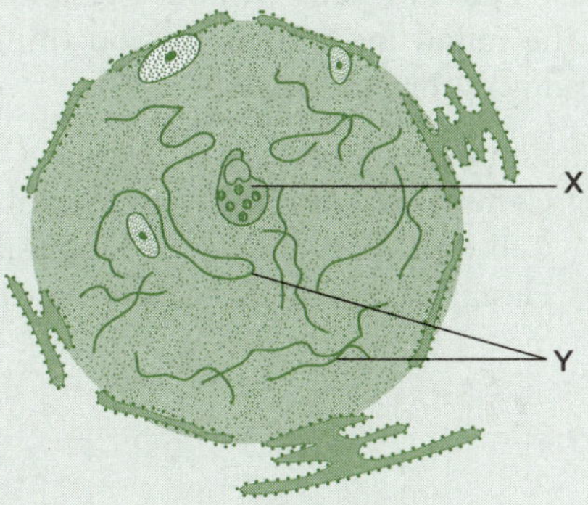

(B) Label X and Y

(C) What is the function of X ?

2.

(A) Identify A and B cells.

A - CELL

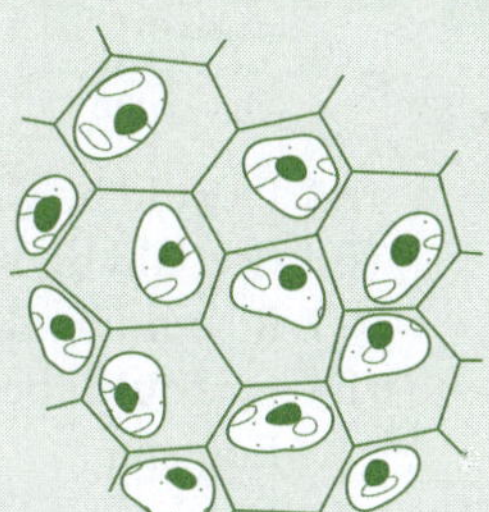

B - CELL

(B) What will happen if B cells are kept in hypotonic solution?

(C) What will happen if A cells are kept in hypertonic solution?

3. Label W, X, Y, and Z.

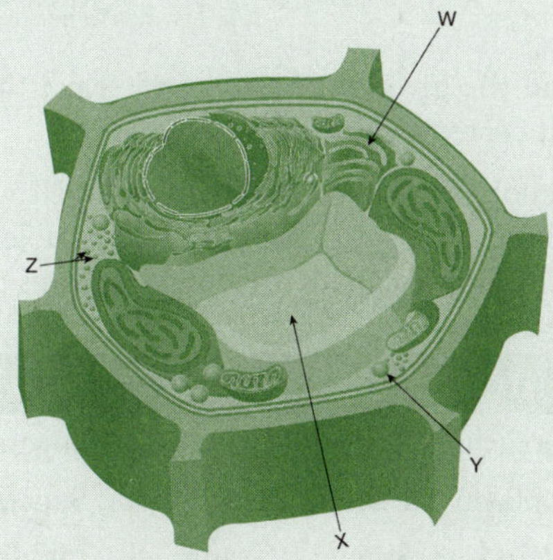

(A) What is the covering membrane of X known as?

(B) Which of them contains hydrolytic enzymes?

(C) Which one of them takes part in storage, modification, and packaging of various chemicals.

4. Give reasons why mitochondria are called 'power houses' and ATP as 'energy currency' of the cell.

5. Give reasons for the following:

(A) Bacteria are prokaryotic cells.

(B) Mitochondria are also called semiautonomous organelles.

6. What will happen if chloroplast is taken out of the cell and illuminated?

7. A solution of 3% glucose and a solution of 8% glucose are kept in a trough separated by a semipermeable membrane. What will you observe after 1 hour?

8. Why does the skin of your finger shrink when you wash clothes for a long time?

ARCHIVE CORNER

1. Read the given paragraph and select the option that correctly fills the blanks.

   Vacuole is a space in the (i) of a cell which his enclosed by a (ii) membrane. Vacuole is filled with a liquid called (iii) which contains dissolved (iv) and (v).

	(i)	(ii)	(iii)	(iv)	(v)
(A)	Cytoplasm	Single	Cell sap	Sugars	Salts
(B)	Cytoplasm	Double	Leucoplast	Sugars	Salts
(C)	Nucleus	Single	Grana	Lipids	Sugars
(D)	Protoplasm	Double	Matrix	Lipids	Salts

2. Aradhya was asked by her teacher to list three basic features that are found in both prokaryotic and eukaryotic cells without exception. Which of the following options do you think can be Aradhya's correct answer?

   (A) Endoplasmic reticulum, Nucleus, Cytoplasm
   (B) Cytoplasm, Plasma membrane, Ribosome
   (C) Cell wall, Mitochondria, Cytoplasm
   (D) Plasma membrane, Mitochondria, Chloroplast

3. Refer to the given figures and select the correct statement regarding them.

   (A) P is double membrane bound cell organelle whereas Q, R, and S are single membrane bound.
   (B) P is involved in synthesis of ATP whereas S is involved in synthesis of proteins.
   (C) Q is involved in storage of proteins whereas R is involved in synthesis of proteins.
   (D) R synthesizes lipids whereas S is involved in storage of lipids.

4. Refer to the given Venn diagram and select the correct option regarding P, Q, and R.

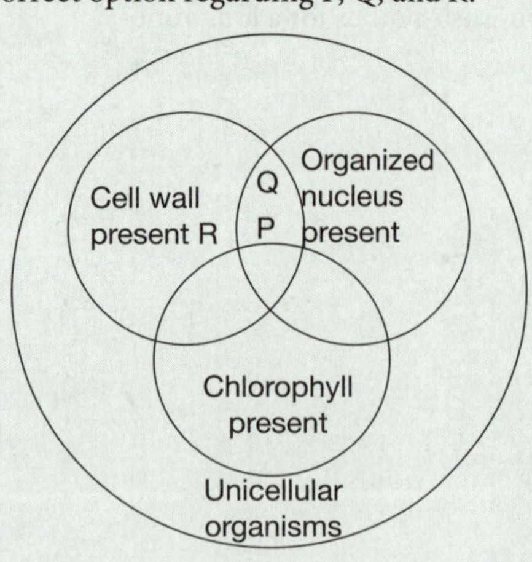

   (A) P could be Chlamydomonas or Aspergillus.
   (B) Q could be Volvox or Penicillium.
   (C) R could be Lactobacillus or Nitrosomonas.
   (D) Q could be clostridium and R could be Euglena.

5. Read the given statements and select the option that c correctly fills in the blanks.

   (i) The process of __________ plays an important role in gaseous exchange between the cell and its external environment.
   (ii) __________ is the common method of feeding among protozoans.
   (iii) Movement of molecules in one direction that is opposite to concentration gradient with the expenditure of energy in the form of ATP is called__________.

	(i)	(ii)	(iii)
(A)	Diffusion	Phagocytosis	Active transport
(B)	Osmosis	Phagocytosis	Endocytosis
(C)	Diffusion	Exocytosis	Osmosis
(D)	Osmosis	Exocytosis	Endocytosis

6. Refer to the given figure. Identify the labelled parts P-S and select the correct statement.

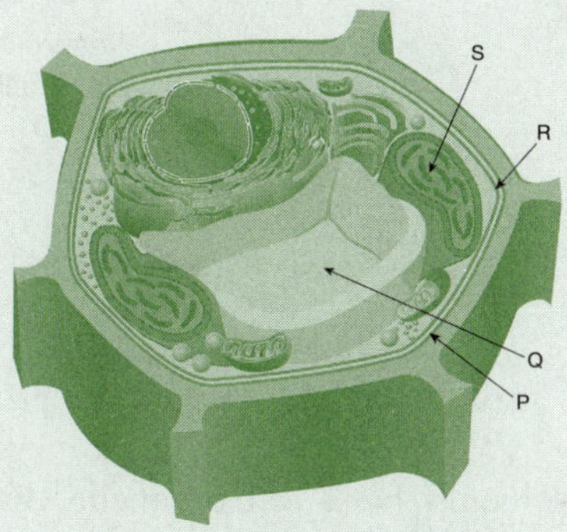

(A) P is present in all eukaryotic and prokaryotic cells without exception.
(B) Q is a membrane bound organelle that remove worn out cell organelles by digesting them.
(C) S provides intermediates for synthesis of various chemical like chlorophyll, steroids, etc.
(D) R is selectively permeable and regulates the exchange of only selected materials.

7. Read the given statements and select he option that correctly identifies them as true (T) and false (F) ones.
(i) Granum is the site of dark reaction during photosynthesis, whereas stroma is the site of light reaction during photosynthesis.
(ii) Lysosomes play an important role during metamorphosis in frog.
(iii) Each 70S ribosome consists of a large 50S subunit and a small 30S subunit.]
(iv) The chromosome in which the centromere is near the end and consequently its one arm is very short and the other arm is very long, is called acrocentric chromosome.

	(i)	(ii)	(iii)	(iv)
(A)	T	T	F	F
(B)	F	T	T	T
(C)	F	F	F	T
(D)	T	F	T	F

8. While observing a stained mount of onion peel under high power compound microscope, Vivaan observed a large cell organelle in the central part of the cell. His teacher told him that this organelle helps in elimination of excess water from the cell. Select the option that correctly identifies this cell organelle?
(A) Nucleus
(B) Mitochondria
(C) Vacuole
(D) Chloroplast

9. Refer to the given figure of a cell and select the correct statement regarding it.

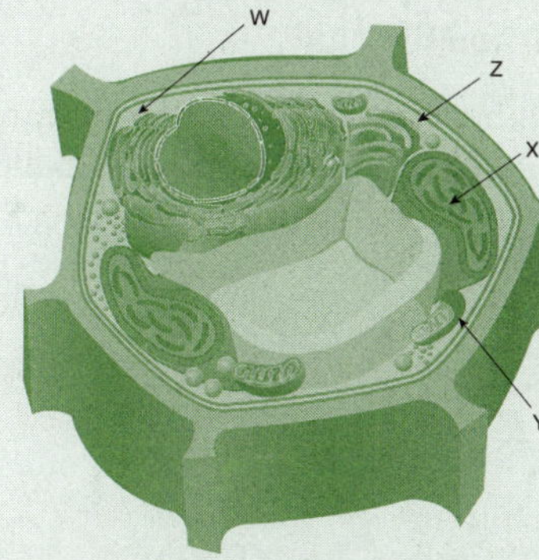

(A) W is engaged in the synthesis of proteins.
(B) Z is present in both prokaryotes and eukaryotes.
In latter, it is 70S type whereas in former, it is 80S type.
(C) Both X and Y are double membrane bound organelles. X is present only in plant cells whereas Y is present only in animal cells.
(D) Acrosome of sperms develop by the modification and maturation of X.

10. Refer to the given figure an select the incorrect statement regarding its labelled parts.

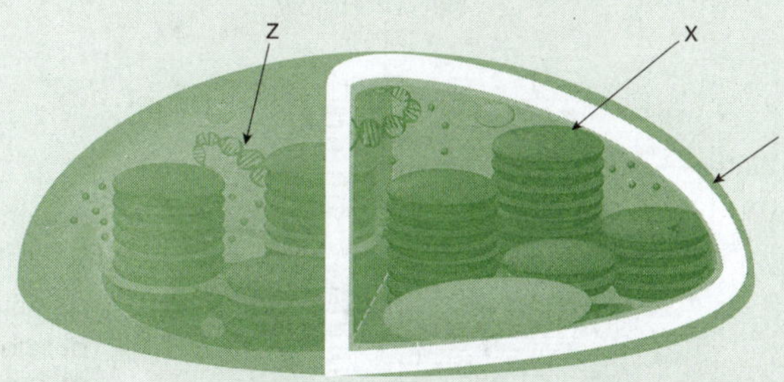

(A) Y has carrier proteins that control passage of molecules.
(B) Z is colorless granular substance containing a circular DNA molecule.
(C) Z is the site of light reaction during photosynthesis.
(D) X contains chlorophyll in its membrane.

11. Which of the following statements about characteristics of organelles are correct?
(i) Chloroplast contains its own DNA.
(ii) Lysosomes are specialised structures that eat worn out cell organelles.
(iii) Ribosomes are only found attached to endoplasmic reticulum.
(iv) Thread-like structures called genes are present in the nucleus.

ARCHIVE CORNER

(A) (i) and (ii) only
(B) (i) only
(C) (ii) and (iv) only
(D) (iii) and (iv) only

12. All members of the Gupta family can roll their tongue. Which of the parts labelled in the given figure carries information regarding this characteristic?

(A) P (B) Q
(C) R (D) S

13. Identify the process shown in the given figure (semipermeable membrane is must for this process) and select the correct statement regarding it.

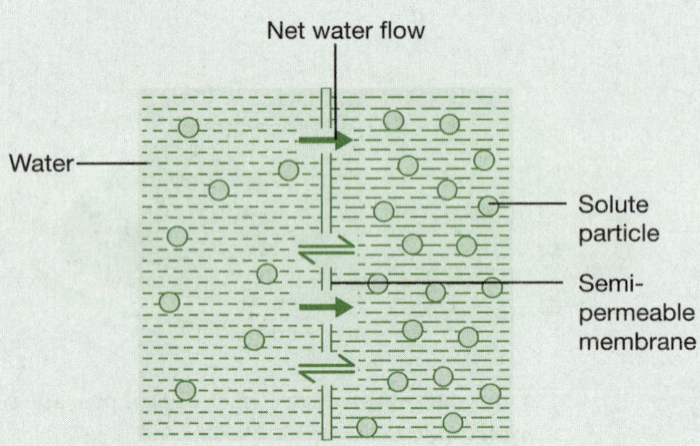

(A) It is a process that can occur in all the mediums.
(B) It is a process that involves flow of solute particles only.
(C) It is a process that is influenced by the number of solute particles dissolved in the solvent.
(D) It helps in the exchange of gases transpiration and photosynthesis.

14. Refer to the given Venn diagram and select the correct statement regarding cell organelles P,Q,R and S.

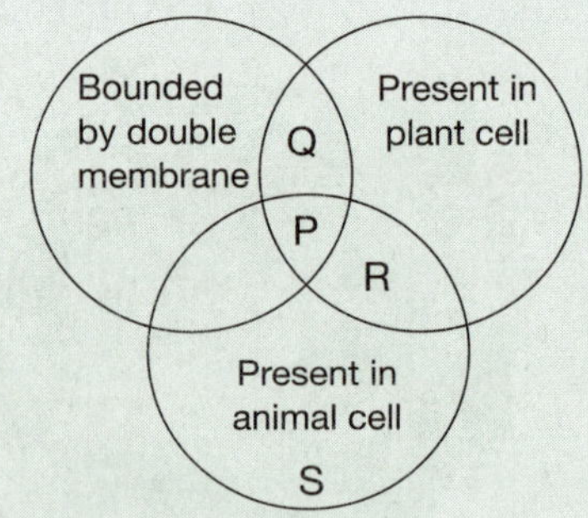

(A) P could be a cell organelle that helps in the storage, modification and packing of secretory products in the vesicle.
(B) R could be an organelle that helps in the oxidation of food stuff.
(C) Q could be an organelle the has structural elements called thylakoids.
(D) S could be an organelle that helps in the synthesis and transport of proteins.

15.

(i) SER	(ii) Golgi apparatus
(iii) Lysosome	(iv) RER
(v) Ribosomes	(vi) Vacuole

Select the option that correctly fills the blanks (a)-(e) using the words given in the box.

1. The (a) ________ provides extensive surface on which h (b) ________ carry out protein synthesis.
2. (c) __________ synthesis hormones such as testosterone and cortisol.
3. (d) _______ Packages materials synthesised in the cell and dispatches them.
4. (e) __________ Plays important role during metamorphosis in frog.

	(a)	(b)	(c)	(d)	(e)
(A)	(iv)	(v)	(i)	(ii)	(iii)
(B)	(iv)	(v)	(vi)	(iii)	(ii)
(C)	(i)	(vi)	(v)	(ii)	(iii)
(D)	(i)	(v)	(iii)	(vi)	(ii)

16. Which of the following statements about the characteristics of organelles are incorrect?
(i) Mitochondria contain their own DNA.
(ii) Lysosomes contain flattened sacs called cisternae.
(iii) Peroxisomes are specialised for carrying our oxidative reactions.
(iv) Ribosomes are always found attached to the Golgi apparatus.

(A) (i) and (ii) only
(B) (ii) and (iv) only
(C) (i),(ii) and (iv) only
(D) (i),(ii).(iii) and (iv)

17. Refer to the graph given here.

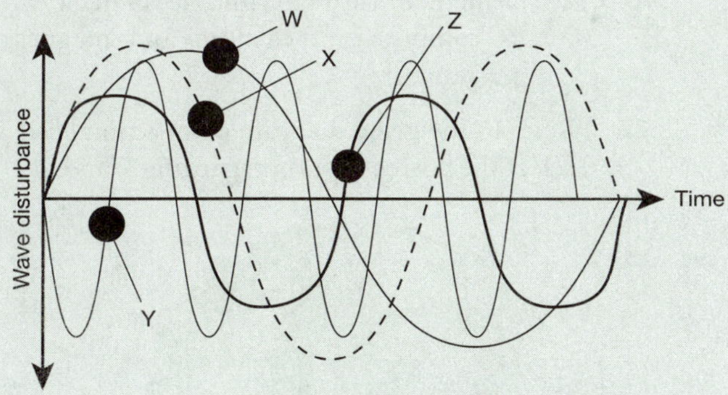

(A) X (B) Z
(C) W (D) Y

18. Which of the following statements is/are incorrect?

I. The inner mitochondria membrane is folded into numerous finger-like processes called cristae.
II. Golgi apparatus is capable of self duplication
III. Smooth endoplasmic reticulum mainly consists of tubules and vesicles whereas rough endoplasmic reticulum mainly consists of cisternae and a few tubules.
IV. Chromatin contains DNA and basic histone proteins in almost equal mass.

(A) II and III only (B) II only
(C) I and IV only (D) I and II only

19. Read the given statements and select the option that correctly identifies them as true (T) and false (F) ones.

(i) Granum is the site of dark reaction during photosynthesis, whereas stroma is the site of light reaction during photosynthesis.
(ii) Lysosomes are formed by the joint activity of endoplasmic reticulum and Golgi complex.
(iii) Each 70S ribosome consists of a large 50 S subunit and a small 30 S subunit.
(iv) The chromosome in which the centromeres near the end and consequently its one arm is very short and the other arm very long, is called acrocentric chromosome.

	(i)	(ii)	(iii)	(iv)
(A)	T	T	F	F
(B)	F	T	T	T
(C)	F	F	F	T
(D)	T	F	T	F

20. Refer to the given structure of a prokaryotic cell and selected the correct statement regarding it.

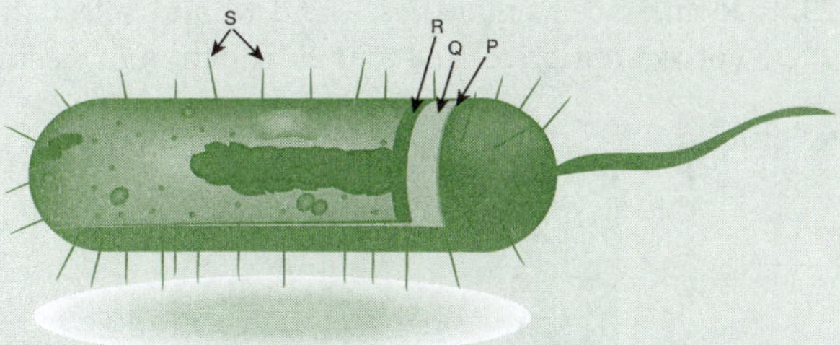

(A) P is layer of non-cellulosic polysaccharides.
(B) Q is double layered in Gram + ve bacteria whereas it is single layered in Gram-ve bacteria.
(C) R is an impermeable covering that restricts entry and exit of molecules into and out of the cell.
(D) S could be tubular outgrowths that are involved in locomotion only.

21. Refer to the given table and select the correct option regarding it.

Type of cell	Solvent	Result
RBC	Ringer's solution	X
RBC	Concentrated salt solution	Y
RBC	Water	Z

	X	Y	Z
(A)	Swollen RBC	Shrunken RBC	Normal RBC
(B)	Normal RBC	Shrunken RBC	Swollen RBC
(C)	Normal RBC	Swollen RBC	Shrunken RBC
(D)	Swollen RBC	Normal RBC	Shrunken RBC

22. "X" is a type of transport across plasma membrane that occurs against the concentration gradient and it requires energy in the form of ATP.

Identify "X" and select the incorrect option regarding it.

(A) Process X helps to maintain concentrations of ions and other substances within living cells.
(B) Process X is very slow and could occur in opposite directions simultaneously.
(C) Process X helps in selective uptake of materials.
(D) Uptake of glucose and some amino acids by some cells occurs with the help of process X.

ARCHIVE CORNER

23. Identify cell organelles L and M and select the correct option related to their function in a cell.

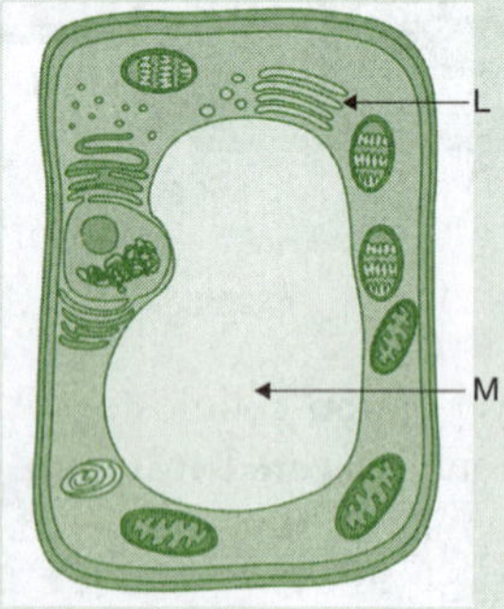

	L	M
(A)	Formation of turgor	Maintenance of cell lysosomes
(B)	Synthesis of lipids	Spindle formation during cell division
(C)	Digestion of foreign materials	Storing by-products
(D)	Synthesis of protein	Production of ATP

24. Which of the following statements is correct?
(A) Lysosomes play an important role at the time of fertilization.
(B) 80S ribosome consists of a large 50S subunit and small 30S subunit.
(C) Smooth endoplasmic reticulum mainly consists of cisternae whereas rough endoplasmic reticulum mainly consists of tubules and vesicles.
(D) All of these

25. Select the incorrectly matched pair.
(A) Mitochondria – Production of energy
(B) Vacuole – Storage of useful minerals
(C) centrosome – Formation of spindle
(D) Peroxisomes – formation of lysosomes

26. Select the correct statement regarding cell wall of plant cells.

(A) Primary cell wall is chiefly composed of a soluble fibrous polysaccharide called suberin.
(B) Secondary cell wall is mainly composed of lignin and is deposited on the outer surface of primary walls whereas they are absent in secondary walls.
(C) Pits are present in primary walls whereas they are absent in secondary walls.
(D) The primary cell walls of adjacent cells are cemented through middle lamella which is composed of calcium and magnesium pectate.

27. Refer to the given diagram of an animal cell and select the correct option regarding P and Q.

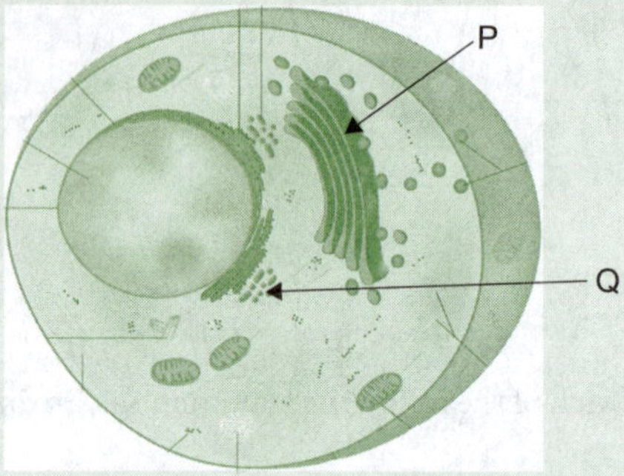

(A) Some of the vesicles of P store digestive enzymes obtained form Q in inactive state to form primary lysosomes.
(B) Polypeptides synthesized at P are transport to Q where they are modified into functional proteins for secretion.
(C) Q synthesises acrosome which plays an important role in the fertilization process in humans.
(D) P is absent in pancreatic cells and cells of salivary glands whereas Q is absent in live cells.

28. A Visking tubing is filled with solution X and placed in a boiling stub of solution Y. After 20 minutes, the Visking tubing appeared to be large and heavier. Which of the following correctly identified solution X and Y?

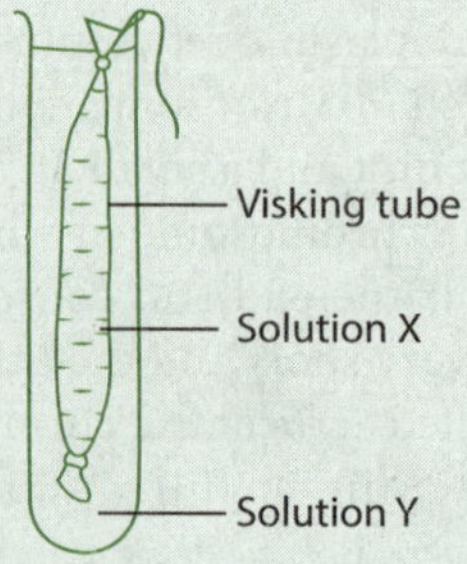

	Solution X	Solution Y
(A)	2 M sucrose solution	0.1 M sucrose solution
(B)	0.5 M sucrose solution	1 M sucrose solution
(C)	1 M sucrose solution	5 M sucrose solution
(D)	Distilled water	2 M sucrose solution

29. What would happen to the air bubble in the following set-up after 30 minutes?

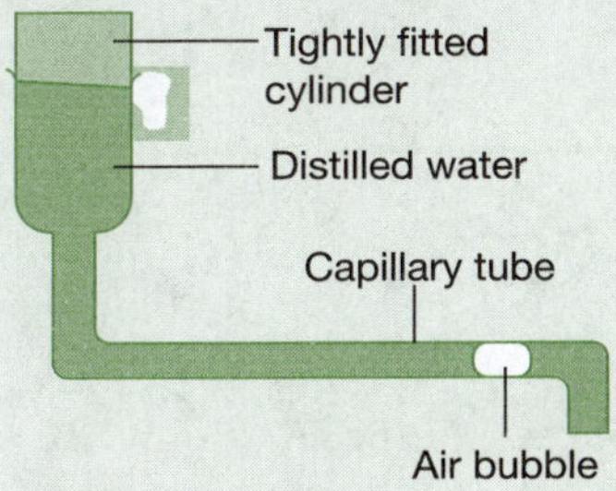

(A) It will disappear.
(B) It will move to the left.
(C) It will move to the right.
(D) It will remain stationary.

30. Refer to the given Venn diagram and select the incorrect option regarding structures V,W,X, Y, and Z.

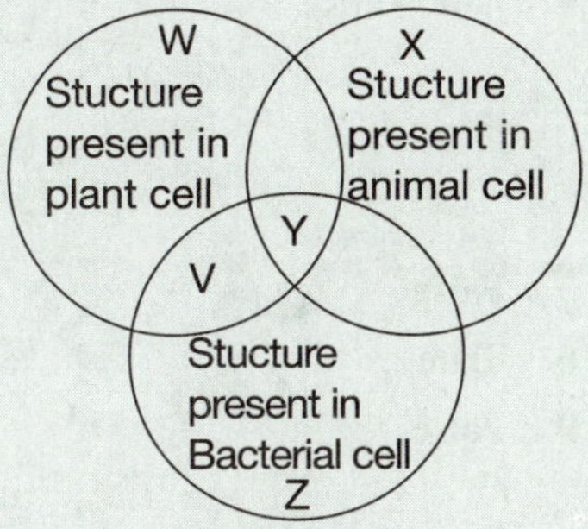

(A) V could be an outermost protective covering which is composed of lipopolysaccharides in bacteria and cellulose in plants.
(B) Y could be a membrane-less organelle involved in protein synthesis whereas Z could be an ingrowth of cell membrane that contains respiratory enzymes.
(C) Both W and X could be double membrane structures but inner membrane of W is smooth whereas that of X is thrown into folds.
(D) W takes part in photosynthesis whereas Z connects genetic material with plasma membrane.

31. Select the incorrect statement.
(A) Osmosis is a slow process, occurs down the concentration gradient and does not expend energy.
(B) Electron microscope uses electromagnets instead of glass lenses and beam of electrons instead of light.
(C) A semipermeable membrane does not allow both solvent and solute molecules to pass through it.
(D) Active transport of materials across plasma membrane is rapid and usually occurs against the concentration gradient involving carrier proteins and energy in the form of ATP.

ANSWER KEYS

Level 1

Fixed Response Type

Multiple Choice Questions

1. D 2. C 3. C 4. A 5. A 6. C 7. A 8. A 9. B 10. A
11. A 12. B 13. C 14. A 15. C 16. C 17. D 18. A 19. C 20. C
21. D 22. B 23. D 24. C 25. A 26. B 27. B 28. C 29. C 30. A

Fill in the Blanks

1. Chromosomes
2. Eukaryotic cells
3. Endoplasmic reticulum
4. Lysosomes
5. Plants
6. Nucleic acids and proteins
7. Cell
8. Prokaryotic
9. Ribosome
10. Cristae

True / False

1. True
2. True
3. False
4. False
5. True
6. True
7. False
8. True
9. False
10. True

Match Type Questions

1. (i)–(d), (ii)–(e), (iii)–(b), (iv)–(f), (v)–(c), (vi)–(a)
2. (i)–(b), (ii)–(d), (iii)–(e), (iv)–(a), (v)–(c)
3. (i)–(c), (ii)–(e), (iii)–(d), (iv)–(a), (v)–(b)

Assertion and Reasons Type Questions

1. B 2. A 3. A 4. A 5. A 6. A 7. D 8. C 9. A 10. B

Level 2

Multiple Choice Questions

1. C 2. B 3. B 4. C 5. A 6. B 7. C 8. D 9. A 10. A
11. C 12. A 13. D 14. D 15. D 16. C 17. D 18. B 19. C 20. B

Archive Corner

1. A	2. B	3. B	4. C	5. A	6. D	7. B	8. C	9. A	10. C
11. A	12. B	13. C	14. C	15. A	16. B	17. C	18. B	19. B	20. A
21. B	22. B	23. A	24. A	25. D	26. D	27. A	28. A	29. B	30. C
31. C									

CHAPTER 2

Tissues

Learning Outcomes

After reading this chapter, you would be able to:

- discuss plant tissues.
- classify the types of plant tissue.
- explain animal tissue.

Geekspeak

- Plant tissue
- Meristematic tissue
- Permanent tissue
- Animal tissue
- Epithelium tissue
- Connective tissue
- Muscular tissue
- Nervous tissue

Introduction

We know that everything starts with cells. Also, in some species, it ends in a cell. For others, however, cells come together to form tissues, tissues form organs, organs form organ systems, and organ systems combine to form organisms.

Prokaryotes are unicellular or colonial organisms that do not have a membrane-bound nucleus or organelles. In contrast, eukaryotic cells have membrane-bound organelles and a membrane-bound nucleus. In larger organisms, cells associate to form tissues. Tissues are groups of similar cells that perform similar or related functions. An organ is a collection of tissues that are grouped together and perform a common function. Organs are not only found in animals, but also in plants. An organ system is a higher level organization made up of functionally related organs. Mammals have many organ systems. For example, the circulatory system carries blood throughout the body and to and from the lungs. Includes organs such as the heart and blood vessels.

Organisms are individual living entities. For example, all trees in a forest are living things. Single-celled prokaryotes and single-celled eukaryotes are also considered organisms and are usually referred to as microorganisms.

Levels of Organization

The living world can be organized into different levels (as shown in Fig 2.1). For example, many individual organisms can be organized into the following levels:

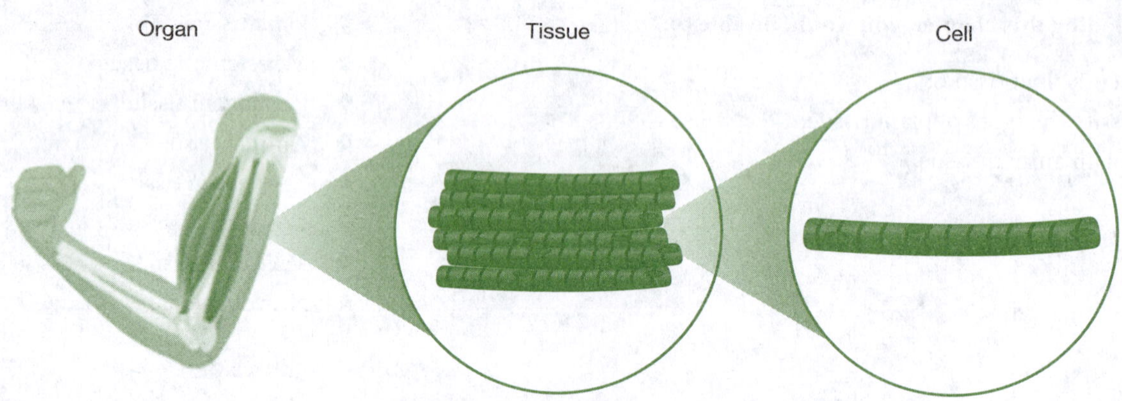

Figure 2.1 Body Organization

- **Cell:** basic unit of structure and function of all living things.
- **Tissue:** group of cells of the same kind.
- **Organ:** A structure made up of one or more types of tissue. The tissues of an organ work together to flavor a particular function. Human organs include the brain, stomach, kidneys, and liver. Plant organs include roots, stems, and leaves.
- **Organ system:** A group of organs that work together to perform a specific function. Examples of human organ systems include the skeletal system, nervous system, and reproductive system.
- **Organism**: A single organism made up of one or more organ systems. In biology, tissue is the biological level of tissue between cells and complete organs. A tissue is a collection of similar cells of the same origin and their extracellular matrix that together perform a specific function. Multiple tissues are then functionally grouped to form organs.

In unicellular organisms, a single cell performs all the vital activities, for example, digestion, respiration, excretion, etc. In case of multicellular organisms, specialized functions are performed by a different group of cells possessing a well-developed division of labour to provide highest possible efficiency of particular function.

As blood flows for transportation of O_2, CO_2, food, hormones, and waste material, muscle cells are involved in movement, etc., so cells make a group called Tissue.

Keystone

Division of labour has been made possible by specialization whereby cells come to have a definite shape, size, structure, and function.

Tissue

A group of cells having similar in shape, having a common origin and usually performing a common function is called tissue.

Keystone

The term tissue was coined by **Nehemiah** Grew. The study of tissues is known as histology.

Importance of Tissues

- Workload of individual cell has decreased.
- Tissues are organized to form organs and organs into organ systems.
- The formation of tissues is linked to the division of labor in multicellular organisms.
- Multicellular organisms have higher survival due to improved body organization and higher efficiency of functions. Plant and animal cells are very different in nature, some of the difference are discussed in Table 2.1.

Table 2.1 Difference between Plant Tissue and Animal Tissue

Plant Tissues	Animal Tissues
Dead supporting tissue is more common than living tissue.	Living tissue is more common than dead tissue.
They require less maintenance energy.	They require more maintenance energy.
There is differentiation of meristematic and permanent tissues.	Such differentiation is absent.
Organization is simple.	Organization is complex with the development of more specialized and localized organs and organ systems.
Tissue organization is towards stationary habit.	Tissue organization is towards high mobility.

Plant Tissue

On the basis of dividing capacity of the tissue, plant tissues are of two types:

1. Meristematic tissue (growing tissue)
2. Permanent tissue

Differences in meristematic and permanent tissue are discussed in Table 2.2.

Table 2.2 Difference between Meristematic and Permanent Tissue

Meristematic Tissue	Permanent Tissue
The cells are capable of division.	The matured cells are incapable of division.
The cells are undifferentiated.	The cells are fully differentiated.
The cells are smaller in size.	The cells wall largest in size.
The cells wall is thin.	The cells wall is relatively thick.
Large prominent nucleus.	Small nucleus.
Vacuoles are small or absent.	Large central vacuole is present.
Intercellular space is absent.	Intercellular space is present.

Meristematic Tissue

These are simple biological tissues containing thin-walled, compactly arranged immature cells that can divide and form new cells (as shown in Fig 2.3).

Features:

- Actively dividing cells are present in growing regions of plants, e.g., root and shoot tips.
- Cells are small and thin wall.
- Intercellular spaces are absent (compact tissue).
- Generally, vacuoles are absent, dense cytoplasm and prominent nuclei are present.
- Large number of cell organelles are present.
- Active metabolic state, stored food is absent.

Classification on the Basis of Origin

- Primary Meristem:
  - Derived directly from the meristems of embryo (Promeristem) (as shown in Fig 2.2).
  - They contribute to the primary growth of plants.
- Secondary Meristem:
  - Formed by permanent tissues.
  - They have cells that originate from permanent tissue.
  - Generally increases plant diameter.

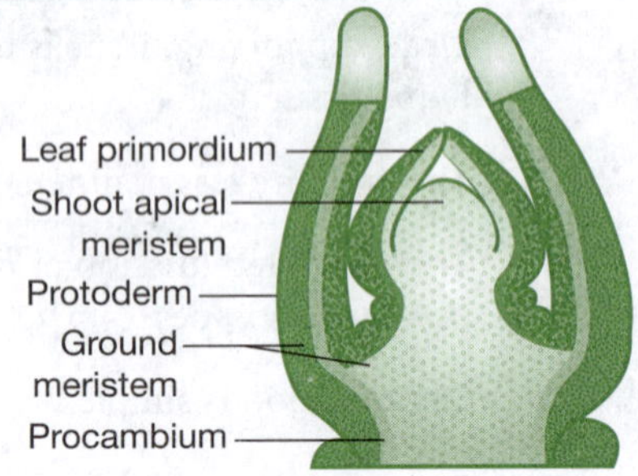

Figure 2.2 Pro-meristem (Embryonal stage)

Meristematic Tissue $\xrightarrow{\text{Differentiation}}$ Permanent Tissue $\xrightarrow{\text{Dedifferentiation}}$ Secondary Meristem

Competition Corner

- Differentiation is the developmental process by which cells acquire a permanent shape and size and perform specific functions.
- Dedifferentiation takes place only in permanent cell. Specialized cells regain the ability to divide and become meristems. Ex. cork cambium.

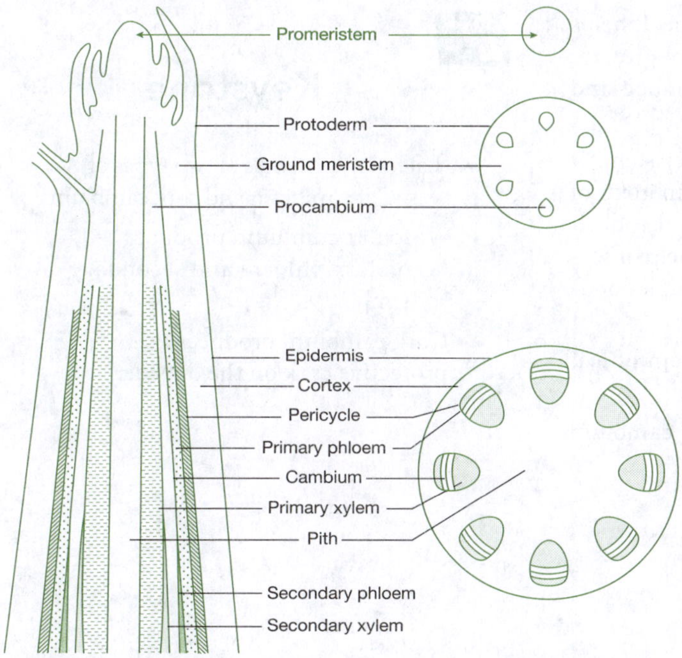

Figure 2.3 Meristems and their Differentiation in L.S. and T.S.

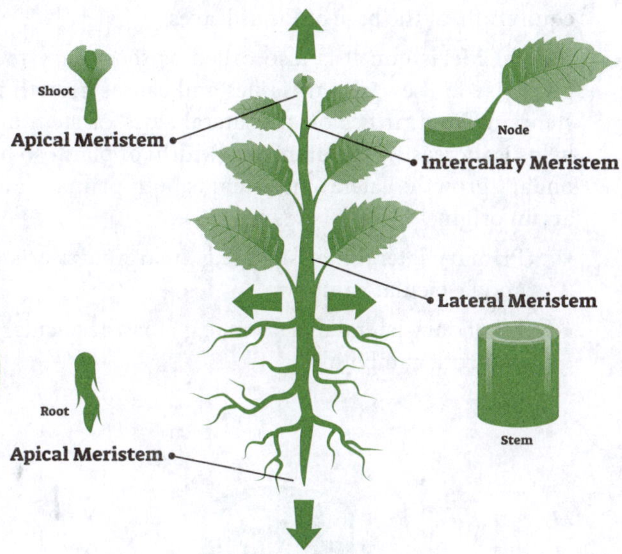

Figure 2.4 Types of Meristems

Classification on the Basis of Location

Meristems are of three types(as shown in Fig 2.4), as follows:

- **Apical Meristem:** It is present at the growing tips of stems and roots (as shown in Fig 2.5). Cell division in this tissue leads to the elongation of stem and root thus it is involved in primary growth of the plant.

  Apical meristem has two regions at embryonic stage.

  First – Promeristem

  Second – Eumeristem

Eumeristem is divided into three regions:

(i) Protoderm (ii) Procambium

(iii) Ground meristem

- **Intercalary Meristem:** It is the part of apical meristem which is left behind during growth period. These are present at the base of leaf and internode region. These lead to the increase in the length of leaf. For example, in grass stem, bamboo stem, mint stem, etc.

Keystone

- Apical and intercalary meristem are responsible for primary growth of plant (growth in length).
- Lateral meristem is responsible for secondary growth.

Competition Corner

In hydrophyte, root cap is multilayered.

- In Pandanus root, cap is absent.
- Root cap contains more amount of Golgi body which secrete mucilage which make the root slimy.
- Apical meristem is absent in Algae and Fungi.

They are short lived and convert into permanent tissue. It helps in longitudinal growth which is also called primary growth. For example, at the base of internode of grasses, bamboo and equisetum, at the base of Pinus leaves.

- **Lateral Meristem:** It is also called as secondary meristem. It gives rise to the vascular tissues and causes growth in girth of stem and root. It lies on the lateral sides of stem and root. It helps is increasing the diameter (width) of plant, so help of secondary growth. Lateral meristem is both primary and secondary in origin.
    - Primary lateral meristem, e.g., marginal meristem of leaf and fascicular cambium.
    - Secondary lateral meristem, e.g., inter fascicular cambium and cork cambium.

Keystone

- Lateral meristem is of two types of vascular cambium and cork cambium.
- Vascular cambium produces secondary phloem and secondary xylem.
- Cork cambium produces a protective cork on the outside.

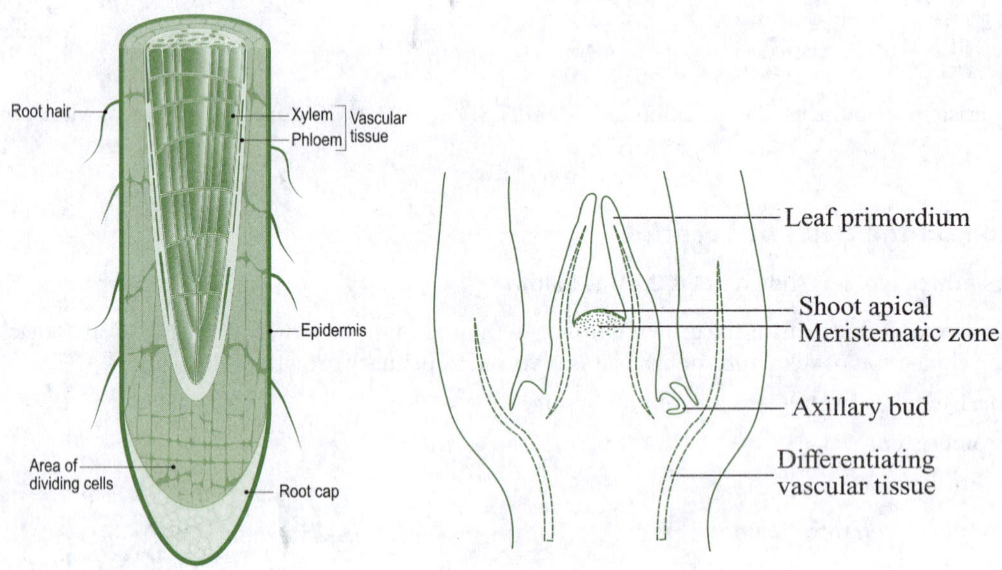

Apical meristem : (a) Root (b) Shoot

Figure 2.5 Types of Apical Meristem

Check Point 1

1. What is position of shoot apical meristem?
2. Which tissue lie at base of internode of plants?
3. Which meristem is responsible for length of plants?
4. Which meristem is responsible for width of plants?

Testing Room 1

Aim: To demonstrate the growth of plants occurs in certain regions only.

Brief procedure: Compare the growth of two onion roots where we cut the tip of one onion root.

Observation: Removal of the root tip stops the root growth.

Explanation: Growth in plants occurs in specific regions. These regions are apical, lateral, and intercalary. These regions contain fast-dividing cell groups called meristematic tissues. When we cut the onion root tip, the apical meristem tissues are cut off. The apical meristem is the main dividing tissue in the root and shoot which increases the length. As a result, the growth of root is stopped in these roots.

Onion roots are fast-dividing cells. We study mitosis from these cells.

Conclusion: Here, we see the root grows only at the tip. It indicates that part of a plant grows only at specific places. If we observe all parts of a plant we see, root tip causes root elongation, shoot tip causes shoot elongation, lateral sides of the stem and root increase the thickness of root and stem. Similarly, lateral sides of leaf grow and make a leaf big.

Length of the root of an onion bulb

Length	Day 1	Day 2	Day 3	Day 4	Day 5
Jar 1	3	3.5	4	4.5	5
Jar 2	3	3.5	4	4*	4

*Root tip removed on day 4

Permanent Tissue

They are composed of cells that have lost the power of division temporarily of permanent. Cells may be living or dead. Cells may be oval, rounded, polygonal, or elongated. The permanent tissue may be dead or living. The division and differentiation of the cells of meristematic tissues give rise to permanent tissues.

They include two types of tissue: protective tissue and supporting tissue

Protective Tissues

These tissues are primarily protective in function. They consist of:

- **Epidermis:** Epidermis forms one cell thick outermost layer of various body organs of plants such as leaves, flowers, stems Epidermis is covered outside by cuticle.
  - Cuticle is a waterproof layer of waxy substance called as cutin which is secreted by the epidermal cells.
  - Cuticle is very thick in xerophytes.
  - Cells of epidermis of leaves are not continuous at some places due to the presence of small pores called as stomata.
  - Each stoma is guarded by a pair of bean shaped cells called as guard cells (as shown in Fig 2.6).
  - These are the only epidermal cells which possess chloroplasts, the rest being colourless.

Functions: The main function of epidermis is to protect the plant from desiccation and infection. Cuticle of epidermis cuts the rate of transpiration and evaporation of water and prevents wilting. Stomata in epidermis allow gaseous exchange to occur during photosynthesis and respiration. Stomata also helps in transpiration.

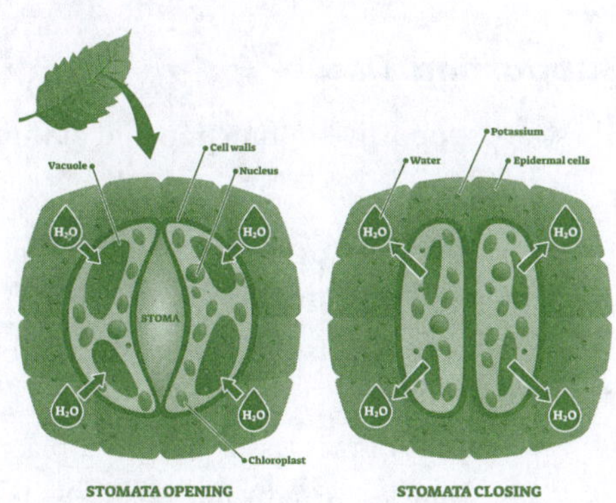

Figure 2.6 Stomatal Opening and Guard Cell

- **Cork or Phellem:** In older roots and stems, tissues at the periphery become cork cells or phellem cells (as shown in Fig 2.7). Cork is made up of dead cells with thick walls and do not have any intercellular spaces. The cell walls in cork deposit waxy substance called as suberin. The cells of cork become impermeable to water and gases due to the deposition of suberin. The cork cells are without any protoplasm but are filled with resins or tannins.

Figure 2.7 Epidermis, Cork Cambium, and Cork Layer

Functions and Uses: Cork is protective in function. Cork cells prevent desiccation, infection, and mechanical injury. Imperviousness, lightness, toughness, compressibility, and elasticity make the cork commercially valuable. Cork is used for insulation, as shock absorber in linoleum. Cork is used in the making of a variety of sport goods such as cricket balls, table tennis, shuttle-cocks, wooden paddles, etc.

Testing Room 2

Aim: Peel the rhoeo leaf and observe it under the microscope.

Observation: We see flat epidermal cells and a few stomatal cells.

Explanation: Rhoeo is a common ornamental plant. Its leaf is easily peeled off and can be observed under the microscope. The thin layer consists of epidermal cells. The epidermal cells are flat cells with low intercellular spaces and thick cell wall. It contains small pores called stoma for exchange of vapours and gases. Two bean-shaped guard cells regulate the opening and the closing of a stoma.

Supporting Tissue

These are supportive in function and of three types.

- **Parenchyma:**
  - It is a living and basic packing tissue which consists of relatively unspecialized cells.
  - Cells of this tissue have thin cell wall which is made up of cellulose.
  - Cells of this tissue have cytoplasm with small nucleus and large vacuole.
  - They are usually loosely packed because intercellular spaces are present between cells.
  - **Function:** This tissue provides support to the plant and help in storage of food.

> **Keystone**
>
> Parenchyma is the first evolved permanent tissue which is present in all soft part of plant (therefore called as universal tissue).

- **Modification of parenchyma:**
  - **Parenchyma:** Parenchyma that stores food is called as parenchyma (as shown in Fig 2.8).
  - **Chlorenchyma:** It is a parenchyma that stores abundant quantity of chloroplast. It helps in synthesis food.
  - **Aerenchyma:** It is a type of parenchyma that is made up of rounded cells which surrounds the large air cavities. It is found in aquatic plants of hydrophytes. It provides buoyancy to aquatic plants to help them to float.
  - **Idioblast:** Parenchyma involved in excretory substance storage are called as idioblast. They help in storing materials like resin, tannin, gums, or oils.

Keystone

Collenchyma are usually absent in all the wood parts, roots, stem, and leaves of monocots and root of dicot plant while present in herbaceous stem and leaves of dicot plant.

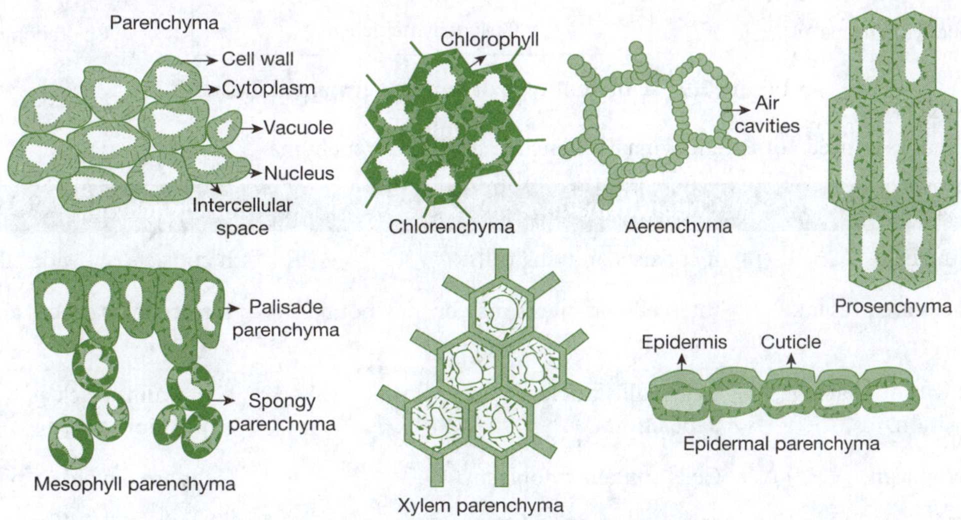

Figure 2.8 Different Modification of Parenchyma

- **Collenchyma:**

Cells of this tissue are living, elongated or vary in structure. Cells of this tissue are irregularly thickened at the corners due to the deposition of pectin. It is present below the epidermis of leaf stalk and leaf margin. Intercellular spaces are very little or absent between cells of this tissue.

  - **Functions:** It provides mechanical support (tensile strength) and elasticity. It allows easy bending in various parts of plant (leaf and stem) without breaking. It provides flexibility to plant.

- **Sclerenchyma:**

Sclerenchyma cells are dead, narrow, and long cells and they are devoid of protoplasm. The walls of cells of sclerenchyma are greatly thickened with deposition of lignin. Such cell walls are called lignified. The cells of sclerenchyma are closely packed without intercellular spaces. They are found in stems (around the vascular bundle), roots, veins of leaves, hard coverings of seed and nuts.

  - **Functions:** It is the main mechanical tissue that provides mechanical support. It makes the plant hard and stiff. Sclerenchymatous cells are of two types in structure—Fibres and Sclereids.
  - **Sclerenchyma Fibres:** They constitute the major mechanical tissue of the plants (as shown in Figure 2.9). Commercial fibres obtained from plants (e.g., Jute, flax, hemp, husk of coconut) usually are sclerenchymatous fibres.

Keystone

Lignin is a complex polymer that acts as a cement and hardens cell wall. Lignin makes the cell wall impermeable so important substances are unable to pass through it. As a result, cell that are heavily lignified do not have living content (protoplasm).

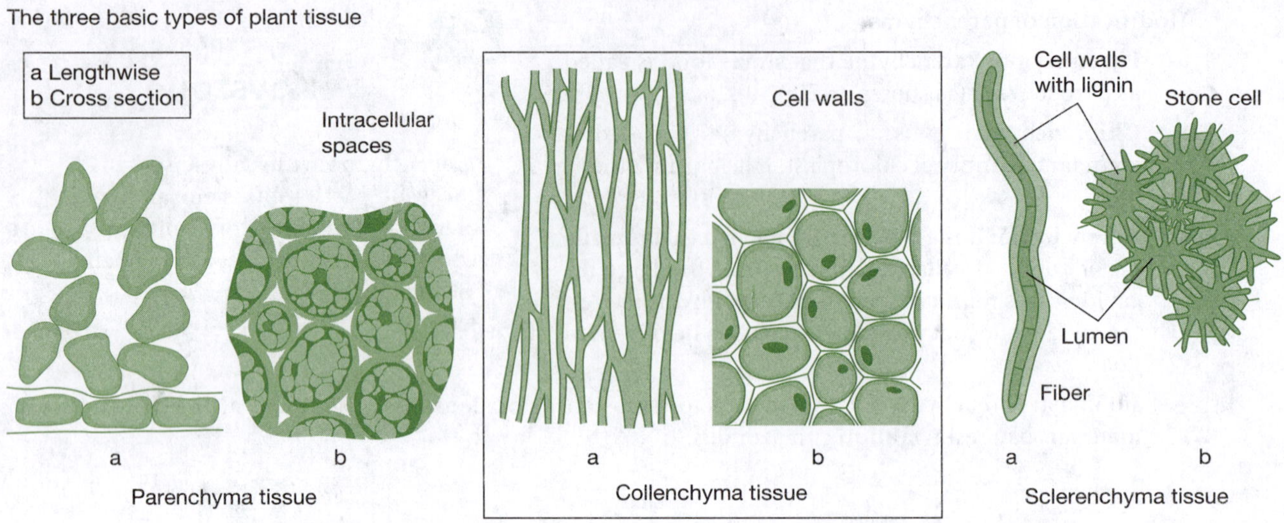

Figure 2.9 Different type of Simple Permanent Tissues

Table 2.3 Differences between of Parenchyma, Collenchyma and Sclerenchyma

Parenchyma	Collenchyma	Sclerenchyma
It consists of living cells.	It consists of living cells.	It consists of dead cells.
Intercellular spaces are present.	Intercellular spaces may or may not be present.	Intercellular spaces are absent.
Cell wall is thin without having secondary deposition.	Cell wall is thick as it has pectin deposition.	Cell wall is thick as it has lignin deposition.
Cell contains cytoplasm.	Cells contain cytoplasm.	Cells are devoid of cytoplasm.
They have vital functions like synthesis and storage of food.	They have both vital as well as mechanical function, providing support and elasticity to plant body.	It is chiefly a mechanical tissue.

- **Sclereids (grit or stone cells):** They are highly thickened and irregularly shaped dead cells. Sclereids provide strength to seed covering and are present in drupe fruit (mango, coconut, walnut).

Complex Permanent Tissue

It consists of more than one type of cells which work together as a unit. It helps in transportation of organic materials, water and minerals. It is also known as conducting or vascular tissue. Xylem and phloem together form vascular bundles.

Xylem

It is also known as wood. It is a vascular and mechanical tissue. Thick-walled cells are found in the form of tubular passages.

Xylem consists of four types of cells called as elements (as shown in Fig 2.10):

- **Tracheids:** They are elongated angular dead cells (primitive elements) mainly involved in conduction of water and minerals in gymnosperms.
- **Vessels:** They are advance elements (generally found in angiosperms). Vessels are cylindrical tube-like structures placed one above the other end to end which form a continuous channel for efficient conduction of water.

Keystone

Ropes and mats that we commonly use in our everyday life for various purposes are obtained from sclerenchyma cells. Linen and hemp are prepared from the fibres obtained from sclerenchyma. Linen and hemp are used in preparation of textiles.

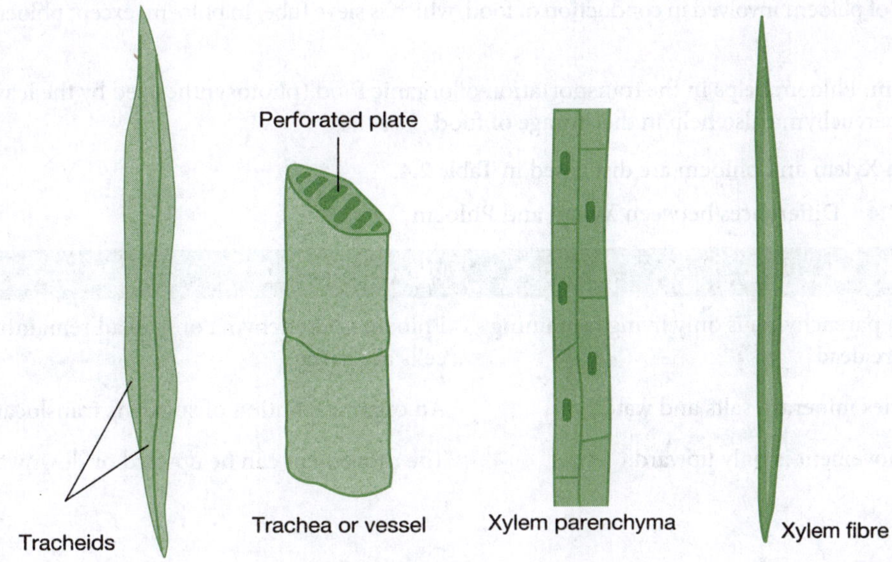

Figure 2.10 Xylem Elements

- **Xylem parenchyma:** They are small and thick-walled parenchymatous cells subjected for storage of starch (food).
- **Xylem sclerenchyma:** They are non-living fibres with thick walls and narrow cavities provide mechanical support. Except xylem parenchyma all other xylem elements are dead.

Hadrome: Tracheids and vessels are collectively called hadrome, as main conducting elements in xylem.

Function of Xylem: The main function of xylem is the upward movement of water and dissolved minerals (ascent of sap) from the roots to different parts of shoots. Tracheids, vessels, and xylem sclerenchyma provide mechanical strength to the plant body.

> **Keystone**
>
> The annual rings present in the trunk of a tree are xylem rings. By counting the number of annual rings, we can determine the age of a tree.

Phloem

Phloem is a living conducting or vascular tissue (as shown in Fig 2.11).

Phloem consists of four types of elements:

- **Sieve tubes:** Sieve tubes are slender tube-like structures made up of elongated, thin-walled cells placed end to end. The end walls of sieve tube cells are perforated by numerous pores are called as sieve plates. Nucleus of sieve cell degenerates at maturity; however, cytoplasm persists.
- **Companion cells:** Companion cells have dense cytoplasm and prominent nuclei. Sieve cells and companion cells are so called sister cells because they originate from single mother cell.
- **Phloem sclerenchyma:** They give mechanical support to sieve tubes.
- **Phloem parenchyma:** They store food and help in radial conduction of food.

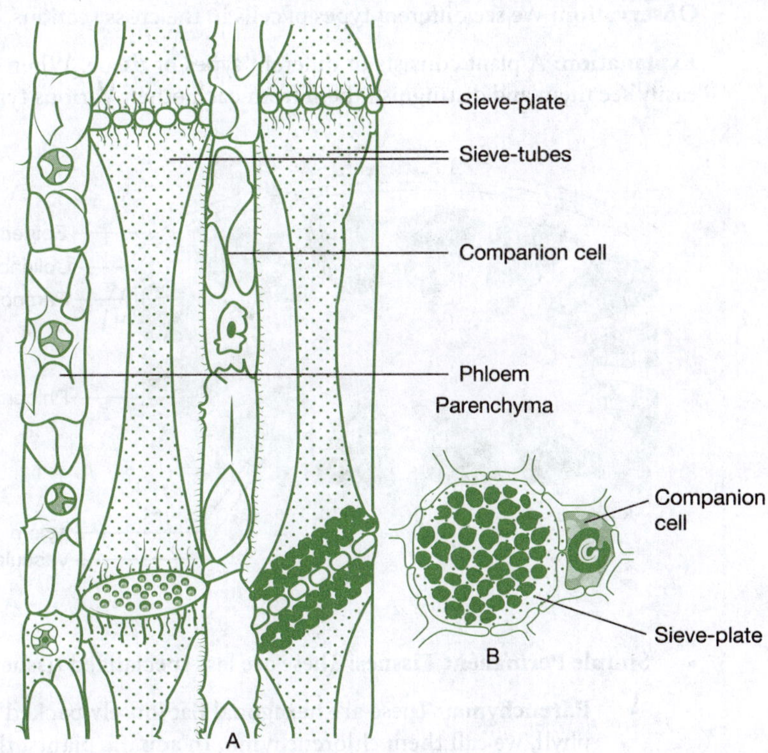

Figure 2.11 Phloem

Leptome: Main part of phloem involved in conduction of food, which is sieve tube. In phloem, except phloem sclerenchyma, all elements are living.

Functions of Phloem: Phloem helps in the transportation of organic food (photosynthesized by the leaves) to all the parts of a plant. Phloem parenchyma also help in the storage of food.

Differences between Xylem and phloem are discussed in Table 2.4.

Table 2.4 Differences between Xylem and Phloem

Xylem	Phloem
Xylem parenchyma is only living remaining cells are dead.	Phloem sclerenchyma only dead remaining all cells are living.
It carries minerals, salts and water.	An organic solution of sugars is translocated.
The movement is only upward.	The movement can be upward or downward.

Keystone

Sieve tubes are devoid of nuclei, but still they remain living. This is because of the fact that the sieve tubes are dependent on the adjoining companion cells which develop from the same meristematic cell. The two cells together form a functional unit.

Testing Room 3

Aim: To observe the cross-section of the stem of a plant under the microscope.

Observation: We see different types of cells in the cross sections.

Explanation: A plant consists of different types of tissue. When we put them on the microscopic slide, we can easily see them and distinguish them from each other. Various types of cells are:

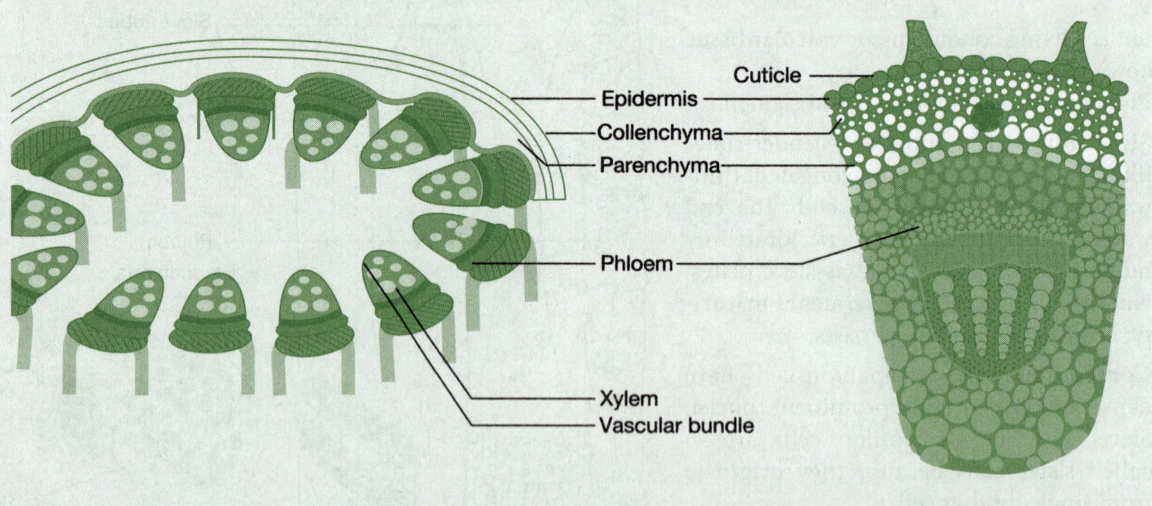

- **Simple Permanent Tissues:** These are less specialized tissues made of similar type of cells. They are:
  - **Parenchyma:** These are hexagonal flat loosely packed cells which store food. If they contain chlorophyll, we call them chlorenchyma. In aquatic plants, they contain big vacuoles to provide buoyancy. We call them aerenchyma.

- **Collenchyma:** These are elongated, irregularly thickened cells with low intercellular spaces. They provide support to the plant. Example, tendril and stem of a climber.
- **Sclerenchyma:** These are elongated, thickened cells with lignified walls and no intercellular spaces. They are dead cells and provide strength and protection to the plant. Example, Coir of coconut.

- **Complex Permanent Tissues:** These tissues contain different types of cells combined to form a specific function.
  - **Xylem:** These are water-conducting tissues of a plant. They consist of xylem fibres, tracheid, vessels, and xylem parenchyma cells. Tracheids and vessels have a tubular structure to conduct water while xylem fibres provide support and parenchyma stores food.
  - **Phloem:** Phloem is food conducting tissues. They consist of sieve cells, sieve tubes, companion cells, phloem fibres, and phloem parenchyma cells. Food passes through long conductive tubes: sieve cells and sieve tubes. Companion cells assist them in the transport while fibre cells provide support and parenchyma provide food.

Note: All fibrous cells are dead cell and serve only supportive and protective purposes.

❖ INTEXT QUESTIONS

1. Which tissue is formed by division and differentiation of meristematic tissue?
   Ans: Permanent tissue
2. Differentiate between meristematic and permanent tissue.

Meristematic Tissue	Permanent Tissue
Cells are small and may be rounded, oval, rectangular or polygonal.	Cells are large and of different shapes according to the types of tissue.
Cells are thin-walled.	Cells are thin or thick-walled.
Cells are rich in cytoplasm.	Cytoplasm is present as a layer along the cell wall.
A prominent nucleus is present.	Nucleus is relatively small in size.
Vacuoles are small; may even be absent.	Usually, a large central vacuole is present.
Intercellular spaces are absent.	Intercellular spaces are often present.
Cells are undifferentiated and given rise to different permanent tissues.	Cells are differentiated.
Power of cells division is present.	Lack the power of cell division.
Always living.	Maybe living or dead.

Check Point 2

5. Write the name of simple of permanent tissue which have lignified elongated dead cell.
6. Which tissue makes up the husk of coconut?
7. Which chemical is deposited in the cell wall of sclerenchymatous cells?
8. Write the name of tissue which provides tensile and mechanical strength.

Animal Tissue

Based upon the structure and functions, simple tissues in multicellular animals are categorized into four types. These are:

(a) Epithelial tissue (b) Connective tissue

(c) Muscular tissue (d) Nervous tissue

Epithelial Tissue

'Epi' means above and 'thelium' means growing layer. Always grows on some other types of tissues. Cells of epithelium are set very close to each other and the tissue rests on a non-cellular basement membrane. Consists of single layer of cells. There is no direct blood supply to this tissue. It is non-nervous in nature.

Functions

The epithelial tissue performs a number of functions. Some of them are:

- It is primarily protective in function and covers all the organs from outside. Example, epidermis of skin and forms the linings of hollow organs.
- It prevents the underlying cells from drying, injury, and chemical effects.
- Epidermis of skin also protects the body from infections.

Epithelial tissues (as shown in Fig 2.12) are classified as:

Squamous Epithelium

It is also called pavement epithelium because its compact structure gives an impression like tiles on floor. Cells are polygonal in surface view. It forms the delicate lining of cavities (mouth, oesophagus, nose, pericardium, alveoli, etc.) blood vessels and covering of the tongue and skin.

Epithelial cells are arranged in many layers (stratum) to prevent wear and tear in skin. This pattern is stratified squamous epithelium.

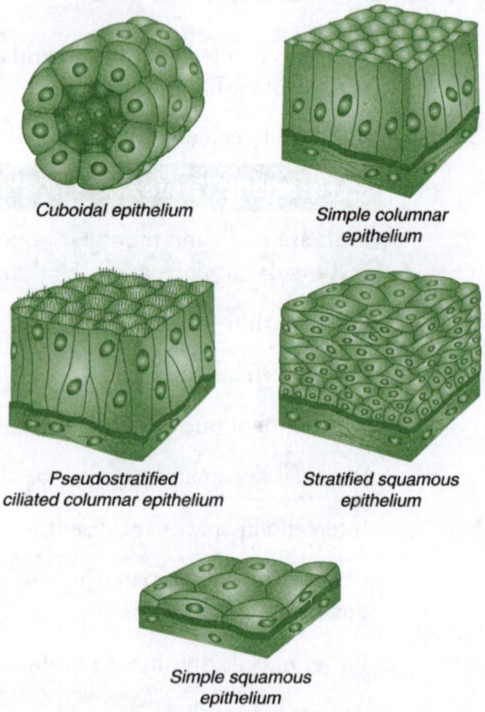

Figure 2.12 Various types of epithelial tissues

Keystone

Pseudostratified epithelium means a tissue which looks stratified, but it is not because its cells are arranged with their nuclei at different level.

Competition Corner

Skin is called as organ because it is made up of different tissues which collectively perform a specialized function (protection). The two main layers of skin:

(a) epidermis (epithelial tissue),

(b) dermis (connective tissue).

Cuboidal Epithelium

They are cube like cells that fit closely, cells look like squares in section (as shown in Fig 2.13), but free surface appears hexagonal. It is found in kidney tubules, thyroid vesicles and in glands (salivary glands, sweat glands). It forms germinal epithelium of gonads (testes and ovaries). It is involved in absorption, excretion, and secretion. It also provides mechanical support.

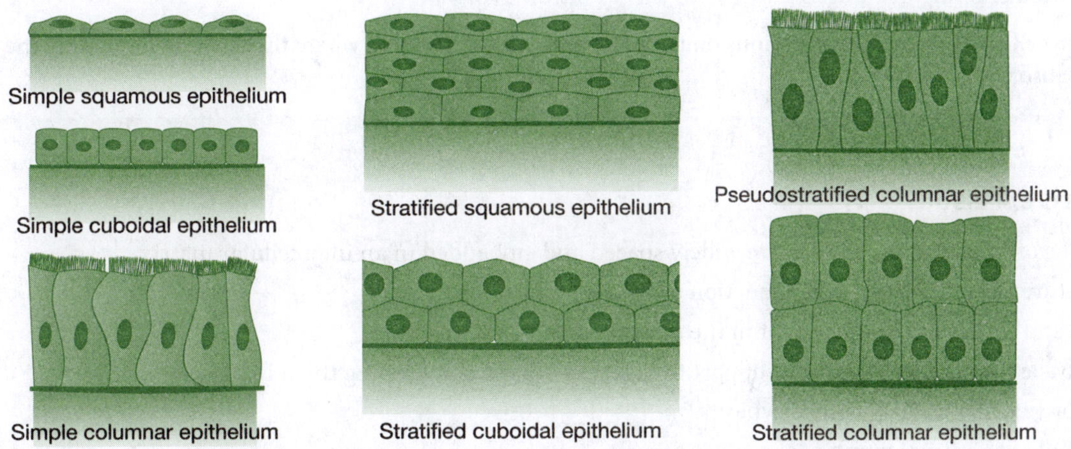

Figure 2.13 Different kinds of Simple and Stratified Epithelium

Columnar Epithelium

Columnar means 'pillar-like' epithelium. It forms lining of stomach, small intestine and colon, forming mucous membranes. Border of microvilli is present at the free surface end of each cell which increases absorption efficiency in small intestine.

Ciliated Epithelium

In this type of epithelium, the cells may be cuboidal or columnar. On its free surface are present very fine hair-like protoplasmic outgrowths. It is found lining the body of nephrons, trachea, and fallopian tube.

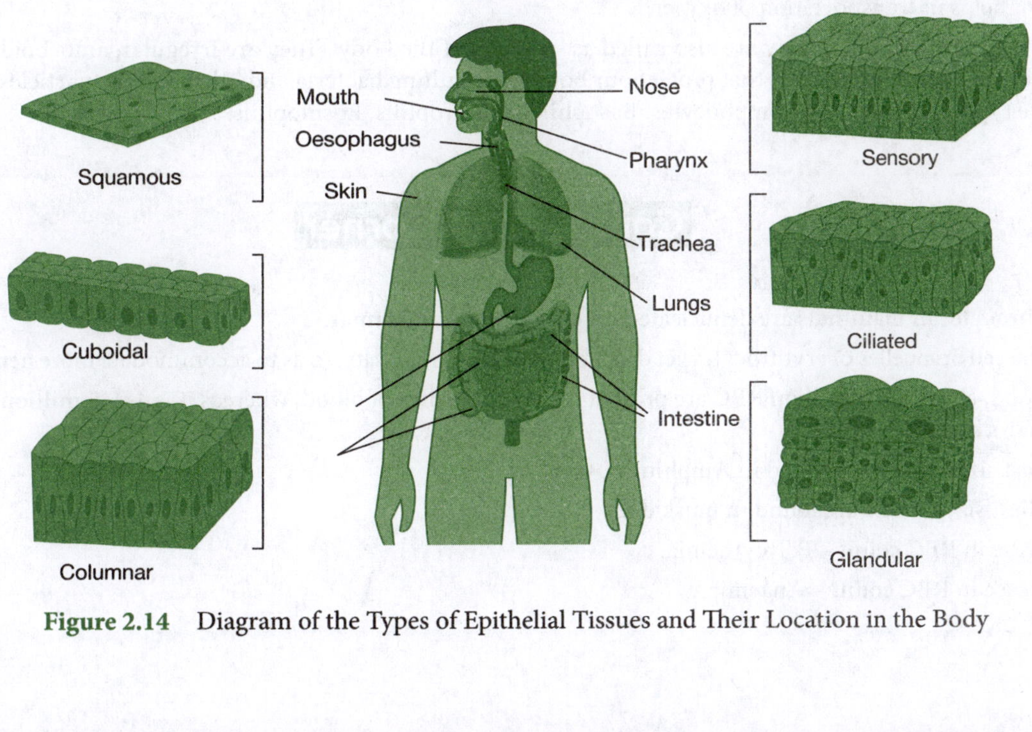

Figure 2.14 Diagram of the Types of Epithelial Tissues and Their Location in the Body

Competition Corner

The functions of cilia and microvilli present on surface of epithelial tissue are:

Cilia show rhythmic beating movements in the respiratory tract. Thus, this beating of cilia helps to keep unwanted particle from entering the lungs.

The microvilli are finger-like projections on the epithelial cells of intestine where they help in increasing the surface area for absorption.

Connective Tissue

- The cells of the connective tissue are widely spaced and embedded in an intercellular matrix.
- The nature of matrix decides the function of tissue.
- White and yellow fibres are present in the matrix.
- Their basic function is to provide support to different organs and keeping them in place.
- Fluid or vascular tissue: It is two types:
  (i) Blood (ii) Lymph

Blood

- Blood is a fluid connective tissue.
- It is softest connective tissue.
- It divides into two parts.

Blood composition:

- **Plasma:** Plasma constitutes 55% of blood, plasma itself is 90-91% water. The remaining 10% of plasma is made up of proteins, salts, hormones and other materials meant for transportation of digested food, gases, excretory products etc.
- **Corpuscles:** Corpuscles forms 45% of blood, they contain RBC, WBC and Platelets.
  - **RBCs:** They are also called as erythrocytes, containing red-coloured respiratory pigment called hemoglobin that helps in transportation of oxygen.
  - **WBC's (Leucocytes):** They are also called as 'Soldiers of the body'. They are irregular, amoeboid, phagocytic cells (as shown in Fig 2.15) that protect our body by engulfing bacteria and other foreign particles. They are of five types – Monocytes, Lymphocytes, Basophiles, Neutrophils, Eosinophils.

Competition Corner

- Erythrocytes in mammals are denucleated except in camel and lamas.
- All the cell organelles of erythrocytes get degenerated during maturity, so as to accommodate more hemoglobin.
- In blood, about 5-4.4 million RBC are present in one cubic mm of blood, whereas it is 4-4. 5 million per cc in woman's blood.
- Largest sized RBCs are found in Amphiuma.
- Smallest sized RBCs are found in musk deer.
- Increase in RBC count – Polycythemia.
- Decrease in RBC count – Anaemia.

- **Blood Platelets or Thrombocytes:** They are spindle-shaped cells which are involved in clotting of blood.

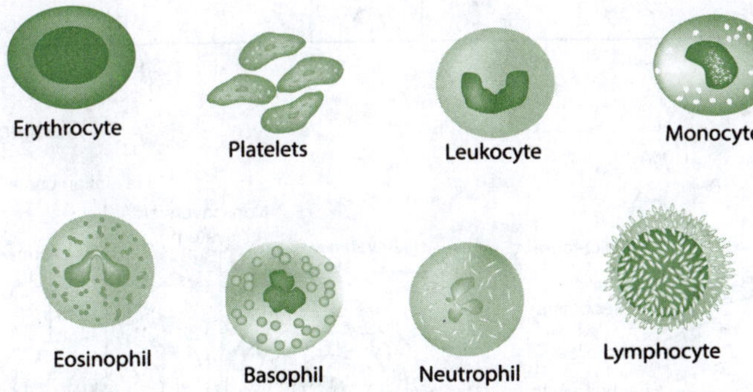

Figure 2.15 Types of blood cells

> **Keystone**
>
> In each cube mm of blood are present 2,00,000 to 3,00,000 platelets.
>
> Increase in platelet count – Thrombocytosis.
>
> Decrease in platelet count – Thrombocytopenia.

> **Competition Corner**
>
> In each cubic mm of blood, 6000–8000 leucocytes are present.
> Most abundant WBC: Neutrophil
> Largest WBC – Monocyte
> Smallest WBC – Lymphocyte
> Decrease in WBC count – Leucopenia.
> Increase in WBC count – Leucocytosis.

Functions of Blood:

- Transportation of digested food.
- Transportation of oxygen to body cells.
- Transportation of carbon dioxide from body cells to lungs.
- Transportation of excretory substances to kidneys for elimination.
- Transportation of hormones.
- WBCs help in fighting against diseases.
- Platelets help in clotting of blood.

> **Keystone**
>
> Heparin, is a natural anti-coagulant in our blood that prevents the blood from clotting inside the blood vessels.

Lymph

It is colourless or light yellow-coloured fluid that bathes all the body organs and is filled in spaces between them. It is blood without the RBC's and blood proteins. Lymph is made up of plasma and lymphocytes.

Functions: It acts as a 'middle man' for the exchange of various materials between the blood and various body tissues.

Skeletal Tissue

It is hard connective tissue that forms supportive framework of the body (as shown in Fig 2.16). It is of two types:

- **Bone:** Matrix of bone is very hard because of salts such as calcium phosphate, $CaCO_3$ (60 – 70%), etc., and a protein ossein.

The long bones are usually hollow containing a cavity called bone marrow cavity. It is full of bone marrow. In the solid matrix are present longitudinal canals called haversian canals. The matrix is present in the form of layers called lamellae. These lamellae are present in the form of crescentic rings around the marrow cavity and around the canals. In these lamellae are present ring-shaped fluid-filled spaces called lacunae. The lacunae contain bone-forming cells called, osteocytes.

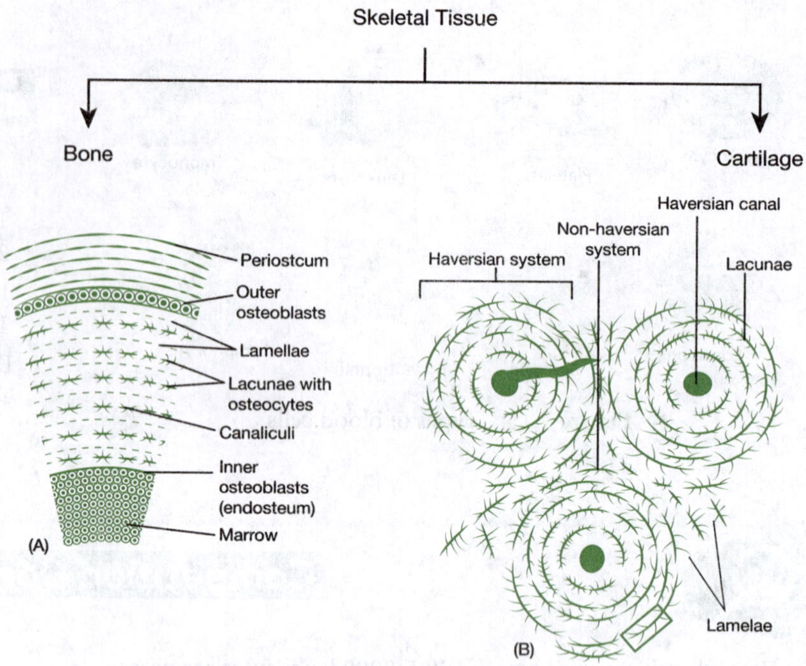

(A) T.S. of amphiblan bone. (B) T.S. of mammalian bone.

Figure 2.16 A part of Decalcified Bone in T.S. and L.S.

> **Keystone**
>
> Covering of the bone is called as periosteum. Bone is the hardest tissue of our body but the hardest substance in our body is enamel, found as covering on teeth.

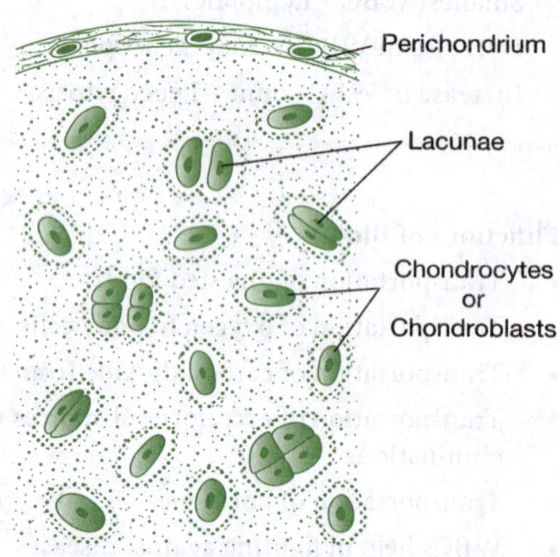

Figure 2.17 T. S. of Hyaline Cartilage

- **Cartilage:** This tissue is elastic and strong but softer than bone.

Elasticity is due to the presence of chondrin (protein). Cells are called as chondrocyte (as shown in Fig 2.17), which are widely-spaced and matrix is reinforced by fibres. It forms the embryonic skeleton of vertebrates and the adult skeleton of sharks and rays. It also occurs in the human body in the ears, tip of the nose and surrounding ends of joints such as knees.

Connective tissue proper

It is the most abundant type of connective tissue.

It is further divided into following types:

- **Areolar Tissue:** It is the most widely distributed connective tissue in the body. This tissue fills spaces inside organs and is found between the skin and muscles, around blood vessels, nerves and in the bone marrow (as shown in Fig 2.18). These are of types:

- **Functions:**
    - It helps to hold various tissues together in any organ.
    - It helps to repair body tissues after injury
    - Mast cells in this tissue are concerned with allergy.
    - It binds skin with underlying tissues.

Keystone

Osteoclast – Bone resorbing cell
Osteoblast – Immature bone cell
Osteocyte – Mature bone cell
Volkmann Canal – Canal which run perpendicular to haversian canal

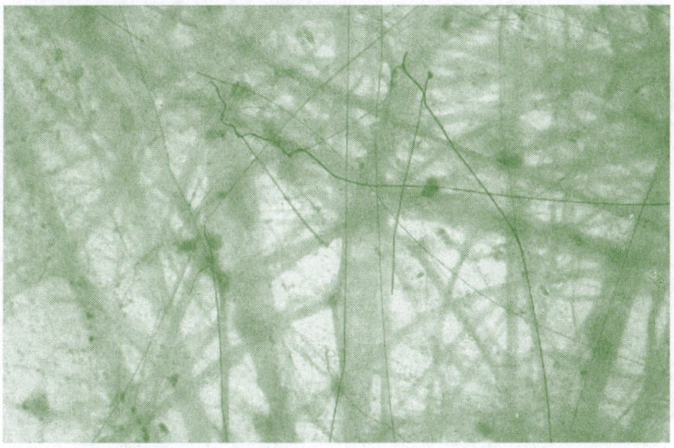

Figure 2.18 Areolar Tissue

Keystone

- **Covering of Cartilage** – Perichondrium
- **Chondroblast** – Immature cartilage cells
- **Chondrocyte** – Mature cartilage cells

- **Adipose Tissue:** These are oval and round cells (as shown in Fig 2.19), filled with fat globules. The cells are called as adipocytes.
    - **Function:**
        - It acts as insulator and prevents loss of heat from the body.
        - It helps in the storage of food in the form of fats.
        - It forms cushion like shock-absorbing structures below vital organs such as heart, kidney, eyeballs, etc.

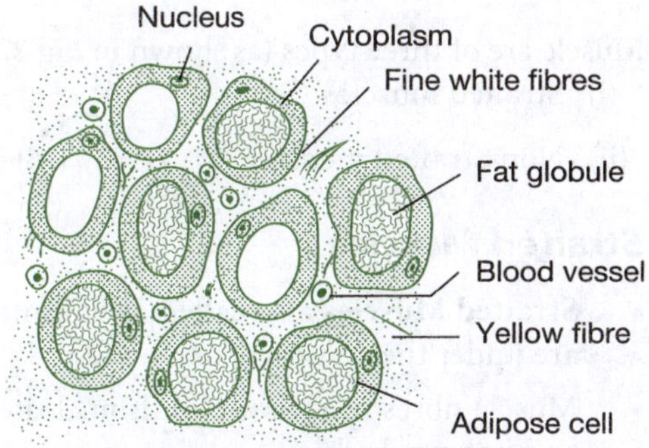

Figure 2.19 Adipose Tissue

- **White Fibrous Connective Tissue:** They are very little matrix containing abundant white fibres forming layers (as shown in Fig 2.20). Bundles of this tissue are called as tendons, which attaches muscles to the bones.
- **Yellow Fibrous Connective Tissue:** They are very elastic due to the presence of a network of yellow fibres in its matrix called as ligament which attaches bone to bone (as shown in Fig 2.21).
- **Reticular Tissue:** The cells in this tissue are star-shaped and form a network-like structure. Reticular fibres are made of Reticulin protein. It is found in the spleen, lymph nodes, tonsils, etc.
    - **Functions:** It forms lymphoid tissues in the body.

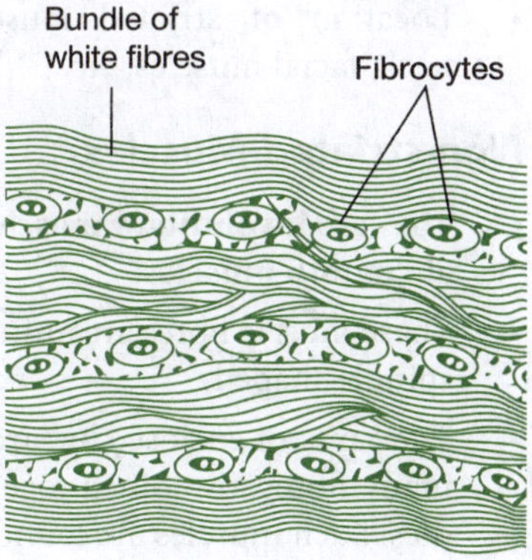

Figure 2.20 White Fibrous Connective Tissue

Muscular Tissue

Muscular tissue is distinguished from other tissues by its unique ability to contract and relax and thereby perform mechanical work. It is responsible for movement of body organs and location of body.

General Structure of Muscle

(a) The structural unit of muscle tissue it the muscle cells which because of its elongated shape is also called muscle fibre.
(b) The contractility is due to the presence of contractile proteins (Actin and Myosin) in the muscle fibre.
(c) The plasma Membrane of muscle cells is called sarcolemma and endoplasmic reticulum of muscle cell is called sarcoplasmic reticulum.

Table 2.5 Differences between Tendon and Ligament

Tendon	Ligament
It is made up of white fibrous tissue.	It is made up of yellow elastic tissue.
Fibroblasts lie in almost continuous.	Fibroblasts lie scattered.
Tendon connects a skeletal muscle to a bone.	Ligament connects a bone to another bone.
It is tough and inelastic.	It is strong but elastic.

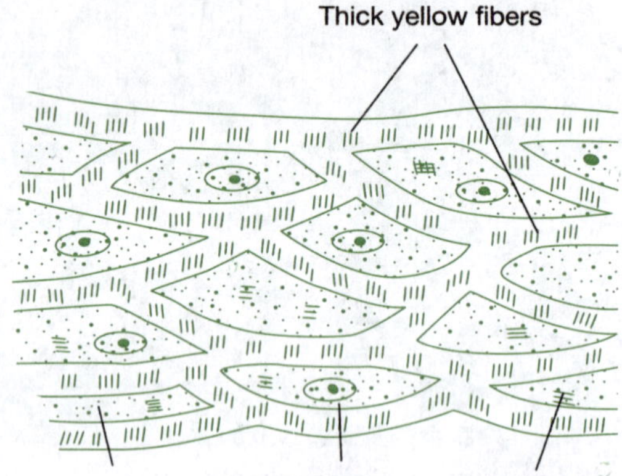

Figure 2.21 Yellow Fibrous Connective Tissue

Keystone

Excessive pulling or overstretching or ligaments produces sprain.

Muscle are of three types (as shown in Fig 2.22):
(i) Straited muscles
(ii) Non-straited muscles
(iii) Cardiac muscles

Straited Muscles

- **Straited Muscles** also called as **voluntary muscles** because these are under the control of one's will.
- Muscle fibres or cells are multinucleated and unbranched.
- These muscles get tired and need rest.
- Location of striated muscles: Limbs, neck, facial muscles, etc.

Non-striated Muscles

- They are **involuntary muscles** also called as **smooth muscles.**
- These muscle fibres are uninucleated and spindle shaped.
- They are not enclosed by sarcolemma but many fibres are joined together in bundles. Such muscles are found in the walls of stomach, intestine, urinary bladder, bronchi, iris of eye, etc.
- Peristaltic movements in alimentary canal are brought about by smooth muscles.

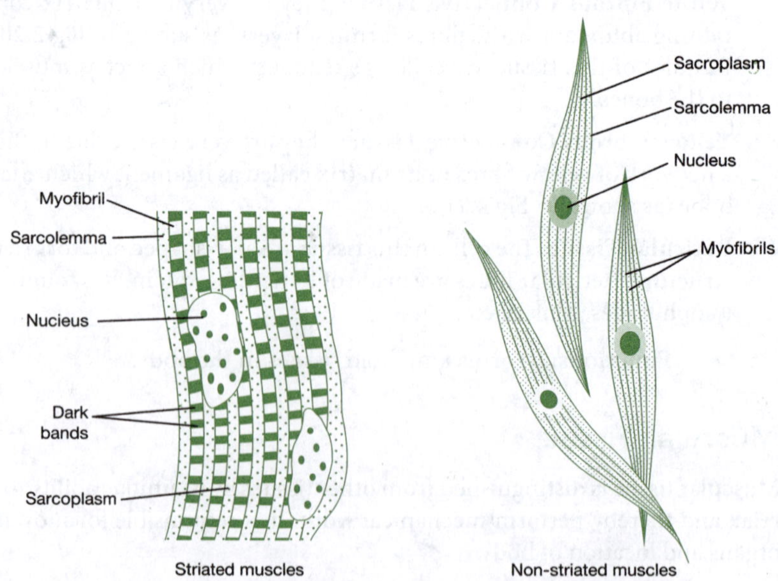

Figure 2.22 Striated Muscles and Non-Striated Muscles

Cardiac Muscle Fibres

- **Cardiac Muscle** are involuntary muscles.
- Only found in the walls of heart.
- Their structure is in between the striated and non-striated muscles (as shown in Fig 2.23).
- They are uninucleated and branched.
- Branches are united by intercalated disc.
- In these muscles rhythmic contraction and relaxation occurs throughout the life.

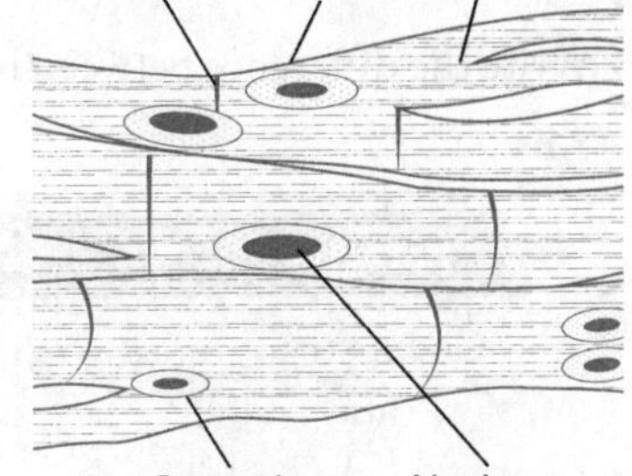

Figure 2.23 Cardiac Muscle Fibres

Nervous Tissue

The nervous tissue, contains densely packed cells called nerve cells or neurons (as shown in Fig 2.24), is present in the brain, spinal cord and nerves. The neurons are specialized for conduction of nerve impulses. Each neuron has following 2 parts:

- **Cyton or Cell Body:** Contains a central nucleus and cytoplasm with characteristic deeply stained particles called Nissle's granules (i.e., clumps of ribosomes).
- **Cell Processes:**
  - **Dendrites:** These may be one to many, generally short and branched cytoplasmic processes. They receive impulse from receptor or another neuron and bring it to cyton.
  - **Axon:** It is single generally long process which conducts impulse away from cyton to other neuron.

Keystone

Nerve cells are the longest cells which may be upto one metre in length. Axon has uniform thickness, but it has terminal thin branches called telodendria. Terminal end buttons or synaptic knobs occur at the end of telodendria.

Functions:

- They control all the body activities
- They co-ordinate between various body parts during any body function.
- Spinal cord and brain are made up of nervous tissue.

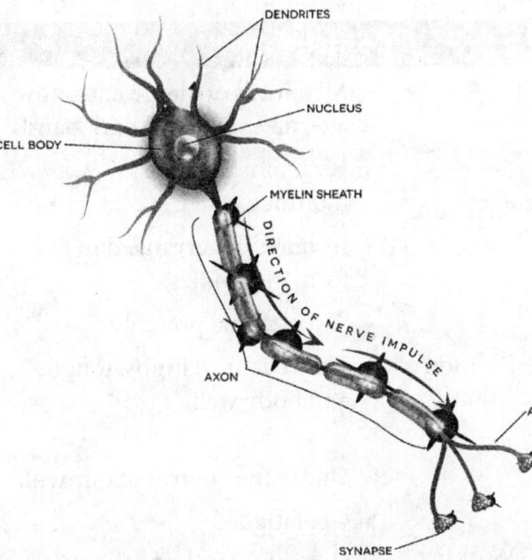

Figure 2.24 Structure of Neuron

Keystone

Myelin sheath is not a continuous layer, the gap between myelin sheath is called as node of Ranvier.

Competition Corner

Synapse is a junction between two neurons. The terminal knobbed branch end of an axon is connected with dendrite branches of an adjacent neuron. This gap junction helps in transmission of impulse from one neuron to the next. The transmission of impulse is generally carried out with the help of a neurotransmitter chemical like acetylcholine.

❖ INTEXT QUESTIONS

3. Write the difference between bones and cartilage.

Ans:

Character	Cartilage	Bone
Chemistry	Formed of organic matter, called condrin protein.	Formed of both organic matter (ossein protein) and inorganic matter (calcium phosphate).
Natural of cells	Chondroblasts present in group of 2 or 4.	Irregular cells osteocytes that occur singly in lacunae.
Nature of lacunae	With no canaliculi.	With canaliculi.
Canals	With no canals.	With haversian canal and Volkmann's canal.
Arrangement of matrix	Not arranged in rings.	In rings called lamellae.
Cavity	Solid internally.	With marrow cavity.
Growth	Unidirectional.	Bidirectional.

4. Write a comparison between striated, nonstriated, and cardiac muscles.

Ans.

	Striated	Unstriped	Cardiac
Structure	• Myofibrils are large and show alternate light and dark bands. • Each muscle cell is multinucleated. • Its fibres are arranged in the form of bundles. • Sarcolemma present.	• Myofibrils are indistinct without light and dark bands. • Each muscles cell is uninucleated. • Its fibres are arranged in the form of sheets. • Sarcolemma absent.	• Myofibrils distinct with light and dark bands. • Each muscles cell is uni-nucleated. • Its fibres are arranged in the form of network. • Sarcolemma present.
Position	• They occur in limbs, tongue and body wall.	• They occur in the walls of alimentary canal, blood vessels, etc.	• They occur in the walls of heart.
Working	• Under the control of our will. • Get fatigued. • Cannot remain contracted for a very long time.	• Not under our control. • Do not get fatigued. • Can remain contracted for relatively longer time.	• Not under our control. • Do not get fatigued. • Contract quickly and rhythmically.

5. Write the difference between blood and lymph.

Ans.

Character	Blood	Lymph
Type of tissue.	Red vascular tissue.	White vascular tissue.
Occurrence in blood vessels.	In lymph vessels.	In lymph vessels and around the body tissues.
Composition	Formed of plasma, erythrocytes, leucocytes and platelets.	Formed of plasma and only leucocytes.
Haemoglobin	Present in RBC's	Absent
Nature of plasma	With more proteins, calcium and phosphorus.	Less
Function	Transportation of materials, defense, blood clotting, etc.	Acts as middle-man between blood and body cells.

Check Point 3

9. What are neurons? Where are they found in the body? What function do they perform in the body of an organism?

10. Draw a well-labelled diagram of cardiac muscle found in the human body. Write two differences between striated and smooth muscles.

11. What is the function of areolar tissues?

STRUCTURAL OUTLINE

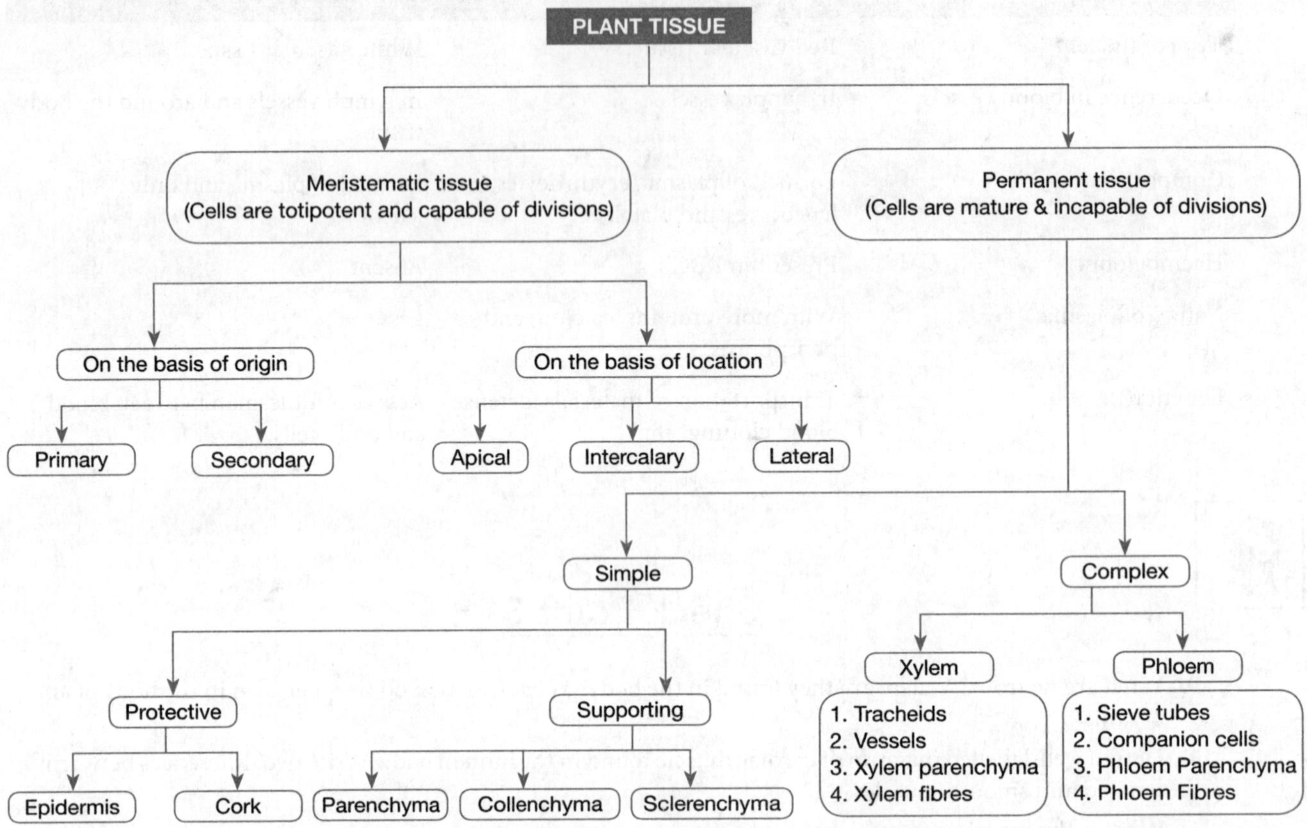

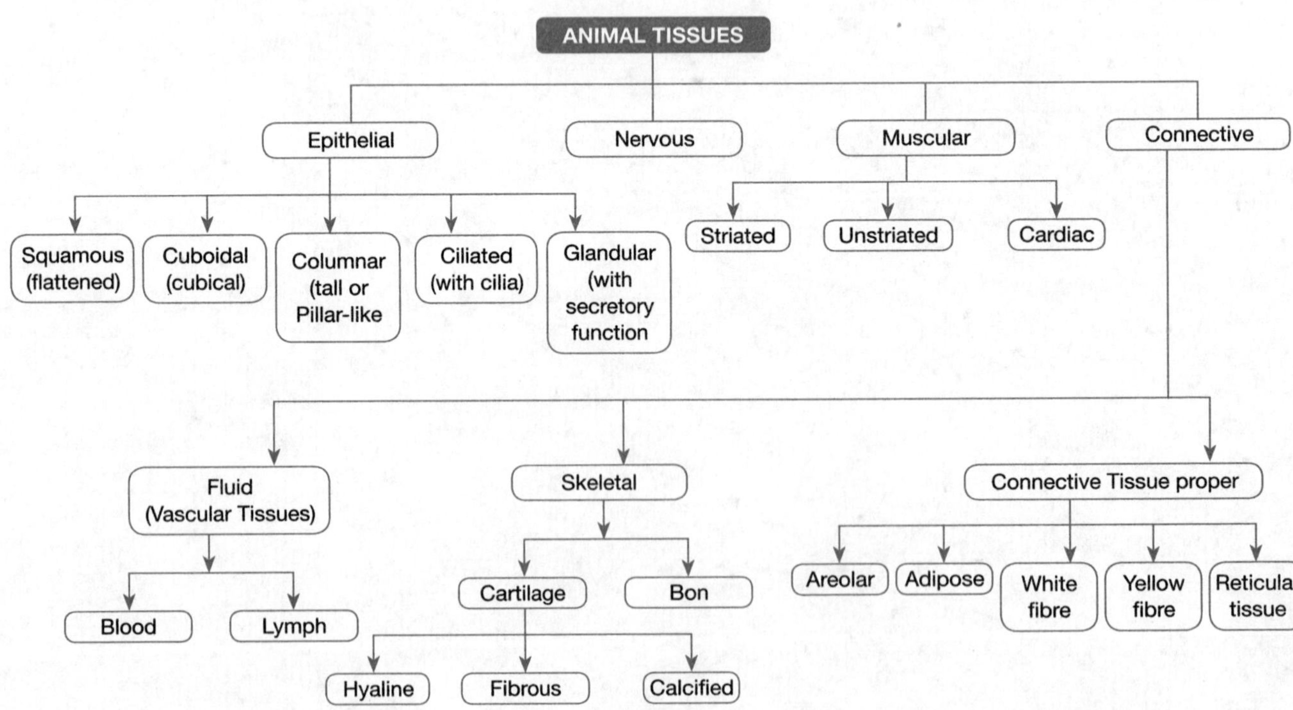

ABRIDGEMENT

Class 11th

Anatomy of flowering plants

- Simple and permanent plant tissues
- Anatomy of dicot, monocot stem and root
- Secondary growth
- Vascular and cork cambium
- Annual rings

Structural organization of animals

Animal Tissues

- Epithelial tissue
- Connective tissues
- Muscle tissues
- Neural tissues
- Endocrine gland

EXEMPLIFICATION

1. Name the basic packing tissue of plant.

Ans. Parenchyma.

2. Which body cell provides resistance against infections?

Ans. White blood cells (WBCs) provide resistance against infections.

3. List any four salient features of meristematic tissue.

Ans. The salient features of meristematic tissue are:

- This tissue consists of cells which continuously divide to produce new cells.
- The cells of this tissue lack vacuoles.
- The cells of this tissue have dense cytoplasm.
- The cells of this tissue have thin cellulosic cell walls and prominent nuclei.

4. Write the functions of collenchyma in plants.

Ans. Collenchyma allows easy bending in various parts of a plant (leaf, stem) without breaking. It also provides mechanical support to plants like in the leaf stalks below the epidermis.

5. What are the two main components of blood? Why is blood considered a type of connective tissue?

Ans. Blood is a special connective tissue consisting of a fluid matrix, plasma, and formed elements. The formed elements are red blood cells (RBCs), white blood cells (WBCs) and blood platelets. Blood is considered as a type of connective tissue as they have the same origin as other types of connective tissue and helps to connect the different parts of the body to facilitate exchange of various components like nutrients and gases.

6. What are neurons? Where are they found in the body? What function do they perform in the body of an organism?

Ans. The cells of nervous tissue are called nerve cells or neurons. Neurons are the structural and functional unit of the nervous system. They are found in the brain, spinal cord, and nerves.

Their functions are: They are highly specialized for transmitting the stimulus from one place to another within the body on being stimulated. They help to coordinate the various functions of the body.

7. Differentiate between voluntary and involuntary muscles. Give one example of each type.

Ans. Voluntary muscles are present in our limbs as skeletal muscles and can be moved by our conscious will whenever we want. Involuntary muscles cannot function on their own. They cannot be controlled by our will or desire. The cardiac muscle and the smooth muscles are involuntary in nature.

8. Animals of colder regions and fishes of cold water have thicker layer of subcutaneous fat. Describe why.

Ans. The thick layer of subcutaneous fat acts as insulator and prevents the heat of the body to escape out. The layer of fat acts as a subcutaneous insulation of body for thermoregulation.

9. Differentiate between voluntary and involuntary muscles. Give one example of each type.

Ans. Voluntary muscles are present in our limbs as skeletal muscles and can be moved by our conscious will whenever we want. Involuntary muscles cannot function on their own. They cannot be controlled by our will or desire. The cardiac muscle and the smooth muscles are involuntary in nature.

10. Draw a labelled diagram of unstriated muscle tissue and mention its occurrence, features, and functions.

Ans.

(i) The cells are long and spindle-shaped.

(ii) They do not have striations.

(iii) Involuntary in nature as they are not under control of our will.

(iv) The cells of smooth muscles are uninucleate.

(v) Smooth muscle fibres are present in iris of the eye, ureters, blood vessels, alimentary canal and bronchi of lungs.

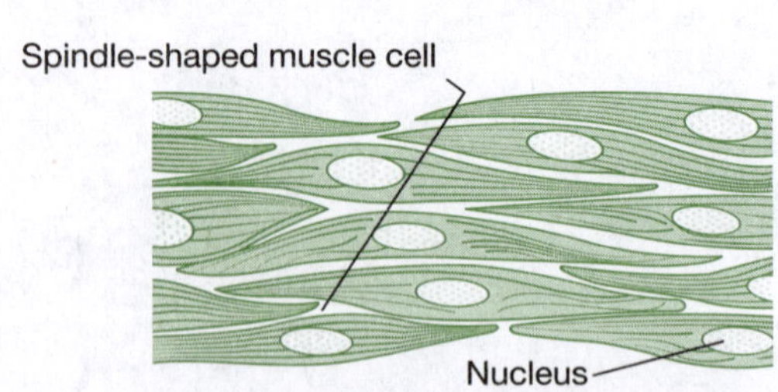

Unstriated muscle fibres

NCERT COMPENDIUM

1. Define the term tissues.

Answer: Tissues be defined as a group or cluster of cells that are similar in structure and work together to achieve a particular function. Tissue as a cluster of cells performs a particular function at a definite place in the body. Within a tissue, cells are arranged or designed to give the highest possible efficiency of.

Functions: blood, phloem and muscle are all examples of tissues.

2. How many types of elements together make up the xylem tissue? Name them.

Answer: Xylem tissue are complex tissues, are made of more than one type of cells. Xylem tissue consists of tracheids, vessels, xylem parenchyma, and xylem fibres. the cells have thick walls, and many of them are dead cells. Tracheids and vessels are tubular structures. This allows them transport water and minerals vertically. the parenchyma stores food and helps in the sideways conduction of water. Fibres are mainly supportive in function.

3. How are simple tissues different from complex tissues in plants?

Answer: Differences between simple and complex tissues in plants.

Simple Tissue	Complex Tissue
These are made up of only one type of cells, which look like each other.	These are made up of more than one type of cells.
All cells have common origin and structure.	The cells of complex tissue have different origin as well as structure.
They are called epidermis.	They are called vascular tissue.
Their main role is to store and provide structural support.	Their main function is transport of water, Minerals, sugars and other metabolites.
Examples – Collenchyma, Parenchyma and sclerenchyma.	Examples – Xylem and phloem.

4. Differentiate between parenchyma, collenchyma, and sclerenchyma on the basis of their cell wall.

Answer: Differences between parenchyma, collenchyma and sclerenchyma on the basis of their cell wall.

Parenchyma	Collenchyma	Sclerenchyma
The cell wall is thin and is made up of cellulose.	The cell wall is thick due to deposition of lignin.	The cell wall is thick at the corners due to deposition of pectin.

5. What are the functions of the stomata?

Answer: Stomata are small pores present in the epidermis of the leaf. Stomata are enclosed by two kidneys shaped cells called guard cells. The main function of stomata is for exchanging gases like CO_2 or O_2 with the atmosphere. Photosynthesis is not possible without them. They are responsible for transpiration in which water is lost in the form of water vapour from the plant surface. This ultimately helps in absorption of minerals by root tissues on account of buildup root pressure.

6. Diagrammatically show the difference between the three types of muscle fibres.

Answer:

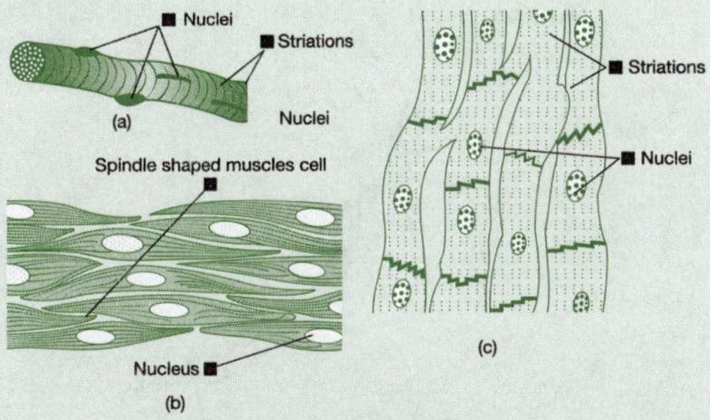

7. What is the specific function of the cardiac muscle?

Answer: The specific function of cardiac muscle to contract and relax rhythmically throughout life and to ensure the blood circulation through entire body. Heart muscle cells are cylindrical, branched, and uninucleate.

8. Differentiate between striated, un striated and cardiac muscles on the basis of their structure and site/location in the body.

NCERT COMPENDIUM

Answer: Differences between striated, unstriated, and cardiac muscles

Striated Muscle	Unstriated Muscle	Cardiac Muscle
The fibres or cells are ling and cylindrical.	The cells are long, narrow, spindle-shaped.	The cells are short, cylindrical and branched.
The fibres or cells are unbranched.	The fibres or cells are unbranched.	At some places, they develop lateral outgrowths to form cross-connections.
Multiple nuclei are present on the periphery.	Single centrally located nucleus.	Cardiac cell are uninucleatd and have a centrally located single nucleus.
They are present in Hand, feet and other skeletal muscles.	They are present in Walls of stomach, intestine, ureter and bronchi.	Striations present, but not as prominent as they are present in striated muscle. They are present in the heart.

9. Draw a labelled diagram of a neuron.

Answer:

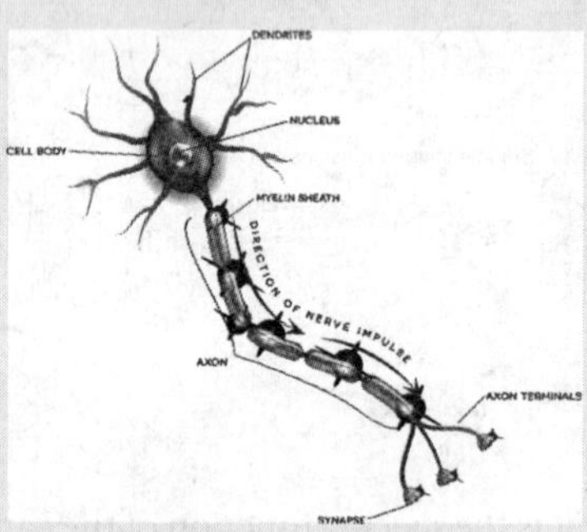

10. Name the following.
(a) Tissue that forms the inner lining of our mouth.
(b) Tissue that connects muscle to bone in humans.
(c) Tissue that transports food in plants.
(d) Tissue that stores fat in our body.
(e) Connective tissue with a fluid matrix.
(f) Tissue presents in the brain.

Answer:
(a) Tissue that forms the inner lining of our mouth – **squamous epithelium**
(b) Tissue that connects muscle to bone in humans – **tendon**
(c) Tissue that transports food in plants – **phloem**
(d) Tissue that stores fat in our body – **adipose tissue**
(e) Connective tissue with a fluid matrix – **blood**
(f) Tissue presents in the brain – **nervous tissue**

11. Identify the type of tissue in the following: skin, bark of tree, bone, lining of kidney tubule, vascular bundle.

Answer:

Given	Type of tissue
Skin	Squamous epithelium
Bark of tree	Cork or secondary epidermis (tissue)
Bone	Connective tissue
Lining of kindey tubule	Cuboidal epithelium
Vascular bundle	Conductive tissue (xylem and phloem)

12. Name the regions in which parenchyma tissue is present.

Answer: Parenchyma tissue are cluster of living cells. They consist of relatively unspecialized cells with thin cell walls. They are usually loosely packed and have large intercellular spaces. this tissue is mainly found in all soft parts of the plant such as stem, root, leaves, flowers, fruits. It is also found in the ground tissue of petioles, mesophyll of leaves as well as in vascular bundles.

13. What is the role of epidermis in plants?

Answer: Role of epidermis in plants:
1. Protection of the underlying cells and tissues.
2. Prevention of water loss.
3. Prevention of mechanical injury and invasion by parasite fungi.
4. Absorption of water.
5. Exchange of gases and transpiration through stomata.

14. How does the cork act as a protective tissue?

Answer: Cork is a multi-layered structure of epidermal. these cells are dead and compactly arranged without intercellular space. They also have a chemical called suberin in their walls which makes them impervious to water and gases.

15. Complete the table:

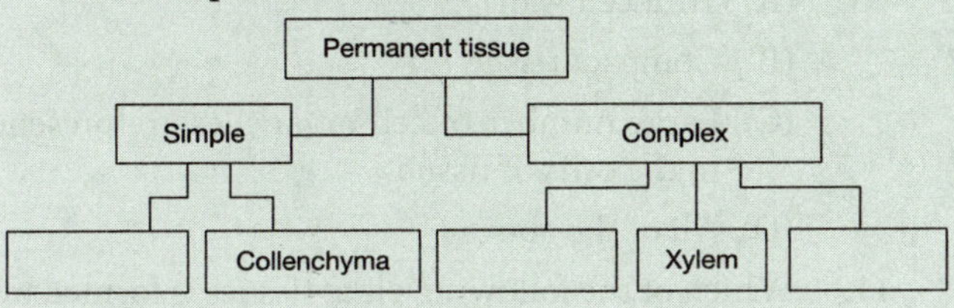

Answer:

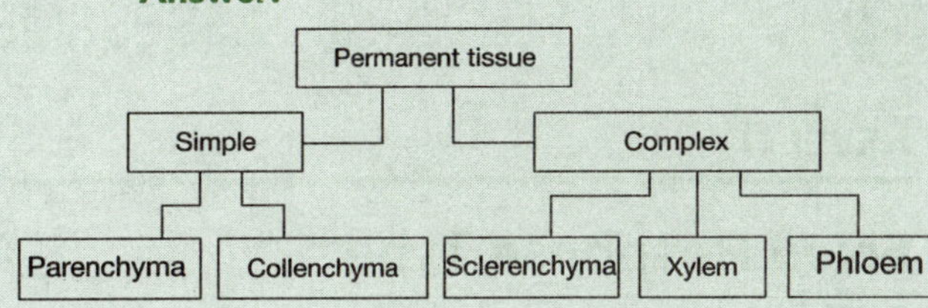

ASSESSMENT CORNER

Level 1

Fixed Response Type

Multiple Choice Questions

1. A group of cells having a common origin and performing similar function is called:
(A) tissue (B) organ
(C) organ system (D) cell aggregate

2. Tissue term was coined by:
(A) Bichat (B) Nägeli
(C) Robert Hooke (D) Robert Brown

3. Study of tissue is known as:
(A) Histology (B) Cytology
(C) Cell biology (D) None of these

4. Meristems are cells that:
(A) store food
(B) help in excretion
(C) provide support
(D) divide continuously to produce new cells

5. Plant length is increased by the activity of:
(A) apical meristem
(B) lateral meristem
(C) cambium
(D) all of the above

6. In plants, cell division is restricted upto:
(A) meristematic cells (B) permanent cells
(C) xylem (D) phloem

7. In grasses, the length of internodes increases by the activity of:
(A) apical meristem
(B) intercalary meristem
(C) lateral meristem
(D) secondary meristem

8. Special feature of dividing cells is:
(A) large lacuna
(B) thick cell walls
(C) dense cytoplasm devoid of lacuna
(D) large intercellular spaces

9. Which of the following tissues has dead cells?
(A) Parenchyma (B) Sclerenchyma
(C) Collenchyma (D) Epithelial tissue

10. Which of the following is a feature of meristematic tissues?
(A) Thin cell wall
(B) Compact tissue
(C) Large number of cell organelles are present in the cells of tissues
(D) All of the above

11. Which of the following plant tissues is formed by permanent tissue?
(A) Primary tissue (B) Secondary tissue
(C) Both of above (D) None of above

12. Which of the following plant tissues causes growth in girth of stem and root?
(A) Apical meristem
(B) Intercalary meristem
(C) Lateral meristem
(D) None of the above

13. Find out incorrect sentence
(A) Parenchymatous tissues have intercellular spaces
(B) Collenchymatous tissues are irregularly thickened at corners
(C) Apical and intercalary meristems are permanent tissues
(D) Meristematic tissues, in its early stage, lack vacuoles

14. A permanent plant tissue consisting of thin-walled living cells is:
(A) parenchyma (B) collenchyma
(C) sclerenchyma (D) xylem

15. A permanent plant tissue made up of living cells having thickening at the corners is:
(A) sclerenchyma (B) collenchyma
(C) parenchyma (D) phloem

16. The main function of sclerenchyma is to help in the:
(A) conduction of food (B) synthesis of food
(C) exchange of gases (D) mechanical support

17. The wall of cork cells is thickened by the deposition of:
(A) cutin (B) suberin
(C) lignin (D) pectin

18. A protective noncellular layer found on the outside of plant organ is:
(A) Epidermis (B) Cuticle
(C) Vascular tissue layer (D) Hypodermis

19. The outer wall of epidermis in stems and leaves has a waxy covering made up of:
(A) lignin (B) suberin
(C) pectin (D) cutin

20. Collenchyma differs from sclerenchyma in:
(A) retaining cytoplasm at maturity
(B) having thick walls
(C) having a wide lumen
(D) being meristematic

21. Lignified elongated dead cells are:
(A) parenchyma (B) collenchyma
(C) sclerenchyma (D) none of these

22. Which of the following plant tissue lacks protoplasm at maturity?
(A) Sclerenchyma (B) Collenchyma
(C) Parenchyma (D) Epidermis

23. Girth of stem increases due to
(A) apical meristem
(B) lateral meristem
(C) intercalary meristem
(D) vertical meristem

24. Which cell does not have perforated cell wall?
(A) Tracheids (B) Companion cells
(C) Sieve tubes (D) Vessels

25. Columnar epithelium is present in:
(A) kidney tubules (B) small intestine
(C) skin (D) thyroid vesicles

26. Which one of the following is a fluid connective tissue?
(A) Areolar tissue (B) Cartilage
(C) Blood (D) Ligaments

27. The tissue that attaches muscles to the bones is:
(A) cartilage (B) tendon
(C) ligament (D) blood

28. The tissue that joins one bone to the other is:
(A) ligament (B) tendon
(C) blood (D) cartilage

29. Areolar tissue is a:
(A) nervous tissue (B) muscular tissue
(C) connective tissue (D) epithelial tissue

30. Which of these cells are called as 'soldiers of the body'?
(A) RBC (B) WBC
(C) Platelets (D) None of these

Fill in the Blanks

1. Matrix of cartilage contains ____________ and of bone ____________ protein.
2. Cork cells possess ____________ on their walls that makes it impervious to gases and water.
3. ____________ have tubular cells with perforated walls and are living in nature.
4. Formation of RBC in liver, spleen and red bone marrow is called ____________.
5. Striated muscle fibres in the sarcoplasm contains many ____________ numerous ____________ and Glycogen granules for the supply of adequate ____________.
6. Neuron receive impulses through ____________ and pass them on to the next neuron through ____________.
7. Bone possesses a hard matrix composed of ____________ and ____________.
8. Nonvascular tissues like parenchyma, collenchyma and sclerenchyma are the examples of ____________ tissues.
9. Vascular tissues, xylem and phloem are examples of ____________ tissues.
10. Chlorenchyma tissues performs the function of ____________.
11. Cork cambium is purely a ____________.
12. Due to secondary growth on the surface of trees stem, small pores are developed called ________.

True/False

1. Muscle fibres or cells are multinucleated and unbranched.
2. Cork tissue is permeable for water.
3. Meristematic tissues have large central vacuole.
4. Primary meristem usually add the diameter to the plant.
5. Matrix of bone is hard due to calcium phosphate, $CaCO_3$ (60-70%), etc., and a protein ossein.
6. Platelets help in clotting of blood.

7. Ciliated epithelium is found on the lining of nephrons, trachea and fallopian tube.
8. Parenchyma is basic packing tissue of plant.
9. The parenchyma stores food and helps in the sideways conduction of water.
10. Only one type of tissue forms an organ.

Match Type Questions

1. Match the following I and II.

Column – I	Column–II
(i) Pith	(a) Secondary meristem
(ii) Cork cambium	(b) Parenchyma
(iii) Cambium	(c) Primary meristem
(iv) Pits	(d) Xylem vessels

2. Match the following I and II.

Column – I	Column–II
(i) Node of Ranvier	(a) Tear Gland
(ii) Exocrine gland	(b) Phagocytosis
(iii) Macrophage	(c) Myelinated nerve fibres
(iv) Dendrite	(d) Nerve impulse

3. Match the following I and II.

Column – I	Column–II
(i) Parenchyma	(a) Carbon fixation
(ii) Photosynthesis	(b) Thin walled, packing cells
(iii) Aerenchyma	(c) Localized thickenings
(iv) Collenchyma	(d) Buoyancy

Assertion and Reason Type Questions

Instructions: In the following questions, an Assertion (A) is given followed by a Reason (R). Mark your responses from the following options.

(A) Both Assertion and Reason are true and Reason is the correct explanation of Assertion
(B) Both Assertion and Reason are true and Reason is not the correct explanation of Assertion
(C) Assertion is true but Reason is false
(D) Assertion is false but Reason is true
(E) Both assertion and reason are false

1. **Assertion:** Every living organism is not multicellular
Reason: Few multicellular organisms do not have tissue.

2. **Assertion:** Node of Ranvier occur in myelinated nerve fibre.
Reason: Myelin sheath is discontinuous

3. **Assertion:** Apical meristem is present at the growing tips of stems and roots
Reason: Apical meristem is always located upper side of plant.

4. **Assertion:** Permanent tissue is composed of mature cells.
Reason: Meristematic tissue is a group of actively dividing cells.

5. **Assertion:** Vessel and sieve tube both are meant for transport purposes.
Reason: Vessels are lignified.

6. **Assertion:** Ciliated epithelium helps in movement of particles.
Reason: Cilia help in movement.

7. **Assertion:** Meristematic tissues constitute the major portion of the plant body.
Reason: Meristematic tissues consist of differentiated cells.

8. **Assertion:** Collenchyma is thick-walled tissue.
Reason: Collenchyma is thickened due to deposition of pectin.

9. **Assertion:** Striated muscles are attached to the bones in different body parts.
Reason: These are independent of voluntary control.

10. **Assertion:** Parenchyma tissues are non-living.
Reason: Parenchyma cells have intercellular spaces.

Comprehension Type Questions

Passage 1:
If you germinate a kidney bean seed in a Petri dish, then the reserve food material present in plant part undergoes oxidation to release energy. This energy is used in cell division and hence sprouting takes place. The two small plant parts that come out of the seed are plumule and radicle, respectively.

1. Plumule helps in the formation of:
(A) Fruit (B) Seed
(C) Flower (D) None of these

2. Root that helps in anchorage are specialized structures of:
(A) Plumule
(B) Radicle
(C) Embryo
(D) None of these

3. Height of the plant above the soil increases due to meristematic tissue present in:
   (A) Root tip (B) Shoot tip
   (C) Both (b) and (c) (D) None of these

Passage 2:
Squamous epithelium is also called pavement epithelium because its compact structure is like tiles on floor. Cells are polygonal and form the delicate lining of cavities (mouth, oesophagus, nose, pericardium, alveoli, etc.) blood vessels and covering of the tongue and skin. Epithelial cells are arranged in many layers (stratum) to prevent wear and tear in skin. This pattern is stratified squamous epithelium.

4. Write the name of epithelium found on the lining of mouth.
5. What is the structural appearance of squamous epithelium?
6. At some places of human body, epithelial cells are found in many layers. What is the name of this epithelium?
7. Name the body organs where squamous epithelium tissues are found.

Passage 3:
Muscular tissue consists of elongated cells, also called muscle fibres. This tissue is responsible for movement in our body. Muscles contain special proteins called contractile proteins, which contract and relax to cause movement. We can move some muscles by conscious will. Such muscles are called voluntary muscles. These muscles are also called skeletal muscles as they are mostly attached to bones and help in body movement. Under the microscope, these muscles show alternate light and dark bands or striations, hence they are also called striated muscles. The cells of this tissue are long, cylindrical, unbranched, and multinucleate. The movement of food in the alimentary canal or the contraction and relaxation of blood vessels are involuntary movements. We can't control these muscle movements. The Smooth muscles or involuntary muscles control such movements. They are also found in the iris of the eye, in ureters and in the bronchi of the lungs. The cells are long with pointed ends (spindle-shaped) and uninucleate. They are also called unstriated muscles. The muscles of the heart show rhythmic contraction and relaxation throughout life. These involuntary muscles are called cardiac. Heart muscle cells are cylindrical, branched and uninucleate.

8. Which of the following muscle tissue are voluntary in nature?
   (A) Cardiac muscle
   (B) Smooth muscle
   (C) Auto rhythmic muscle
   (D) None of the above
9. The muscles whose contraction is under our control are known as:
   (A) Voluntary muscles
   (B) Involuntary movements
   (C) Cardiac muscle
   (D) Unstrained muscle
10. The smooth muscle is found in the:
    (A) Iris of eye
    (B) Uterus
    (C) Bronchi of lungs
    (D) All of above
11. Give the characteristics of striated muscles.
12. Give the characteristics of unstriated muscles.

Free Response Type

Very Short Answer Type Questions

1. Name the plant tissue having dead cells.
2. Write any 2 functions of adipose tissues.
3. Which plant tissue remains in active metabolic state always?
4. Which meristematic tissue causes elongation of stem and root in primary growth of a plant?
5. What is the role of lateral meristem in plant?
6. Straited muscles are found in which part of body.
7. Defined dedifferentiation?
8. Which type of epithelial tissues are involve in absorption, excretion and secretion?
9. How many types of connective tissue present in human body?
10. Write name of different kinds of animals tissue?

Short Answer Type Questions

1. Differentiate between primary and secondary meristem.
2. Mention the role of parenchyma, collenchyma and sclerenchyma.
3. Write the functions of adipose tissue?

4. Differentiate leptome and hedrome.
5. Write down the difference between bones and cartilage.
6. Write down the differences between striated and non-striated muscle.
7. What are the functions of blood?
8. Draw and identify different elements of phloem?
9. Write short note on complex permanent tissue?
10. Write down the example of the following tissues:
    (i) Areolar
    (ii) Adipose
    (iii) Yellow fibre connective tissue
    (iv) White fibre connective tissue

Long Answer Type Questions

1. Write a detailed description on the protective tissue in plants.
2. List the characteristics of cork. How are they formed? Mention their role.
3. Write in detail about the types of simple permanent tissues.
4. Describe the structure and function of different types of epithelial tissues along with suitable diagram.
5. Describe the types of connective tissue along with their functions.

Case Based Questions

Case 1: Identify the given two slides A and B as a parenchyma or sclerenchyma. Sclerenchyma can be identified by which characteristic?

Slide A

Slide B

Case 2: Tissue A and tissue B constitute tissue C. A carries water while B carries food for the plants. Identify A, B, C.

Case 3: Bone is a solid, hard porous tissue. It forms the natural skeleton and gives the body its basic structure and also supports the body. Its matrix is impregnated with phosphates and carbonates of calcium and magnesium which provides hardness to it. The matrix also contains ossein protein. The matrix is arranged in concentric rings which are called lamellae. Bone cells lie between the lamellae in fluid-filled spaces called lacunae.

1. Bone cells are also called:
   (a) Lacunae
   (b) Osteocytes
   (c) Neutrophils
   (d) Erythrocytes
2. The matrix inside the bone is arranged in concentric rings called:
   (a) Cytoplasm
   (b) Osteocyte
   (c) Lacunae
   (d) Lamellae
3. To form natural skeleton and to give support to the body is the main function of:
   (a) Cells
   (b) Muscles
   (c) Bones
   (d) Ligaments
4. The matrix of bone is impregnated with:
   (a) Carbon dioxide and oxygen
   (b) Carbon dioxide and water
   (c) Sulphates of sodium
   (d) Phosphates and carbonates of calcium and magnesium
5. Bone cells lie between the lamellae in fluid-filled spaces called:
   (a) Lamina
   (b) Osteocytes
   (c) Lacunae
   (d) Ossein

Level 2

Multiple Choice Questions

1. Fluid part of blood after removal of corpuscles is:
(A) plasma (B) lymph
(C) serum (D) vaccine

2. Yellow muscle fibers are also known as:
(A) bone (B) muscle
(C) ligament (D) none of these

3. Blood platelets are also called as:
(A) leucocytes (B) erythrocytes
(C) thrombocytes (D) None of these

4. Contraction and relaxation are unique features of:
(A) epithelial tissue (B) connective tissue
(C) muscle tissue (D) nervous tissue

5. The tissue which is under the control of animal's will is:
(A) cardiac muscle (B) striated muscle
(C) non-striated muscle (D) cartilage

6. The muscle which works throughout life without undergoing fatigue is:
(A) striated muscle (B) non-striated muscle
(C) cardiac muscle (D) all of the above

7. Meristematic tissues in plants are
(A) localised and permanent
(B) not limited to certain regions
(C) localised and dividing cells
(D) growing in volume

8. Wall of urinary bladder consists of:
(A) striated muscles (B) unstriated muscles
(C) both of above (D) none of these

9. Intercalated discs are present in:
(A) striated muscles (B) unstriated muscle
(C) cardiac muscles (D) all of the above

10. Voluntary tissue forms wall of which of the following organ?
(A) Intestine (B) Stomach
(C) Bronchi (D) All of the above

11. Movements in body are brought about by:
(A) muscular tissues
(B) epithelial tissues
(C) bones
(D) tendons and ligaments

12. The functional unit of nervous tissue is called as:
(A) cyton (B) synapse
(C) neuron (D) axon

13. Which is not a function of epidermis?
(A) Protection from adverse condition
(B) Gaseous exchange
(C) Conduction of water
(D) Transpiration

14. Cartilage is formed by:
(A) Osteoblasts (B) Fibroblasts
(C) Chondroclast (D) Chondroblasts

15. The membrane that covers cartilage is known as:
(A) Periosteum (B) Perichondrium
(C) Perineurium (D) Pericardium

16. The dead element present in the phloem is
(A) companion cells (B) phloem fibres
(C) phloem parenchyma (D) sieve tubes

17. Haversian canals are found in:
(A) Bone marrow (B) Hyaline cartilage
(C) Bone matrix (D) Calcified cartilage

18. The tendons are formed of:
(A) White fibrous tissue (connective)
(B) Yellow fibrous tissue (connective)
(C) Areolar tissue
(D) Adipose tissue

19. Schwann cell surrounds a/an:
(A) Axon (B) Cyton
(C) Dendrite (D) Dendron

20. Cambium is a:
(A) root meristem
(B) apical meristem
(C) lateral meristem
(D) intercalary meristem

Higher Order Thinking Skills (HOTS)

1. What will happen if:
(i) Apical meristem is damaged or cut?
(ii) Cork is not formed in older stems and roots?
(iii) Cells of epithelial tissue are not compactly packed?
(iv) Lymph is not returned to blood?

2.
(i) Identify figures: A, B, and C.
(ii) Which one of them provides both mechanical strength as well as flexibility?
(iii) Which one of them is commercially exploited to obtain hemp and jute?
(iv) Which one of them can be modified to form air cavities in aquatic plants?

(v) Which one of them has heavy deposition of lignin?

Fig. A

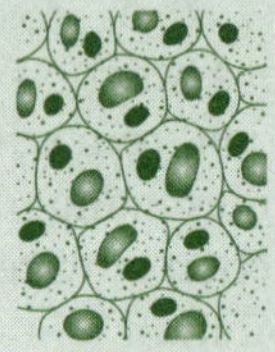

Fig. B

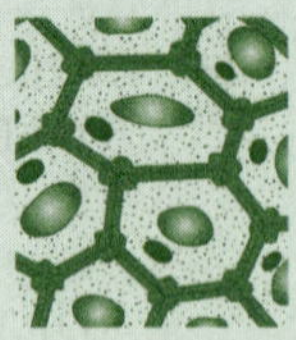

Fig. C

3. (i) Identify the figure. What is its function?

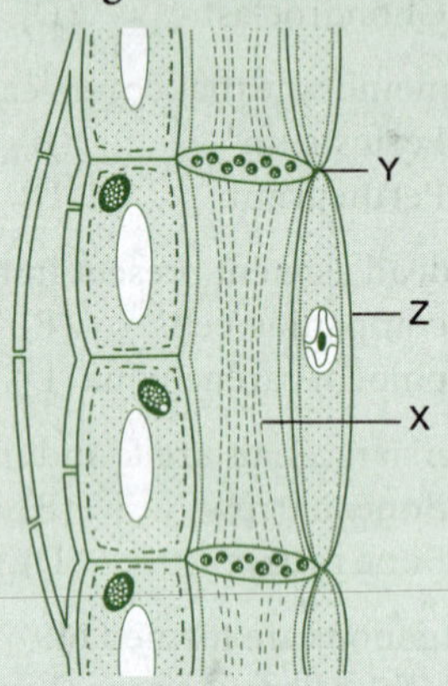

(ii) Label X, Y, and Z.

(iii) Which ones of them develop from the same mother cell?

(iv) X loses its nucleus in mature state. Still, it remains alive. How?

4. A nail is inserted in the trunk of a tree at a height of 1 metre from the ground level. After 3 years, where will the nail be present?

5. Tissue a and tissue b constitute tissue c. A carries water while b carries food for the plants. Identify a, b, c.

6. A person met with an accident in which two long bones of the hand were dislocated. What could be the reason?

7. If the tip of a sugarcane plant is removed from the field, even then it keeps on growing in length. Why?

8. The root tips of a plant were cut, and the plant was replanted. What will happen to the plant and why?

ARCHIVE CORNER

1. Read the given statements and select the correct option.
Statement 1: Parenchyma and collenchyma tissues have thick walls and living cells.
Statement 2: Parenchyma forms hard grit of pear fruit and collenchyma forms hard walls of nuts.
   A. Both statements 1 and 2 are correct.
   B. Statement 1 is correct and statement 2 is incorrect.
   C. Statement 1 is incorrect and statement 2 is correct.
   D. Both statements 1 and 2 are incorrect.

2. Refer to the given diagrammatic representations of two different tissues, X and Y.

X Y

Now, read the following statements and select the correct ones regarding these tissues.
   (i) X is an animal tissue whereas Y is a plant tissue.
   (ii) X is the major water conducting tissue in vascular plants and gives mechanical strength to plant body.
   (iii) X is composed of all dead cells whereas Y is composed of all living cells.
   (iv) X conducts water in vascular plants in downward direction.
   (v) In animals, Y is found below the skin that forms a shock absorbing cushion around the internal organs and stores fat to insulate the body against heat loss.
   A. (i) and (ii) only
   B. (iv) only
   C. (v) only
   D. (iii), (iv) and (v) only

3. Identify structures X, Y, and Z and select the incorrect statement regarding them.

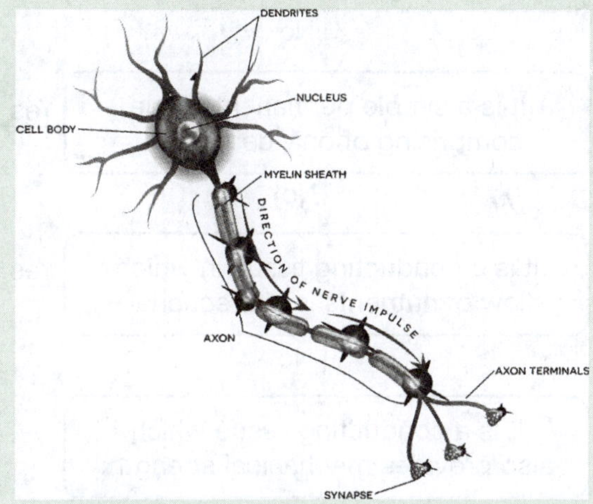

   A. X is cell body having nucleus and cytoplasm.
   B. Y are dendrites which are branched extensions of cell body.
   C. Z is an axon which is a cylindrical process arising from X.
   D. Y transmits nerve impulse from one neuron to another whereas Z receives impulses.

4. Which of the following epithelial tissues lines the coelom and urinary tubules?

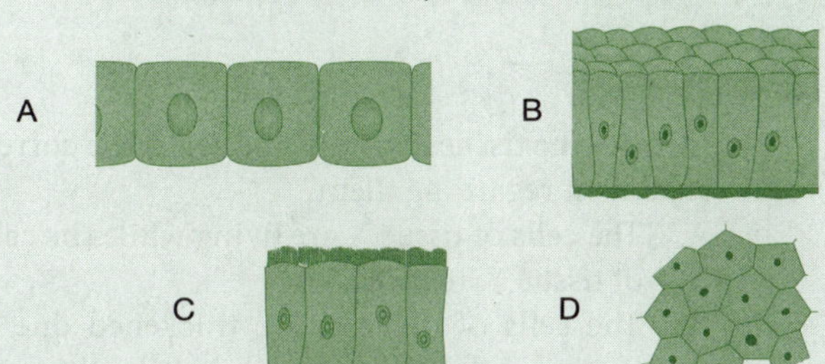

5. Study the given flow chart and select the incorrect statement regarding P, Q, R, and S.
   A. 'P' can be the tissue that is located at growing apices of shoots and roots.
   B. Tissue 'Q' is primarily responsible for storage of food.
   C. Tissue 'R' is responsible for transport of food from leaves to other parts of the plant body.
   D. Tissue 'S' is made up of four types of cells – vessels, tracheid, fibres, and parenchyma.

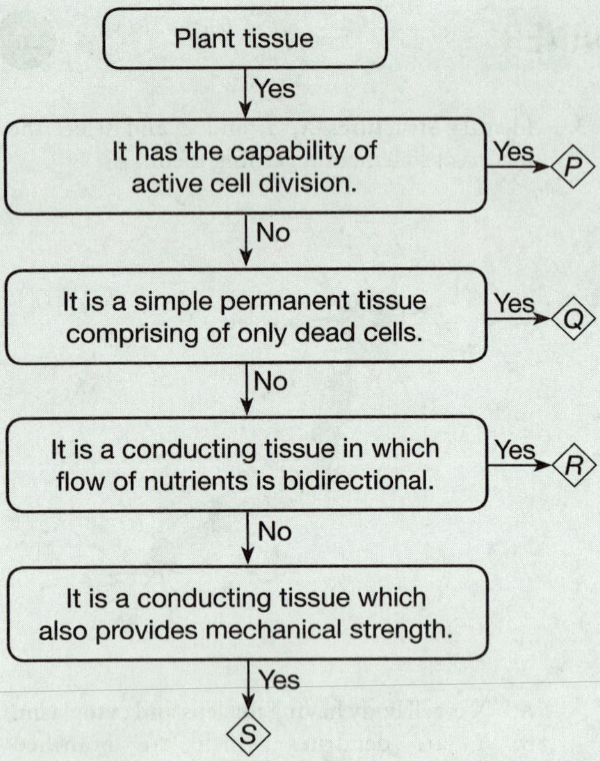

6. Refer to the given figures showing transverse sections of two plant tissues.

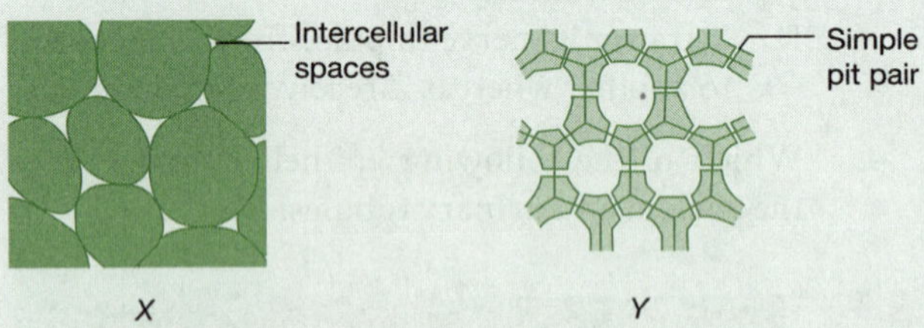

Identify the tissues X and Y and select the correct statement regarding them.

A. The cells of tissue X are living while the cells of tissue Y are dead.
B. The cells of tissue X are thickened due to lignin while cells of tissue Y have thin cell walls.
C. There are large intercellular spaces in both the tissues X and Y.
D. X provides protective covering around seeds and nuts whereas Y helps to resist tearing effect of wind in leaves.

7. Which of the following plant tissues provide mechanical support and a protective covering around seeds?

A. Parenchyma
B. Collenchyma
C. Aerenchyma
D. Sclerenchyma

8. Read the given statements and select the incorrect one.

A. In plants, the testing room of apical meristem causes the plant to increase in length.
B. In grass, intercalary meristem is present at the base of leaves.
C. The vascular cambium and cork cambium of dicots are examples of apical meristem.
D. Lateral meristem in plants is responsible for an increase in stem thickness.

9. Identify the tissue X and select the correct statement regarding its function.

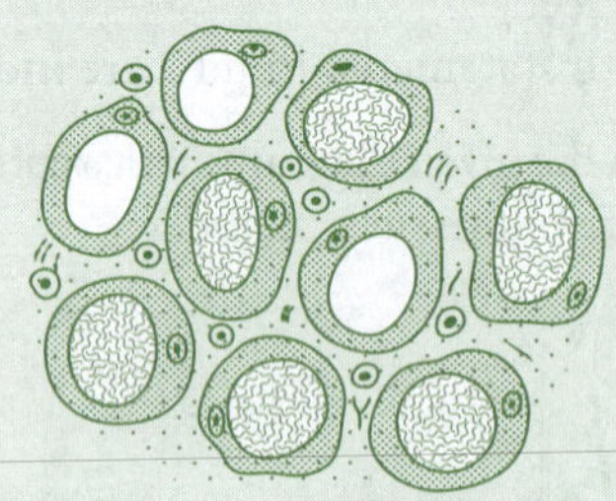

Tissue X

A. Tissue X stores fat and insulates body against heat loss.
B. Tissue X fixes the skin with the muscles.
C. Tissue X serves to bind the bones together.
D. Tissue X connects skeletal muscle with bones.

10. Match column I with column II and select the correct option from the given codes

Column I	Column II
P. Squamous epithelium	(i) Fallopian tube
Q. Ciliated epithelium	(ii) Stomach
R. Cuboidal epithelium	(iii) Blood vessels
S. Columnar epithelium	(iv) Windpipe
	(v) Thyroid glands
	(vi) Pancreatic ducts
	(vii) Alveoli of lungs
	(viii) Intestine

A. P–(i), (viii); Q–(ii), (vi); R–(iii), (v); S–(iv), (vii)
B. P–(ii), (vi); Q–(i), (v); R–(iv), (viii); S–(iii), (vii)
C. P–(iii), (vii); Q–(ii), (vi); R–(iv), (v); S–(i), (viii)
D. P–(iii), (vii); Q–(i), (iv); R–(v), (vi); S–(ii), (viii)

11. Match column I with column II and select the correct option from the given codes.

Column I	Column II
(a) 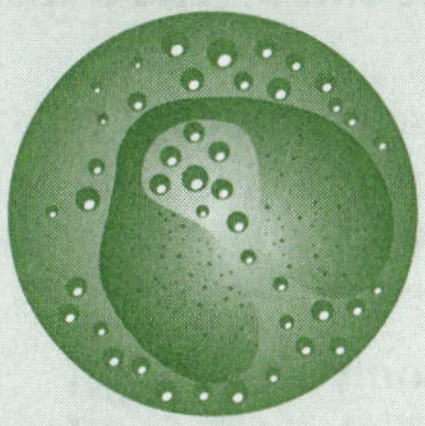	(i) Phagocytosis
(b) 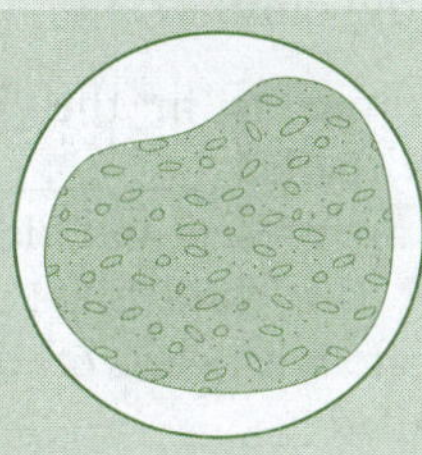	(ii) Release heparin
(c) 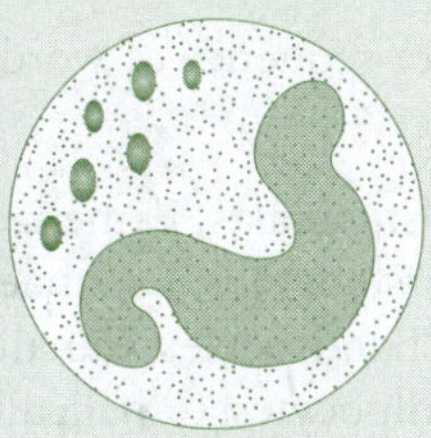	(iii) Allergic response

A. (a)-(i), (b)-(ii), (c)-(iii)
B. (a)-(ii), (b)-(iii), (c)-(i)
C. (a)-(i), (b)-(iii), (c)-(ii)
D. (a)-(iii), (b)-(i), (c)-(ii)

12. Refer to the given table of differences between cartilage and bone and select the incorrect differences.

	Cartilage	Bone
(i)	It is soft, elastic and flexible.	It is hard, tough and inflexible.
(ii)	Its matrix occurs in homogenous mass.	Its matrix occurs in lamellae.
(iii)	Tissues has a rich blood supply.	It does not have a rich blood supply.
(iv)	Growth is bidirectional.	Growth is unidirectional.

A. (i) and (ii) only
B. (iii) and (iv) only
C. (i) and (iv) only
D. (ii) and (iii) only

13. Identify the type of muscular tissue from the given figures and select the correct statement regarding them.

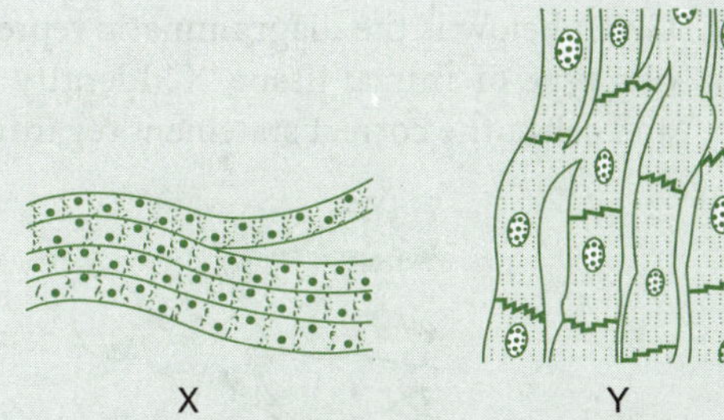

A. Cells of X are uninucleated whereas that of Y are multinucleated.
B. X is voluntary in nature whereas Y is involuntary in nature.
C. X is mainly found in the alimentary canal and blood vessels whereas Y is mainly found in the limbs.
D. Both X and Y show slow contractions.

14. Study the given flow chart and select the incorrect statement regarding P, Q, R and S.

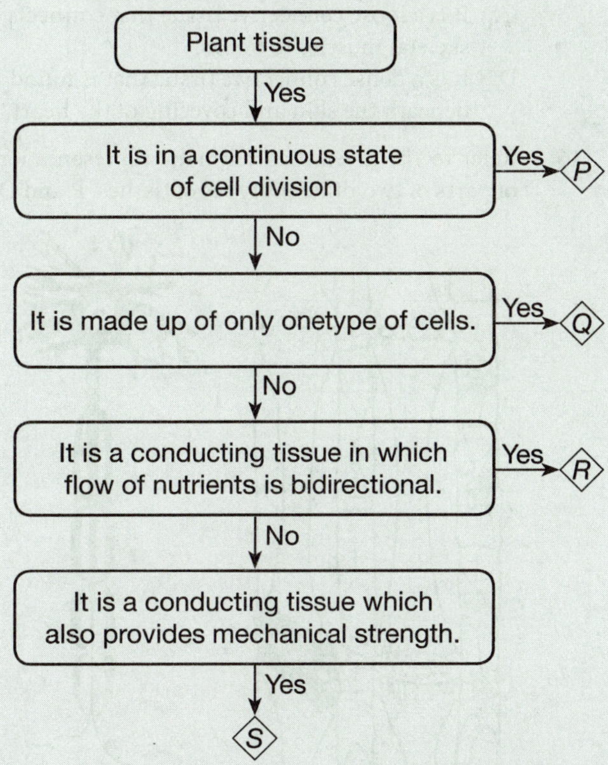

A. P could be the tissue which is present in root tips and shoot tips.
B. Tissue Q could be primarily responsible for storage of food.
C. Tissue R could be responsible for transport of food from leaves to other parts of the plant body.
D. Tissue S could be made up of only one type of dead cells.

15. Given below is the diagrammatic representation of a type of animal tissue 'X'. Identify the tissue and select the correct statement regarding it.

Tissue X

A. It is a dense connective tissue that stores fat and insulates the body against heat loss.
B. It is a loose connective tissue that acts as packing and supporting tissue between organs lying in the body cavity.
C. It is a loose connective tissue that connects skeletal muscles to bones.
D. It is a dense connective tissue that is found beneath the skin and covering of the heart.

16. Refer to the given diagrammatic representation of parts of two different types of tissues, P and Q.

P Q

Read the following statements regarding these tissues and select the correct statements.
(i) P is a plant tissue whereas Q is an animal tissue.
(ii) P is the major water conducting tissue in vascular plants and provides mechanical strength to plant body.
(iii) Q is a specialized tissue in animals for receiving stimuli and transmitting messages.
(iv) P is composed of all dead cells whereas Q is composed of all living cells.

A. (i) and (ii) only
B. (iii) and (iv) only
C. (i) and (iii) only
D. (i), (iii) and (iv) only

17. The matrix of bone is in the form of thin concentric rings, called ________. Bone cells, called ________ are present in fluid-filled spaces called ________. This fluid filled spaces of the bone communicate with each other by network of fine canals, called ________.

Select the correct sequence of words to complete the above passage.

A. Lacunae, Osteoblasts, Lamellae, Canaliculi
B. Lamellae, Osteocytes, Lacunae, Canaliculi
C. Lamellae, Chondrocytes, Canaliculi, Lacunae
D. Lacunae, Adipocytes, Canaliculi, Sarcoplasm

18. Refer to the given structure of a type of plant tissue. Identify its components X, Y, and Z and select the correct statement regarding them.
A. X is a non-living thin-walled cell that helps in storage of food.
B. Y is devoid of nucleus but mitochondria, plastids and endoplasmic reticulum are present in abundance in it.
C. Z is connected to X with the help of plasmodesmata.
D. Both B and C

19. Identify the types of epithelial tissue from the given statements and select the correct option regarding them.
i. L forms delicate lining of blood vessels.
ii. M is found in salivary and sweat glands.
iii. N forms lining of stomach and gall bladder.
iv. O lines Fallopian tubes and nephrons of kidney.

A. L could be cuboidal epithelium whereas M could be columnar epithelium.
B. M could be cuboidal epithelium whereas N could be columnar epithelium.
C. N could be squamous epithelium whereas O could be cuboidal epithelium.
D. L could be columnar epithelium whereas O could be ciliated epithelium.

20. Select the incorrect option regarding tissues P, Q, R, S, T, and U.

A. P is an epithelial tissue whereas Q is a loose connective tissue.
B. T is either greatly reduced or absent but R is exclusively present in aquatic floating plants whereas S is found in Cucurbita stems.
C. R is aerenchyma, S is collenchyma, T is xylem and U is phloem.
D. U is found in grit of guava, pear, etc., whereas the matrix of tissue P contains a flexible material called chondrin.

21. Select the correct match of tissue and its location.
A. P-Wall of Bowman's capsule, S-Epidermal covering of legume seeds
B. Q-Blubber of whale, R-Covering of nuts
C. R-Petiole of lotus, U-Hump of camel
D. Q-In subcutaneous tissue, T-Stele or vascular cylinder of monocot root

22. Refer to the given picture of blood smear and select the correct option regarding different blood corpuscles (P-S).

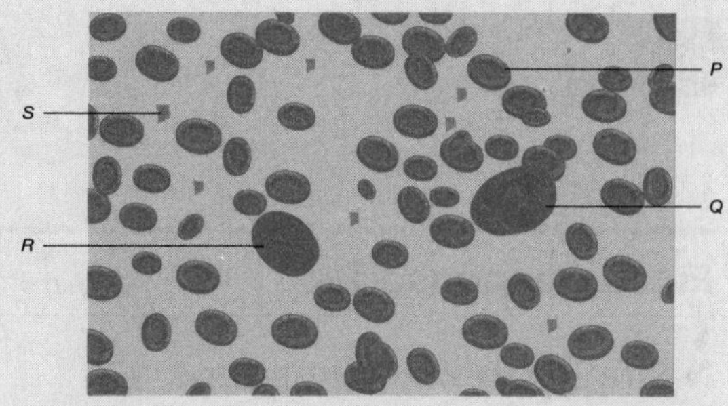

A. Blood cell Q plays a major role in transport of gases within the body.
B. A person who is unable to produce blood cell S bleeds continuously even from a minor injury.
C. Blood cell P produces antibodies in response to a pathogenic infection in the body.
D. Blood cell R contains a red pigment called haemoglobin that shows affinity for oxygen.

ARCHIVE CORNER

ANSWER KEYS

LEVEL 1

Fixed Response Type

Multiple Choice Questions

1. A	2. A	3. A	4. B	5. A	6. A	7. B	8. C	9. B	10. D
11. B	12. C	13. A	14. A	15. B	16. D	17. B	18. B	19. D	20. A
21. C	22. A	23. B	24. A	25. B	26. C	27. B	28. A	29. C	30. B

Fill in the Blanks

1. Chondrin, Ossein
2. Suberin
3. Sieve tubes
4. Erythropoiesis
5. Nuclei, Mitochondria, energy
6. Dendrons, Axons
7. Calcium, Phosphorus
8. Simple
9. Complex
10. Photosynthesis
11. Secondary meristem
12. Lenticles

True/False

1. True
2. False
3. False
4. False
5. True
6. True
7. True
8. True
9. True
10. False

Match Type Questions

1. (i)-(b), (ii)-(a), (iii)-(c), (iv)-(d)
2. (i)-(c), (ii)-(a), (iii)-(b), (iv)-(d)
3. (i)-(b), (ii)-(a), (iii)-(d), (iv)-(c)

Assertion and Reason Type Questions

1. B	2. B	3. C	4. B	5. B	6. A	7. E	8. A	9. C	10. D

LEVEL 2

Multiple Choice Questions

1. A	2. C	3. C	4. C	5. B	6. C	7. C	8. B	9. C	10. D
11. D	12. C	13. C	14. D	15. B	16. B	17. C	18. A	19. A	20. C

Archive Corner

1. D	2. C	3. D	4. D	5. B	6. A	7. C	8. C	9. A
10. D	11. D	12. B	13. C	14. D	15. B	16. B	17. B	18. D
19. B	20. D	21. D	22. B					

ANSWER KEYS

CHAPTER 3

Diversity in Living Organisms

Learning Outcomes

At the end of this chapter, you would be able to:

- explain classification.
- describe nomenclature.
- discuss 2 kingdom, 3 kingdom, 4 kingdom and 5 kingdom system.
- explain the characters of monera, protista, fungi, plantae, animalia.

Geekspeak

- Nomenclature
- Classification
- Taxonomy
- Hierarchy
- Cryptogamae
- Phanerogamae
- Coelom
- Parapodia
- Bilateral
- Triploblastic
- Gills
- Poikilothermal

Introduction

Biodiversity or biological diversity means the variety of living organisms present on a particular region. There are about 20 lac organisms known on the Earth which differ from one another in external form, internal structure, mode of nutrition, habitat, etc.

The warm and humid tropical regions of the Earth between the Tropic of Cancer and the Tropic of Capricorn have a rich diversity of life, i.e., plants, animals, and microorganisms and are called the region of mega biodiversity. There are 12 megadiveristy centres in the world, which are rich in biodiversity.

Countries are Brazil, Colombia, Ecuador, Peru, Mexico, Zaire, Madagascar, Australia, China, Indonesia, Malaysia and India. India is one of the 12 countries which consist of more than half of the biodiversity of the Earth.

Since inception on earth, about 4.2 billion changes and diversifications on account of evolution. According to an estimation, about 5 to 30 million species of living organisms are present on the earth. **Diversity means = variety.** Different places on the earth have their own typical kinds of living beings. Biodiversity refers to all the diverse plants, animals and microorganisms on the earth, which differ from one another in external appearance, size, colour pattern, internal structure, nutrition, behavior and habitat." excretion etc.

Classification

The method of arranging variety of organisms into different groups, on the basis of similarities and dissimilarities between them, is called **classification.**

Taxonomy (Gr. taxis-arrangement; nomos-law): The functional branch of biology dealing with the identification classification and nomenclature of living organisms is called taxonomy. **Carolus Linnaeus (1707 – 1778) is known as "Father of taxonomy". Ernst Mayr** defined taxonomy as the theory and practice of classifying organisms.

Hierarchy: It is the framework by which taxonomic groups are arranged in definite order from higher to lower categories. Or

It is a descending arrangement of taxonomic categories.

Taxon: It refers to any rank or category in the hierarchial order of classification, e.g., kingdom, phylum, etc. The highest taxon is kingdom while the lowest taxon is species. Species are the basic unit of classification.

Hierarchy of Categories

Kingdom→ Phylum/Division → Class → Order → Family → Genus → Species

Some of the characteristics of hierarchy are discussed in Table 3.1.

Keystone

The term '**biodiversity**' is a concise form of **'biological diversity**' and was coined by **Walter G. Rosen** in 1986.

Keystone

Father of Modern Taxonomy → **Carolus Linnaeus**

Term 'taxonomy' was given by → **A.P. de Candolle**

Table 3.1 Different Hierarchy of Categories

S. No.	Hierarchy	Characteristics
1.	Kingdom	It is the highest category of taxonomic studies. All animals are included in kingdom Animalia and all plants are included in kingdom Plantae.
2.	Phylum (or Division)	Many Classes with some common characters are included in Phylum. Example: Chordata.
3.	Class	Similar orders are place together in a class. Example: Mammalia

4.	Order	A number of families having common characters are placed in order. Example: Carnivora
5.	Family	A number of genera having several common characters form a family. Examples: Solanaceae, malvaceae.
6.	Genus	It is a group of closely related species with common ancestry. Examples: Mangifera, solanum, etc.
7.	Species	A group of organisms capable of interbreeding to produce offspring. Examples: Tuberosum (potato), melongena (brinjal).

Taxonomy

Taxonomy includes study of Identification, Nomenclature, Classification and Affinities.

Identification

It is defined as the determination that a particular organism is similar to some other known individual.

Nomenclature

It is the system of naming of any living creature whether it is from a lower phylum or from higher phylum. Nomenclature is done on the basis of a set of rules stated in the ICBN, i.e., **International Code of Binomial Nomenclature.**

Binomial Nomenclature: It is a system of naming the organisms in such a way that each of their names contain two components, first is genus and the second one is species, e.g., scientific name of human is **Homo sapiens**, Scientific name of crow is **Corvus splendens. Homo** and **Corvus** are the genus while **sapiens** and **splendens** are the names of species.

This system was introduced by **Carolus Linnaeus** (Karl van Linne) in his book '*Systema Naturae*' who is also called **Father of Taxonomy.**

Certain convections are followed while writing the scientific names:

- The name of the genus begins with a capital letter.
- The name of the species begins with a small letter.
- When printed, the scientific name is given in italics.
- When written by hand, the genus name and the species name have to be underlined separately.

Classification

Classification is the arrangement of organisms into sets or groups according to the similarities and dissimilarities present between them. This diversity gives rise to the need of classification. So, 'diversity needs classification'.

System of Classification

- **Artificial System:** It based to habit, habitat and few morphological characters, e.g., Aristotle classified living organisms on the basis of habitat water, land and air. Theophrastus grouped plants on the basis of their habits into trees, shrubs, undershrubs and herbs.
- **Natural System:** It was based on morphological and anatomical similarities and differences, e.g., Bentham and Hooker's classification of seed plants.
- **Phylogenetic System:** It was based on evolutionary sequence as well as genetic relationship amongst the organisms. Charles Darwin showed that living organisms evolved by the process of descent with modifications, e.g., Engle and Prantl's classification of flowering plants.

Significance of Classification:

- It establishes hierarchy of groups of organisms on the basis of their common features.
- It makes the systematic study easier.
- It is essential to understand the interrelationship amongst different groups of organisms.
- It serves as a base for the development of other biological sciences as well as different fields of applied biology like public health, environment, etc.

❖ INTEXT QUESTIONS

1. **What is classification?**
   Ans: The grouping of organisms on the basis of their similarities and differences is called classification.
2. **Who is the father of modern taxonomy?**
   Ans: Carolus Linnaeus is the Father of Modern Taxonomy.
3. **In the hierarchy of classification, which grouping will have the smallest number of organisms with a maximum of characteristics in common and which will have the largest number of organisms?**
   Ans: Species will have smallest number of organisms with a maximum of characteristics in common and Kingdom will have largest number of organisms.
4. **Who proposed the five kingdom system of classification?**
   Ans: R.H. Whittaker.

Check Point 1

1. Who was coined the term biodiversity?
2. What is taxonomy?
3. What is the difference between taxon and taxonomy?
4. Which is the lowermost category in the hierarchy of classification?

Different Systems of Classification

- **Two Kingdom System:** It was given by **Carolus Linnaeus in 1758.** Organisms were divided into **Plant Kingdom and Animal Kingdom.** Fungi, Bacteria and Euglena could not find an appropriate position.
- **Three Kingdom System:** It was given by **Ernst Haeckel (1894).** In this, **Kingdom Protista** (for unicellular organisms) was also included along with plant kingdom and animal kingdom.
- **Four Kingdom System:** It was given by **Copeland.** Kingdom **Monera (for prokaryotes)** was also included in this system of classification.
- **Five Kingdom System:** It was given by **Robert Whittaker (1959).** According to him, organisms were divided into five kingdoms – **Monera, Protista, Fungi, Plantae** and **Animalia.**

Kingdom Monera

These are single celled prokaryotic (i.e., lacking a defined nucleus) organisms. It is a kingdom of prokaryotes. Monera is therefore, also called **prokaryota** (as shown in Fig 3.1).

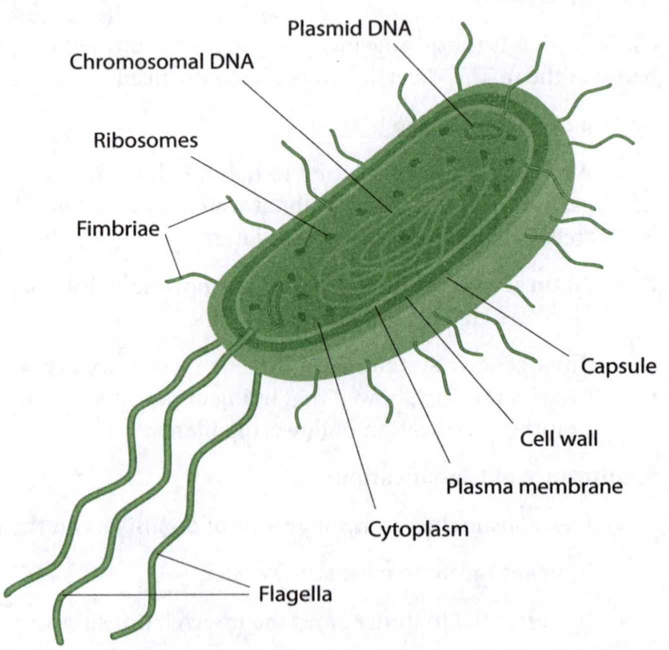

Figure 3.1 Structure of Bacteria

Characteristics:

- **Prokaryotic nature:** Membran-bound cell organelles are absent.
- **Unicellular nature:** Monerans are basically unicellular.
- **Flagella:** Flagella, if present are single-stranded.

- **Cell wall:** It is absent in some (e.g., Mycoplasma) and present in others (e.g., bacteria, cyanobacteria). Basic structure of cell wall is made of **murein or peptidoglycan** (instead of cellulose).
- **Nutrition:** Both autotrophic (Blue-green algae) and heterotrophic (Mycoplasma and bacteria) modes of nutrition.
- **Nitrogen metabolism:** All nitrogen fixing organisms belong to Monera (e.g., rhizobium in root nodules of legumes). Some monerans take part in ammonification, nitrification, and denitrification.

Examples: Mycoplasma (produces diseases in humans, animals and plants), bacteria (e.g., *Vibrio cholerae, Clostridium botulisum, Escherchia coli*) and blue green algae or cyanobacteria (e.g., *Anabaena, Nostoc*).

Kingdom Protista

Protista is the kingdom of unicellular (and colonial) eukaryotes.

Characteristics:

- **Organization:** Protists have simple unicellular and eukaryotic organization.
- **Locomotion:** Locomotion is generally present. It occurs with the help of flagella (e.g., Euglena), cilia (e.g., Paramecium) and Pseudopodia (e.g., Amoeba). Flagella and cilia have 11-stranded structure.

> **Keystone**
>
> All nitrogen fixing organisms belong to kingdom Monera. For example, rhizobium is found in the root nodules of legumes.

- **Cell Wall:** Some protists are covered with cell wall (most photosynthetic protists) while others do not possess it (e.g., protozoan protists).
- **Nutrition:** It is diverse-photosynthetic (e.g., **diatoms**), holozoic (e.g., **Amoeba**) and absorptive (e.g., **Entamoeba**). Photosynthetic nutrition occurs in protistan algae and Euglena like organisms. They are the major producers of aquatic systems. Holozoic nutrition is animal like nutrition where solid food particles are ingested. It is found in protozoan protists. In absorptive nutrition, liquefied digested food is absorbed. It occurs in parasites and saprophytes. Euglena and its relatives perform photosynthesis in light. In dark and in the presence of organic matter, they switch over to saprophytic nutrition. Such a dual nutrition is called mixotrophic nutrition. Such organisms are called plant-animals.
- **Sexual Reproduction**: It is present, but an embryo stage is absent. Examples: Dinoflagellates (e.g., Gonyaulax, *Noctiluca*), diatoms (e.g., Navicula), *Euglena*, Protozoans (e.g., *Amoeba, Paramecium* (as shown in Fig. 3.2)).

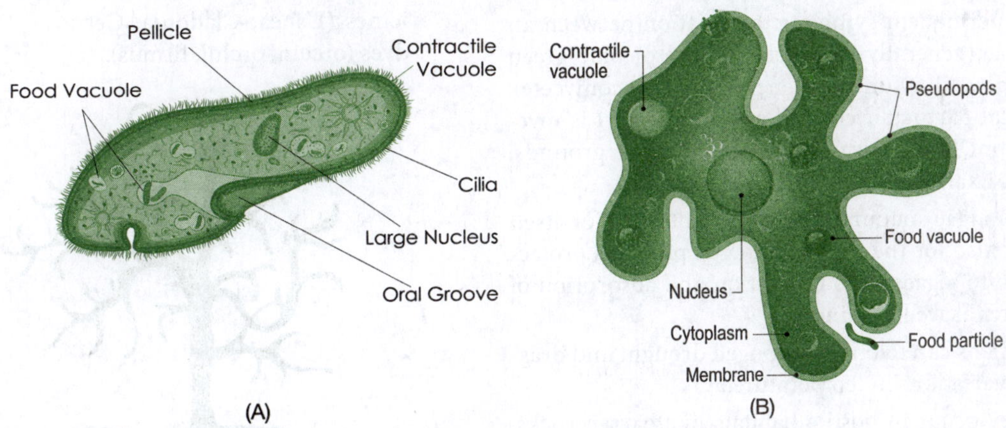

Figure 3.2 Structure of (A) Paramecium (B) Amoeba

Kingdom Fungi

Fungi are achlorophyllous, heterotrophic spore producing, cellwall containing.

Characteristics:

- **Mycelium**: The body of fungi is called mycelium. It is made of a number of fine threads called hyphae (singular hypha).
- **Multicellular Nature:** Fungi are basically multicellular. Yeast is an exception in being unicellular.
- **Cell Wall:** It contains a tough complex sugar called chitin or fungus cellulose.

Keystone

Some of the protists are pathogenic. For example, Entamoeba histolytica, which cause dysentery and Plasmodium vivax that causes malaria.

- **Nutrition**: Fungi are heterotrophic with absorptive nutrition. Most of the mare decomposers (Hence kingdom of multicellular decomposers) or saprophytes which feed on organic remains by first secreting digestive enzymes and then absorbing the digested materials. A few fungi are also parasitic.
- **Reserve Food:** It is glycogen and oil.
- **Sexual Reproduction:** Fungi show progressive reduction in sexuality. An embryo stage is absent.

  Examples: Yeast (Baker's Yeast, Brewer's Yeast), *Agaricus* (Mushroom), *Penicillium* (source of penicillin), *Aspergillus*, *Rhizopus* (Bread Mould) (as shown in Fig. 3.3).

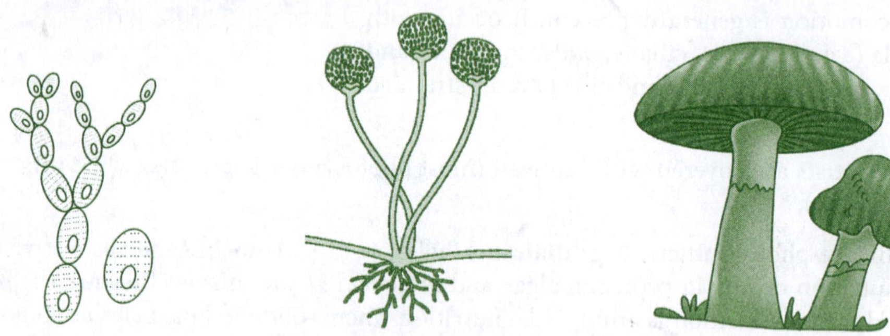

Figure 3.3 Yeast, Rhizopus, Mushroom

Competition Corner

Lichen:

- They are dual organisms which have been formed by permanent symbiotic association between an algae (generally a cyanobacterium or blue-green alga) and a fungus (generally and ascomycete). Algal part is phycobiont and fungal part is mycobiont.They grow on rocks, tree trunks, grounds, etc. Examples: Parmellia, Alectoria, etc.
- The algae manufactures food not only for itself but also for the fungus. Fungus provides protection to algae; helps in fixation and absorption of water as well as minerals.
- Lichens can tolerate prolonged drought and drastic variations in temperature.
- They occur in hostile habitats like barren rocks, walls, tree trunks, icey regions where they can be seen as slow growing large colored patches.
- Lichens are sensitive to air pollution. They are the source of dhoop and havan samagri. Some medicines (Usnea, Cladonia, Cetraria, Lobaria) and dyes (orcein, orchil, litmus).

Lichen

Kingdom Plantae

Plantae is a kingdom of multicellular photosynthetic organisms having cellulose cell wall. Plants are muticellular eukaryotes with cellulose cell walls. They are autotrophs and use chlorophyll for photosynthesis.

Basis of Classification:

- On the basis of differentiation of plant body.
- On the basis of conducting tissue.
- One the basis of ability of bear seeds and seed are enclosed within fruits,

> **Keystone**
>
> - Penicillium was the source of the first discovered antibiotic, penicillin. Yeasts (Saccharomyces) are widely used in baking bread and in wine making, etc.
> - Fungi lack chlorophyll and is heterotrophic but still considered as plant because of the presence of cell wall and absence of centriole.

Sub Kingdom Cryptogamae (Cryptos = hidden, gamous = marriage)

These are also called as lower plants, flowerless or seedless plants. Their reproductive organs are hidden.

Division Thallophyta (Algae)

- Undifferentiated plant body, i.e., absence of root, stem and leaves (as shown in Fig. 3.4).
- Their is no vascular system.
- Reproductive organs are single-celled and there is no embryo formation after fertilization.
- These are aquatic or terrestrial, fresh water or marine.
- Autotrophic, photosynthetic containing various pigments like chlorophyll, carotenoids, xanthophylls etc.
- Unicellular, colonial, filamentous and multicellular.
- Cell wall of cellulose and stored food is starch.
- **Examples:** Blue green algae (*Nostoc*), *Anabaena* Green algae (*Ulothrix, Chara, Cladophora, Ulva, Spirogyra*) Brown algae, Red algae, etc.

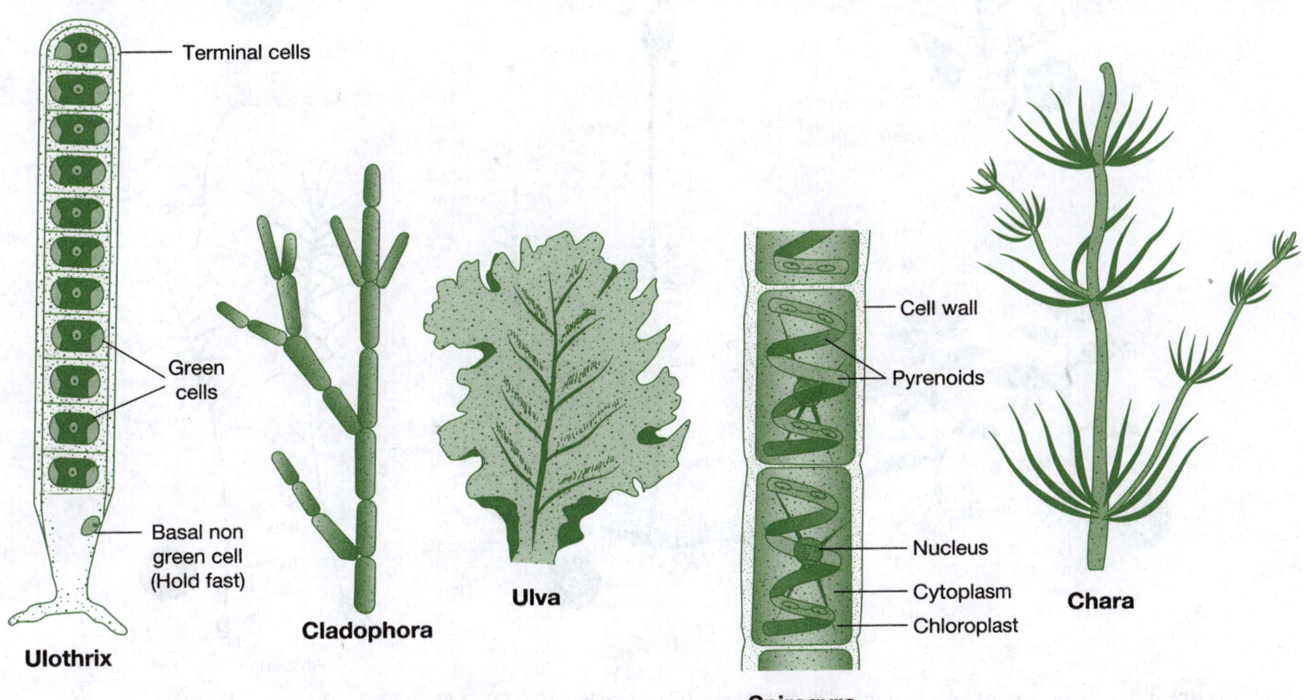

Figure 3.4 Different Types of Algae

Division Bryophyta

- Bryophytes are also known as amphibians of plant kingdom.
- These are the simplest and the most primitive land plant (as shown in Fig. 3.5).
- They have flat plant body which differentiate into stem, leaf and root like structure (Rhizoids).
- Main plant body is attached to substratum by means of rhizoids.
- There is no specialized tissue for the conduction of water and other substances from one part of the plant body to another.

Keystone

In thallophytes, asexual reproduction generally take place by spores. Sex organs are simple single-celled (the male sex organs are calles as antheridia and female sex organ called oogonia) and there is no embryo formation after fertilization.

Figure 3.5 Structure of (A) Bryophytes (B) Ricca (C) Marchantia (D) Pellia (E) Anthoceros (F) Funaria (G) Polytrichum (H) Pogonatum

- Sex organs are jacketed and multicellular. Fertilization produces embryo. They show heteromorphic type of alternation in generation.
- **Examples:** Liverworts (*Riccia, Marchantia*), hornworts (**Anthoceros**) and mosses (*Funaria*).

Division Pteridophyta

- They are seedless vascular plants, primitive tracheophytes or vascular cryptogams.
- Plant body is differentiated into true stem, leaves and roots (as shown in Fig. 3.6).
- They are the most evolved cryptogams.
- Vascular tissues are present.
- Fruits are absent.
- **Examples:** Ferns (Dryopteris, Pteris), Club moss (Lycopodium), Horsetail (Equisetum), Marsilea.

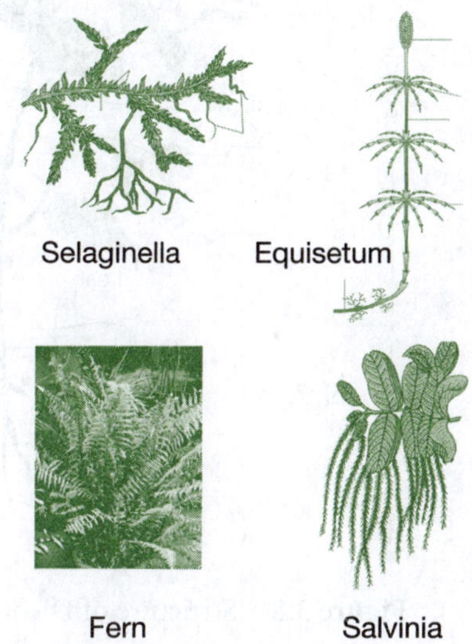

Figure 3.6 Different Types of Pteridophytes

Sub Kingdom Phanerogamae (Phaneros = visible, gamous = marriage)

This is the highest group of plants which includes flowering and seed-bearing plants. They reproduce sexually by means of seeds. The flowering plants are of two types:

(i) Gymnosperms **(ii)** Angiosperms

Division Gymnospermae

- Gymno-means naked and sperma-seed.
- Seeds are not enclosed in fruits. These are naked seeded.
- They have well developed vascular system but xylem lacks vessels and phloem lacks companion cells.
- They occupy an intermediate position between the pteridophytes and the angiosperms.
- Plants are commonly tall trees or shrubs.
- The flowers are represented by unisexual cones, often both cones are present on the same plant.
- Examples: *Cycas, Pinus* (as shown in Fig. 3.7).

Figure 3.7 Structure of Pinus and Cycas

Division Angiospermae

- Angio means covered and sperma means seed.
- These are seed bearing plants. These are represented by trees, herbs, shrubs.
- Body well differentiated into root, stem and leaves. They have highly developed vascular system.
- Seeds remain enclosed in ovary. Plant embryos in seeds have structures called cotyledons. Cotyledons are called seed leaves.
- It is divided into two classes on the basis of number of cotyledons.
  - **Class Dicotyledons (dicots):**
    - Their seeds have 2 cotyledons in the embryo. Leaves are dorsiventral and show reticulate venation.
    - Tap root is present, e.g., neem, peepal, mango, pea, mustard (as shown in Fig. 3.8).

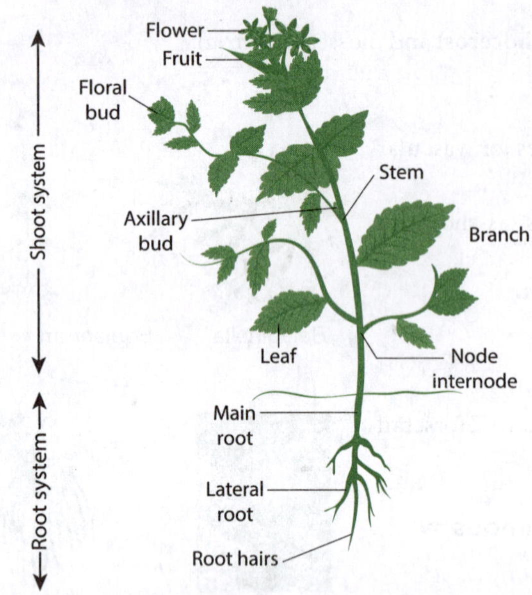

Figure 3.8 Structure of Dicot Plant (Mustard)

Figure 3.9 Structure of Monocot Plant (Maize)

- **Class Monocotyledons (monocots):**
    - Their seeds have one cotyledon in embryo. Leaves are isobilateral with parallel venation.
    - Fibrous root system is present, e.g., wheat, maize (as shown in Fig. 3.9), onion.

❖ INTEXT QUESTIONS

5. Write the difference between bryophytes and pterdophytes.

Ans:

Bryophyta	Pteridophyte
True stem and true leaves are always absent.	True stem and true leaves are present.
Fixation is carried out by rhizoids	Fixation is carried out by roots.
Bryophytes are non-vascular in nature.	Pteridophytes are vascular plant.

6. Differentiate between dicots and monocots.

Ans:

Plant organ	Dicots	Monocots
Root	Tap, adventitious or both.	Only adventitious.
Stem	Vascular bundles arranged in ring with central pith.	Vascular bundles scattered.
Leaves	Mostly with reticulate venation.	Usually parallel venation.
Cotyledons	Two	One
Floral parts	Five or multiple of 5, rarely 4.	Three or multiple of 3, rarely 4, never 5.

7. Differentiate between gymnosperm and angiosperms.

Ans:

Characters	Gymnosperms	Angiosperms
Nature of seeds	Naked as no fruit formation.	Enclosed inside the fruit.
Reproductive organs	Sporophylls form cones.	Flowers.
Xylem	Only tracheid but no vessel.	Vessels shown in present.

Phloem	No companion cells.	Companion cell present.
Ovules	Not enclosed in ovary.	Enclosed in vary.
Examples	Cycas and Pinus.	Monocots and Dicots.

8. Differentiate between algae and fungi.

Ans:

Algae	Fungi
Green, blue, green, red brown coloured.	Colourless.
Contain chlorophyll and other pigments.	Chlorophyll is absent.
Autotrophic.	Heterotrophic.
Body made up of true parenchyma.	Pseudo-parenchyma (a false tissue) present.
A cell-wall of true cellulose is present.	Cell wall contains chitin, cellulose, pectose, etc.
Reserve food is starch.	Reserve food is glycogen and oil.
Aquatic.	Found at damp and moist places.

Check Point 2

5. In which kingdom will you place and organisms which is single celled eukaryotic and photosynthetic?
6. Which division among plant has simplest organism?
7. How are pteridophytes different from the phanerogams?

Animal Kingdom

Animal kingdom is discussed below in detail:

Basis of Classification

- Organization and differentiation of cells to form tissues and organs.
- Body symmetry.
- Formation of body cavities and blood vascular system.
- Features of embryonic development.
- **Level of Organization in Living Beings:** It is structural differentiation of animal body.
  - **Cellular level of Organization:** Tissues do not differentiate. Different types of cells are present, e.g., porifera (sponges).
  - **Tissue Level of Organization:** Multicellular body cells organized into tissues, but organs are absent, e.g., Coelenterate.
  - **Organ Level of Organization:** Cells are organized into tissues and tissues into organ, but organ systems are absent, e.g., Platyhelminthes.**85**
  - **Organ System Level of Organization:** Cells are organized into tissues, tissues into organs, and organ into organ systems, e.g., Nematoda and higher animals.
- **Body Symmetry:** It is similarity in arrangement of parts. Absence of repetition or similarity is called asymmetry (as shown in Fig. 3.10). Symmetry is of two types – radial and bilateral (discussed in Table 3.2).
  - **Radial Symmetry:** The body is cylindrical or discoid when similar parts occur all around the central axis. Any vertical plane passing through, the central axis will divide the body into two equal halves, e.g., many sponge, coelenterates and Echinodermata's. Head is generally absent.

- **Bilateral Symmetry:** The body has a head. Organs and limbs are paired. They are arranged laterally. Body is divisible into two equal halves by only one plane (mid-sagittal plane). Bilateral symmetry is found in Platyhelminthes, Nematoda, Annelida, Mollusca, Arthropoda and Chordate.

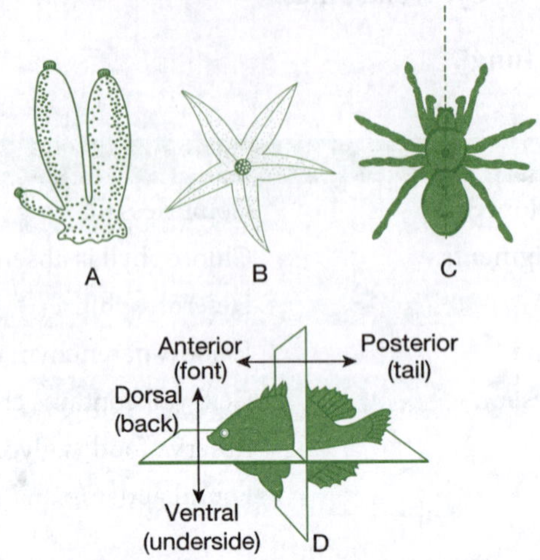

Figure 3.10 Diagrams Showing Body Symmetry (A) Asymmetry in Sponges; (B) Radial Symmetry in Starfish; (C) Bilateral Symmetry in Spider; and (D) Fish – A Bilaterally Symmetrical Animal Having Front (Anterior) End, Tail (Posterior) End and Back (Dorsal), Underside (Ventral) Side.

Table 3.2 Difference Between Bilateral and Radial Symmetry

Bilateral Symmetry	Radial Symmetry
Limbs and organs are paired.	Limbs and organs occur all around the central axis.
Cephalization is present.	Cephalization is absent.
Examples. Fish, Frog, Earthworm, Human.	Examples. Hydra, Starfish.

Keystone

Cephalization is the development of head in the anterior part of the animal body.

- **Germ or Germinal Layers:** They are the germinal layers that differentiate in the embryo. All tissues and organs of the animal body develop from them. Germinal layers can be two or three in number. On this basis, the animals are of two types – diploblastic and triploblastic.
  - **Diploblastic Animals:** Animals having two germinal layers, outer **ectoderm** and inner **endoderm.** Mesoderm is absent (as shown in Fig. 3.11), e.g., Porifera, Coelenterata.
  - **Triploblastic Animals:** Animals having three germinal layers-outer **ectoderm,** middle **mesoderm** and inner **endoderm,** e.g., Platyhelminthes to Chordata.
- **Coelom (Body Cavity):** It is mesoderm lined fluid filled space that occurs between alimentary canal and body wall which provides shock proof environment to various body organs. Depending upon the absence or presence of coelom animals are of three types – **Acoelomate, Pseudocoelomate** and **Eucoelomates.**

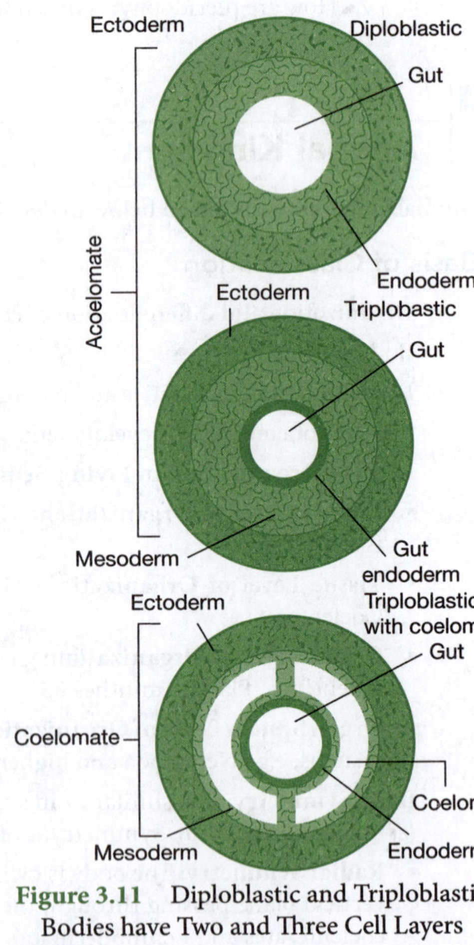

Figure 3.11 Diploblastic and Triploblastic Bodies have Two and Three Cell Layers

- **Acoelomate:** Coelom is absent, **e.g., Porifera, Coelenterate, Platyhelminthes**. In Platyhelminthes, a mesoderm is present, but it does not form cavity.
- **Pseudocoelomate:** A cavity called **pseudocoelom** is present which is not lined by mesoderm. It is generally endodermal in origin. Mesoderm occurs but forms small separate pouches, e.g., **Nematoda.**
- **Coelomate or Eucoelomate:** A true coelom lined by mesoderm is present (as shown in Fig. 3.12). On the basis of origin, true coelom is of two types – **schizocoelom and enterocoelom.**

Figure 3.12 Diagrammatic Sectional View of (A) Coelomate (B) Pseudocoelomate (C) Acoelomate

Non-Chordates

All the Non-chordates are discussed below.

Phylum Protozoa

- They are unicellular, eukaryotes.
- These are the simplest and the most primitive animals. Their body organization is of 'Protoplasmic Level'.
- They are of different shapes, i.e., irregular, elongated or rounded.
- They have different types of locomotory organs like cilia, flagella, pseudopodia (false feet), etc. Nutrition is of different types like holozoic, holophytic, mixotrophic.

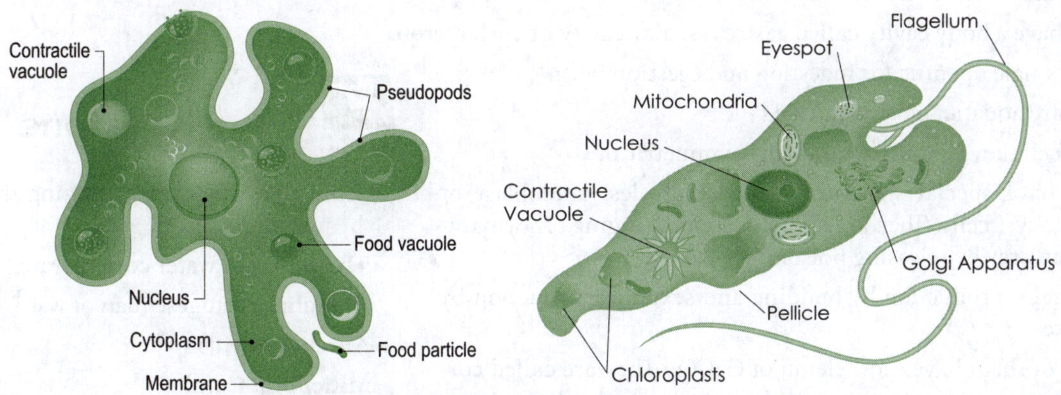

Figure 3.13 Structure of Amoeba and Euglena

- Digestion is intracellular and it takes place in food vacuole.
- Excretion and respiration occur through general body surface by the process of simple diffusion.
- Reproduction may be sexual or asexual.
- Examples: Amoeba (as shown in Fig. 3.13), Entamoeba, Plasmodium, Euglena, Paramecium.

Phylum Porifera

- These are pore bearing organisms i.e., with porous body, also called as **sponges.**
- Aquatic, mostly marine habitats.
- These are sessile and sedentary (attached to substratum) asymmetric or with radial symmetry.
- Sponges are diploblastic.
- Occur in different shapes, i.e., vase–like, round, sac-like, etc.
- Body perforated by numerous pores called ostia which opens into a canal system having canals and chambers lined with choanocytes and have a large sized water outlet called oscula.
- Their cavity is called spongocoel.

- Endoskeleton is made of needle like spicules made of calcium carbonate and silica or spongin.
- They are Hermaphrodite, and perform asexual reproduction by budding.
- E.g., *Sycon, Spongilla, Euplectella* (Venus flower basket) (as shown in Fig. 3.14).

Figure 3.14 Different Examples of Poriferan Animals

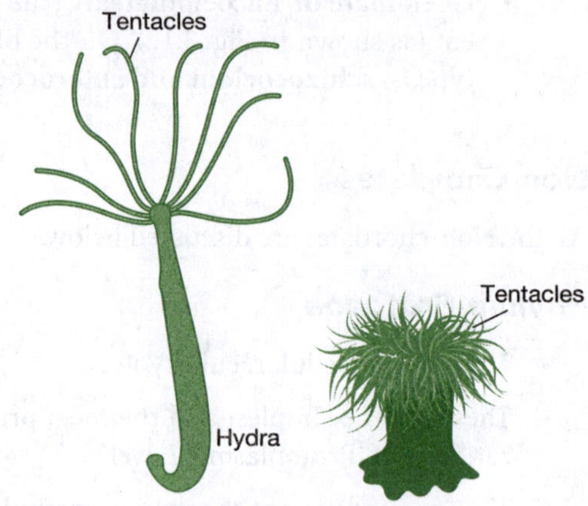

Figure 3.15 Structure of Cnidaria and Sea Anemone

Phylum Coelenterata or Cnidaria

- These are sac-like structures.
- They have a body cavity called gastrovascular cavity or coelenteron.
- It has single opening for ingestion and egestion both.
- They are aquatic, mostly marine.
- Multicellular, diploblastic, radially symmetrical.
- They have special structures called tentacles, cnidoblast or nematocyst cells. They are specialized for stinging. They paralyse the prey by releasing poison.
- Asexual reproduction by budding and sexual reproduction by gametes.
- Some of them have exoskeleton of $CaCO_3$. They are called corals. They live in colonies and when they die, they form coral reefs, or islands.
- **Examples:** Hydra, Jelly fish, Physalia, Sea-anemone (as shown in Fig. 3.15).

> **Keystone**
>
> Cnidoblast helps in paralyzing the prey by injecting poison.
>
> **Hydra:** Fresh water coelenterate.
>
> **Physalia:** Portugese man of war
>
> **Aurelia:** Jelly fish
>
> **Millepora:** Coral

Phylum Platyhelminthes (Platys = flat, helminth = worm)

- Generally called as flatworms.
- Bilaterally symmetrical, triploblastic, dorsoventrally flattened.
- Acoelomates.
- Their digestive cavity has a single opening with mouth only and anus is absent.
- They possess hooks and suckers.
- They have flame cells or protonephridia for excretion.
- Mode of nutrition is parasitic.
- Reproduction is of both types, i.e., asexual and sexual.
- These are hermaphrodite.
- Examples: *Planaria, Fasciola* (liver fluke), *Taenia solium*, Blood fluke (as shown in Fig. 3.16).

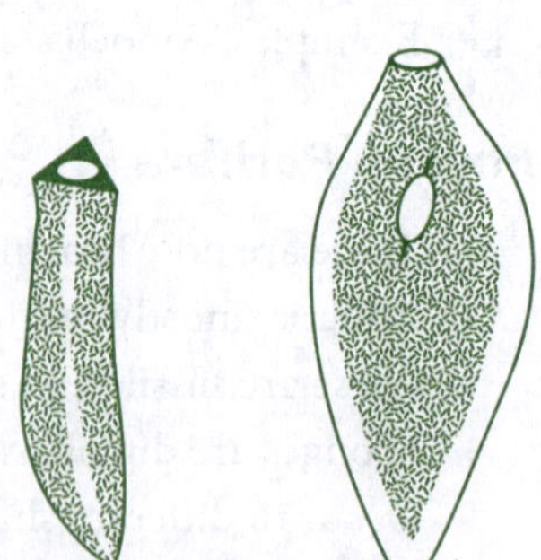

Figure 3.16 Structure of Planaria and Liver Fluke

Phylum Nematoda (Aschelminthes)

- They are also called as roundworms.
- Bilaterally symmetrical, unsegmented triploblast.
- These are pseudocoelomic.
- Their alimentary canal is tubular having both mouth and anus.
- Most are free living, some live in moist soil, some are fresh water while some are marine.
- Some are parasites on plants and animals.
- They lack circulatory system. Female ascaris is longer than male ascaris. It has curved tail.
- Reproduction is sexual and sexes are separate.
- **Examples:** *Ascaris* (round worm) (as shown in Fig. 3.17), Filarial worm (elephantiasis).

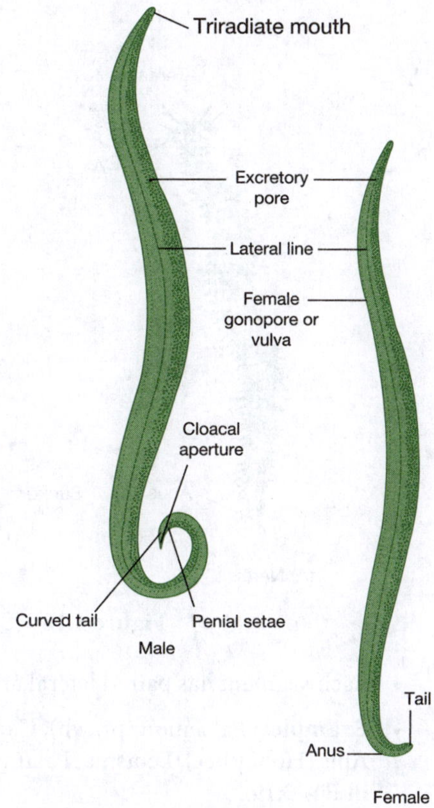

Figure 3.17 Structure of Male and Female Ascaris

Phylum Annelida (Annulus = ring segments)

- Their body is triploblastic, bilaterally symmetrical, soft, elongated, vermiform, cylindrical.
- Body is metamerically segmented.
- Exoskeleton is absent, body is covered by thin cuticle.
- Eucoelomata, i.e., they have true body cavity which first appeared in this phylum.
- Well-developed alimentary canal is present.
- They have closed circulatory system.
- Locomotion is with the help of chitinous projections called chaetae (setae).
- Excretion by nephridia.
- Nervous system has dorsal brain.
- Most are aquatic, marine or fresh water. Some are terrestrial.
- They reproduce sexually.
- **Examples:** Earthworm, Leech, Nereis, Sea mouse (as shown in Fig. 3.18).

> **Keystone**
>
> - Hermaphrodite – male and female reproductive organs are present in same animals.
> - Alimentary canal straight and complete with mouth and anus in nematodes. They are unisexual organisms.

Phylum Arthropoda (Arthros = jointed, poda = legs)

- These are the organisms with jointed appendages.
- This is the largest phylum in animal kingdom.
- Body triploblastic, bilaterally symmetrical and externally segmented.
- They have an exoskeleton made up of protein and chitin (Moulting Periodic shedding off of the exoskeleton to induce the growth).
- They have a complete alimentary canal with mouth and anus.
- Respiration occurs through general body surface, gills, trachea and book lungs.
- They have an open circulatory system with dorsal heart and arteries.
- Body cavity is called haemocoel.
- Excretion by coelom ducts, Malpighian tubules, green glands, coxal glands.
- Sexes are separate.

> **Keystone**
>
> In Annelids, body is metamerically segmented, i.e., body is divided externally by transverse grooves as well as internally by septa. These segments are called metameres.
>
> Locomotion is performed by parapodia or Chitinous setae which are segmentally arranged.

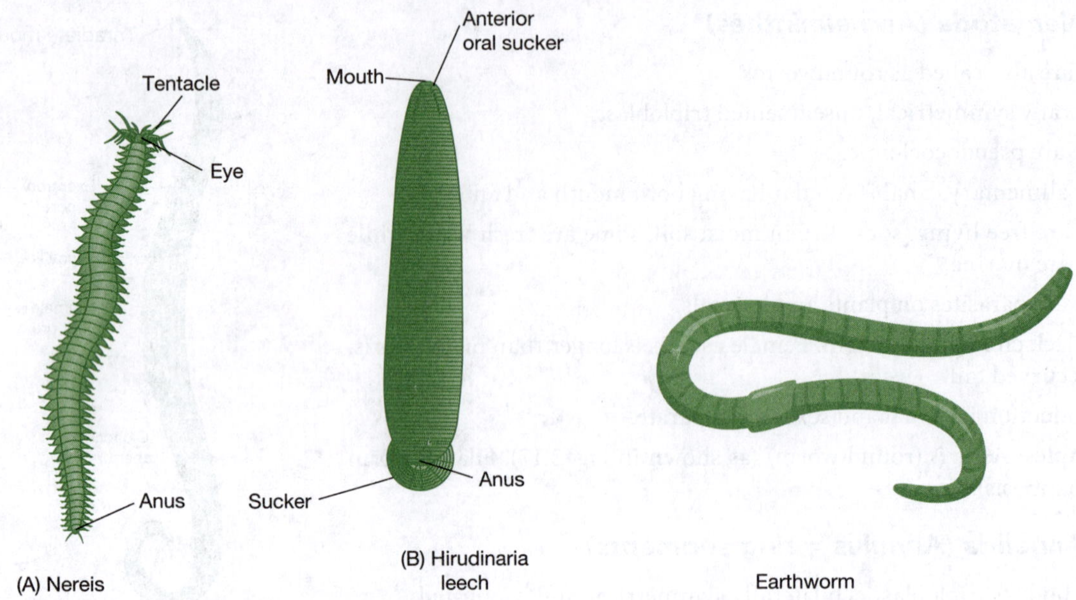

Figure 3.18 Structure of (A) Nereis, (B) Hirudinaria, (C) Earthworm

- Each segment has paired lateral and jointed appendages.
- **Examples:** Palaemon (prawn), Cancer (crab), Periplanata (cockroach), Anopheles (mosquito) and Aranea (spider), Apis (Honey bee), Lepisma, Palamnaeus (scorpion) Scolopendra (centipede), Musca (House fly) Butterfly (as shown in Fig. 3.19).

Figure 3.19 Structure of A. Prawn, B. Cockroach, C. Moth, D. Scorpion, E. Spider, F. Lepisma, G. Musca

Phylum Mollusca (Molluscs = soft)

- It is the second largest group of animals, body soft, unsegmented, asymmetrical and without appendages Neopilina is a segmented mollusca.
- Bilateral symmetry in some mollusca like pila due to torsion (twisting) during growth, the adult is asymmetrical.
- Body divided into a head, foot and visceral mass. A thin skin covering the body is called as mantle, which secretes a calcareous shell.
- Body cavity is haemocoel.
- Respiration by gills (Ctenidial) in aquatic forms but in terrestrial forms space between mantle and body wall called as mantle cavity act as lungs.
- For ingestion they have tongue like structure "radula" they also possess a digestive gland called hepatopancreas.
- Open circulatory system.
- Excretion by metanephridia present near heart.
- Reproduction is sexual and sexes are separate.
- **Examples:** Chiton (8 Calcareous pieces), Pila, Helix (torsion univalve), Dentalium (tusk like shell), Unio, Mytilus (Bivalve), Octopus, Torpedo, Sepia, Indian pearl oyster (as shown in Fig. 3.20).

Figure 3.20 Structure of (A) Chiton, (B) Octopus, (C) Pila, (D) Unio

Phylum Echinodermata (Echinos = spines, Derma = skin)

- Head is absent, oral and aboral surfaces have five radial ambulacra.
- Excretory organs are absent.
- A complex system of water containing tubes and bladders passing through pores of skin called water vascular system is present. From this tube-like structure arise, these tubes look like feet and are called as tube feet that helps in locomotion.
- Reproduction can be asexual, sexual or by regeneration.
- **Examples: Asterias** (star fish), **Echinus** (seaurchin), **Holothuria** (sea cucumber), **Antedon** (feather star).

Phylum Hemichordata

- They are placed in between non-chordates and chordates as they possess some characters of both.
- They include worm like, un-segmented, bilaterally symmetrical animals which are exclusively marine.

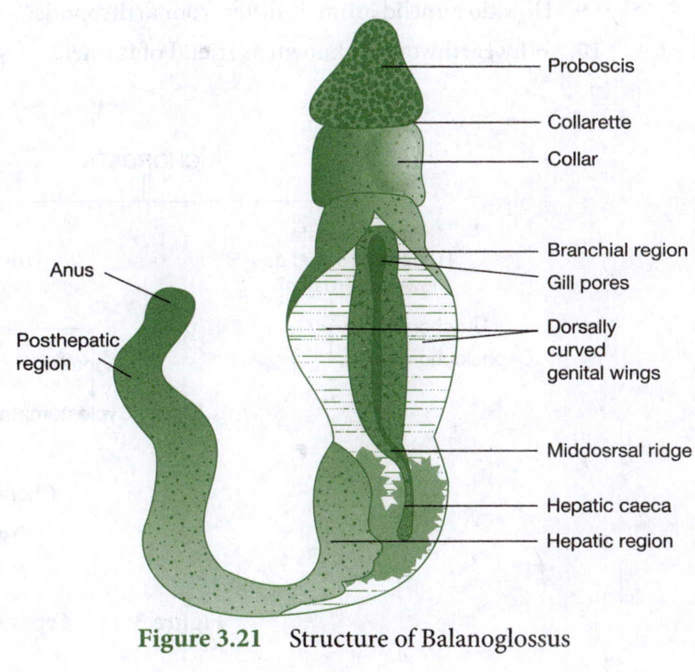

Figure 3.21 Structure of Balanoglossus

- Their body is divided into three regions proboscis, collar and trunk.
- They do not possess notochord, which is a flexible, rod like structure running through the length of the body, above alimentary canal.
- They possess gill slit or gill cleft which is meant for respiration.
- They possess nerve cord in collar region, but it is not a true dorsal nerve cord.
- **Examples:** *Balanoglossus* **(tongue worm) (as shown in Fig. 3.21),** *saccoglossus.*

❖ INTEXT QUESTIONS

9. **Name the largest phylum of kingdom Animalia.**
   Ans: Arthropoda.
10. **Which phylum in animal kingdom consists of pseudocoelomate organisms?**
    Ans: Nematoda
11. **What is the characteristic feature due to which echinoderms are named?**
    Ans: Spiny skin (Echino - spiny; derm - skin)
12. **State the phylum to which liver fluke and planaria belong.**
    Ans: Phylum Platyhelminthes
13. **Prawn, housefly and spider belong to one group.**
    (i) Name the group.
    (ii) Justify the name given to this group.
    Ans:
    (i) Arthropoda.
    (ii) They have jointed legs. The word 'arthropod' means jointed legs

Check Point 3

8. Differentiate between platyhelminthes and aschelminths.
9. How do annelid animals differ from arthropods?
10. Why earthworm is known as friend of farmer?

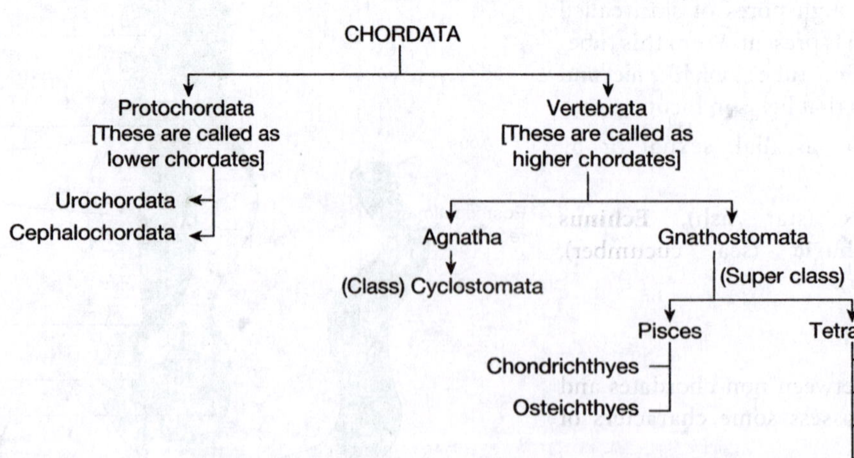

Figure 3.22 Types of Chordata

Phylum Chordata

- This is the most advanced group of animals.
- Notochord is present at some stages of life, supported by a tubular hollow dorsal nerve cord.
- In higher chordates, i.e., vertebrates, the notochord is replaced by vertebral column.
- A set of gill slits is also present at certain stage of life, also called as pharyngeal gill clefts.
- Tail is also present behind the anal aperture that is post anal tail.
- They also possess a proper circulatory system (as shown in Fig. 3.23).
- **Notochord:** It is solid unjointed of vacuolated cells, present on dorsal side between alimentary canal and nervous system in some animal. It is derived from mesoderm and act as primary axial skeleton.

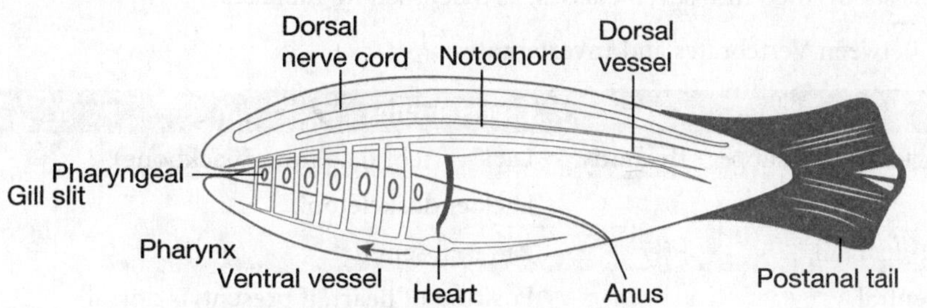

Figure 3.23 Showing Basic Chordate Features

Competition Corner

Phylum Protochordata

- **They** are termed as lower chordates.
- They do not possess brain, cranium, vertebral column, jaw and paired appendages.
- Notochord is present at least in some stages along with other diagnostic chordate characters (dorsal hollow nerve cord, gill slits, post anal tail).
- They are triploblastic, bilaterally symmetrical, enter coelomic, organ system level organization.
- They are marine animals.
- Protochordates are further divided into two groups: urochordata and cephalochordata.

Subphylum Urochordata

- They are commonly known as tunicates.
- The notochord is present in the tail of the larva and disappears in the adult.
- The larva (tadpole) undergoes retrogressive metamorphosis, i.e., changes from a better developed larva to a less developed adult.
- **Examples:** Herdmania (sea squirt), Doliolum, Pyrosoma.

Subphylum Cephalochordata

- Animals are fish like without a head.
- A notochord which extends upto the entire length of the body and persists throughout the life.
- A post anal tail throughout life.
- **Examples:** Branchiostoma (Amphioxus; Lancelet).

Subphylum Vertebrata or Craniata

- Majority of chordates are included in this phylum (as shown in Fig. 3.24).
- They are advanced animals, having a cranium (brain box) around the brain. Nervous system is well developed.

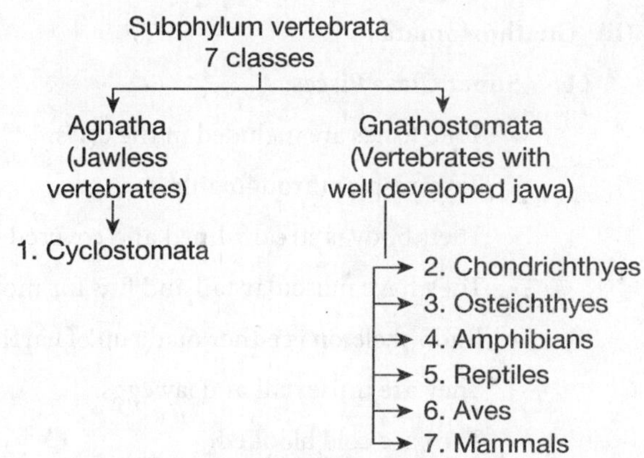

Figure 3.24 Subphylum Vertebrata

- Notochord is replaced by a vertebral column (backbone) in the adults. Endoskeleton is highly developed.
- There are two pairs of limbs or appendages.
- Head is well differentiated.
- The heart is situated ventrally. The circulatory system is closed consisting of blood vascular system and lymphatic system. Red-coloured pigment haemoglobin is present in red blood corpuscles.
- Respiratory organs may be gills (in aquatic animals), skin, buccopharyngeal cavity (in amphibians) or lungs (in land animals).
- Excretion occurs through kidneys.
- Sexes are separate.
- This subphylum is subdivided into seven classes, as discussed in Table 3.3

Table 3.3 Difference Between Vertebrates and Invertebrates

Vertebrates	Invertebrates
Vertebral column (Backbone) to support the body.	Lack vertebral column (backbone).
Possess endoskeleton.	Lack endoskeleton.
Usually possess a post-anal tail.	Tail is absent.
Position of hearts is ventral.	Position of heart, if present, is dorsal.
Nerve cord is tubular and dorsal in position.	Nerve cord (Spinal) is solid and ventral in position.
Red blood cells (RBCs) contain haemoglobin.	Generally, haemoglobin is absent. If present, it remains dissolved in blood.
Two pair s of limbs (appendages) are present.	Limbs (appendages) consist of more than two pairs.

(i) Agnatha

1. Class Cyclostomata (Gr. Cyclos = circular, Stome = mouth; the circular mouthed fishes):

- These are the most primitive vertebrates.
- Animals are jawless and possess a circular mouth.
- They are ectoparasites on fish and use mouth to stick to fish; the mouth is therefore suctorial.
- Notochord is present in the form of a cylindrical rod.
- Head and brain are poorly developed.
- Cartilaginous endoskeleton is present.
- Respiration occurs through gills contained in pouches.
- Heart is two–chambered consisting of one auricle and one ventricle.
- Gonad is single and fertilization is external. e.g., Petromyzon (lamprey) (as shown in Fig. 3.25), Myxine (hag fish).

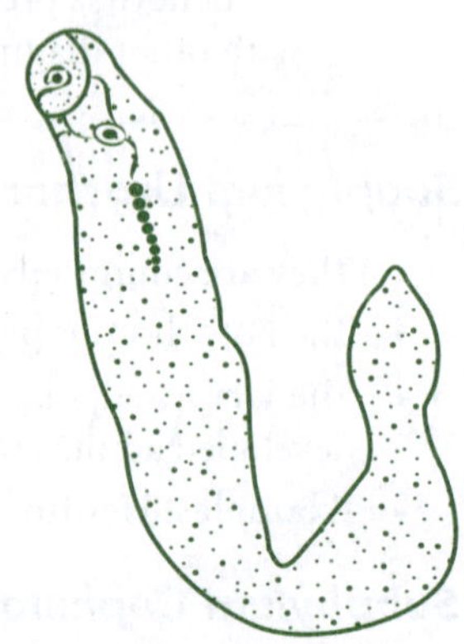

Figure 3.25 Structure of Petromyzon

(ii) Gnathostomata

1. Super Class Pisces:

- True fishes are included in the class.
- They respire through gills.
- Their body is stream-lined and covered by scales/plates.
- They have muscular tail and fins for movement.
- Endo skeleton is either made up of cartilage or bone.
- They are unisexual and lay eggs.
- They are cold blooded.
- Heart is two-chambered.

Keystone

Cold blooded/poikilotherms: There body temperature does not remain constant and varies with atmospheric temperature.

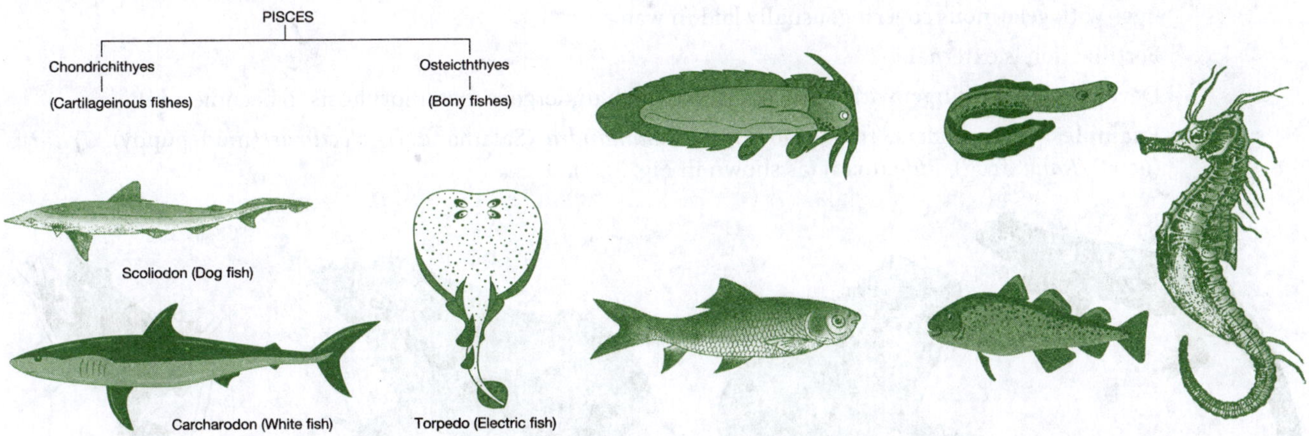

Figure 3.26 Structure of (A) Chondrichthyes (B) Osteichthyes

Table 3.4 Differences Between Chondrichthyes and Osteichthyes

Chondrichthyes	Osteichthyes
Mouth ventral.	Mouth terminal.
Tail fin asymmetrical (heterocercal).	Tail fin symmetrical (homocercal).
5-7 pair of gills are present.	4-5 pairs of gills are present.
Gills are naked.	Gills covered by operculum.
Cloacal aperture is present.	Anus and urinogenital apertures are separate.
No swim bladder.	Swim bladder usually present.
Fertilization is internal.	Fertilization is external.
Examples: Dog fish, sting ray, electric ray, whale shark.	**Examples:** Rohu, climbing perch, angler fish, hippocampus, sea horse, lion fish, flying fish, mandarin fish.

2. **Super Class Tetrapoda:**

Class Amphibia (Gr. amphi = both, bios = life, the vertebrates leading two lives/dual life):

- They are amphibious in nature; found in fresh water and moist places.
- Skin is smooth or rough, rich in glands which keep it moist; skin with pigmented cells, i.e., chromatophores.
- Body is without scales.
- Endoskeleton is mostly bony; notochord does not persist in adults.
- Head and trunk are distinct; neck and tail may or may not be present.
- Limbs tetrapods (four – limbed), there are digits without nails.
- Respiration occurs by lungs, skin or buccal lining, gills are present at least during larval stage for respiration.
- Excrete either ammonia (by tadpole) or urea (by adults).
- Heart three chambered with two auricles and a ventricle, red blood corpuscles are large, biconvex,
- oval and nucleated.
- Brain is not much developed, cranial nerves are 10 pairs.
- Sexes are separate, i.e., dioecious, male without copulatory organ.

Keystone

Amphibians are the first vertebrate which come out of water but these are not able to live on land permanently. These depend on water for their reproduction.

- Eggs with gelatinous covering, usually laid in water.
- Fertilization is external.
- Development is indirect with a tadpole larva which undergoes metamorphosis to become adult.
- **Examples:** Salamanders, frogs and toads. *Salamandra* (Salamander), *Necturus* (mud puppy), *Triturus* (newt), *Rana* (frog), *Bufo* (toad) (as shown in Fig. 3.27).

Figure 3.27 Structure of (a) Salamander (b) Toad (c) Frog (d) Hyla

Class Reptilia (L. reptare = to creep; creeping vertebrates)

- Two pairs of pentadactyl limbs are present, but in snakes, limbs are reduced or absent.
- Body is covered with epidermal horny scales.
- Skin is dry, impermeable and devoid of glands.
- Respiration takes place by lungs only. Gills are absent.
- Heart is incompletely four-chambered, having two auricles and incompletely divided ventricle. In crocodile, heart is completely four chambered.
- Sexes are separate.
- Fertilization is internal (characteristics of land animals).
- There is no larval stage in development.
- **Examples:** Testudo (tortoise), Chelone (turtle) Draco (flying lizard), Chameleon, Hemidactylus (wall lizard), Naja (cobra), etc.

Keystone

- The only poisonous lizard is Heloderma, all other are non-poisonous. Varanus is the largest living lizard present in the world.
- Reptiles are first successful terrestrial animals, but some are aquatic. Body is divided into head, neck, trunk, and tail.

Class Amphibia and Class Reptilia are different in many ways, some of them are discussed in Table 3.5

Table 3.5 Differences Between Amphibia and Reptilia

Amphibia	Reptilia
Skin is smooth and moist.	Skin is dry and cornified.
Scales are absent.	Scales are present over the body.
Digits do not possess claws.	Digits end in claws.
Heart is three-chambered.	Heart is incompletely four-chambered.
Fertilization is external.	Fertilization is internal.
Examples: Frog, Toad.	Examples: Lizard, Snake, Tortoise.

Class Aves (L. Aves = birds):

- The birds are described as 'feathered reptiles' that have developed the power of flight.
- The body is covered with soft feathers (feathery exoskeleton) called Plumage.
- The body is divisible into head, neck, trunk, and tail.

- There are two pairs of limbs. The fore limbs are modified to form wings (in flying birds) or are reduced (as in non-flying birds). Hind limbs are strongly developed for perching, walking.

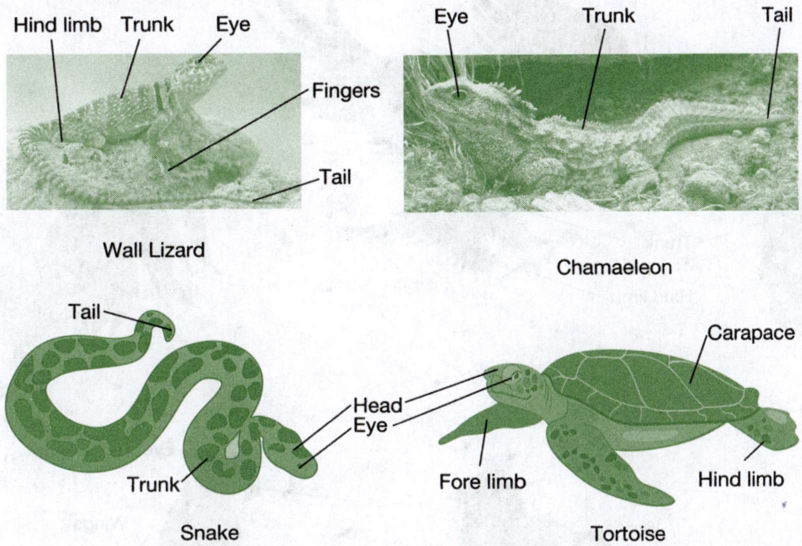

Figure 3.28 Structure of (A) Wall zard, (B) Chamaeleon, (C) Snake, (D) Tortoise

- Endoskeleton is light. The bones have air cavities (Pneumatic bones). This makes the bird light.
- Jaws are modified to form a strong beak.
- Teeth are absent.
- Respiration is by lungs only. Lungs have additional bag like membranous extensions called as air sacs.
- Heart is completely four chambered.
- Sexes are separate.
- Birds are oviparous, i.e., egg laying.
- Fertilization is internal. Fertilized eggs are laid with a yolk (stored food) and with a hard calcareous shell.
- Like reptiles and mammals, they have the embryonic membranes namely the amnion, chorion, yolk-sac and allantois.
- High degree of parental care is exhibited.
- There is no larval stage in development.
- **Examples:** Columba (pigeon), Pavo (peacock), Corvus (crow), Passer (sparrow), Struthio camelus (ostrich), Kiwi and Penguin are flightless birds. White Stork (Ciconia ciconia) Male Tufted duck (Aythya fligula) (as shown in Fig. 3.29).

Keystone

Sound producing organ at the junction of trachea and bronchi of birds is called syrinx.

Penguins, emu, ostrich, and kiwi are flightless birds. Archaeopteryx is the connecting link between reptiles and birds.

Class Mammalia (L. mamma = breast; the mammals): Mammalia is the most evolved group of organisms and are found in diverse habitats ranging from deserts, polar ice caps, oceans, mountains, forests and grasslands. They are named mammals as all of them possess mammary glands (milk producing glands). Mammals are the only animals which feed their young ones with milk.

- Skin is covered with an exoskeleton of hair. Hair is provided with sweat glands which help in the regulation of body temperature. In aquatic mammals, hair being negligible, the subcutaneous layer of fats provides insulation.
- Mammals have two pairs of pentadactyl limbs.
- The body cavity is unequally divided into two parts by a muscular partition called as diaphragm.
- Eyes are provided with movable lids.
- Ears have fleshy external ears or pinnae.

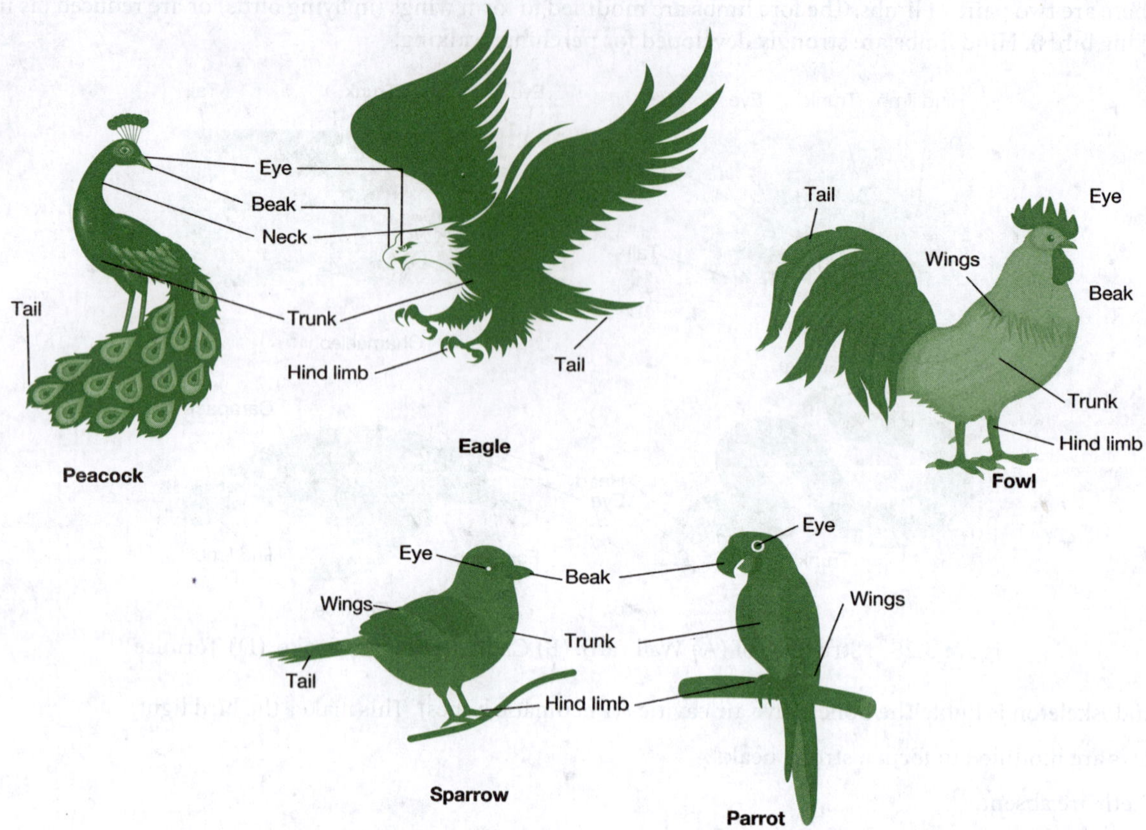

Figure 3.29 Peacock, Eagle, Fowl, Sparrow, Parrot

- Teeth are embedded in sockets (thecodont). Two sets of teeth develop in the lifetime of a mammals – milk teeth and permanent teeth (diphyodont).
- Teeth are of different types (heterodont).
- Respiration occurs by lungs.
- Heart is four-chambered. RBCs are non-nucleated and usually circular.
- Sexes are separate. Gonads are paired. Testes lie commonly in the scrotal sacs outside the abdomen.
- Fertilization is internal. Eggs are small, microscopic without shells and are retained in uterus of female for development.
- Embryonic membranes (amnion, chorion, yolk-sac and allantois) present.
- They give birth to living young ones and are called as viviparous.
- The young ones are fed on milk from mammary glands.

Important Groups of Mammals: Mammals are divided into three main groups:

- **Egg-laying mammals (monotremes):**
  - These mammals show characters of both reptiles and mammals.
  - They lay hard shelled eggs (oviparous).
  - **Examples:** Spiny ant eater, Duck – billed platypus.
- **Marsupial mammals (pouched mammals):**
  - Pouched or marsupial mammals (Latin marsu-pium = pouch) They are viviparous.
  - The young ones, when born, are cared in pouch called marsupium present on the mother's abdomen.
  - In the pouch, they feed on the mother milk.
  - **Examples:** Kangaroo (Macropus), Kola bear.

- **Placental mammals (true mammals):**
  - These mammals with true placenta.
  - The embryo is retained in the uterus.
  - These are the very successful group of land animals, occurring in diverse climatic conditions.
  - **Examples:** Mole, bat, lion, tiger, camel, giraffe, whale, dolphin, monkey, kangaroo, rabbit (as shown in Fig. 3.30), etc.

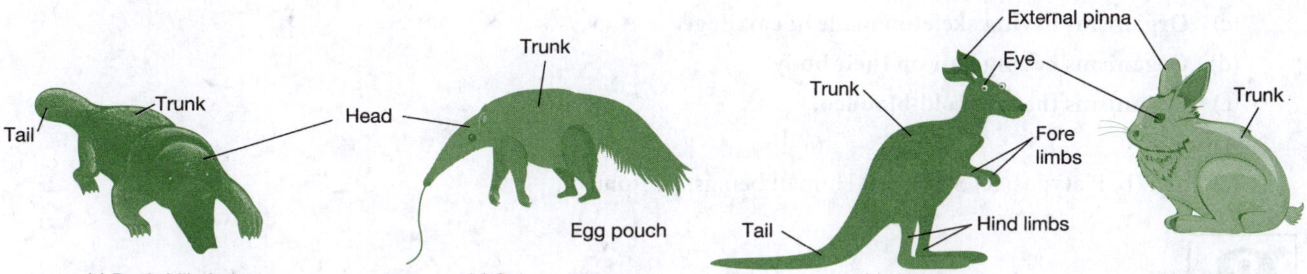

Figure 3.30 Duck-Billed Platypus, (B) Spiny Ant-Eater, (C) Kangaroo, (D) Rabbit

Table 3.6 A Comparative Summery of the Verebrates

Character	Pisces	Amphibia	Reptilia	Aves	Mammalia
Habitat	Aquatic	Terrestrial and aquatic	Terrestiral	Aroreal	Terrestrial, aquatic, and arboreal.
Body Temperature	Cold-blooded	Cold-blooded	Cold-blooded	Warm-blooded	Warm-blooded
Exoskeleton	Slimy scales	Absent	Dry and Scaly	Feathers, claws	Hairs, nails etc.
Respiratory organ	Gills	Gills, lungs and skin	Lungs	Lungs	Lungs
Locomotory organs	Fins	Limbs	Limbs	Wings and legs	Limbs
Heart	2-chambered	3- chambered	Incompletely four chambered	4-chambered	4- chambered
Propagation	Oviparous	Oviparous	Oviparous	Oviparous	Viviparous
Fertilization	External	External	Internal	Internal	Intra-uterine

❖ INTEXT QUESTIONS

14. Name two egg laying mammals.

Ans: (i) Platypus (ii) Echidna.

15. State any two characteristics of Mammalia. Name two egg laying mammals.

Ans: Characteristics of Mammalia:

- Mammals are warm-blooded animals having hairs on body.
- They have four chambered hearts.
- They have mammary glands for the production of milk to nourish their young ones.
- Skin has sweat or oil glands.
- Egg laying mammals: Platypus, Echidna.

16. Explain the following terms:

(i) Bilateral symmetry, (ii) Triploblastic animals and (iii) Open circulatory system.

Ans:

(i) Bilateral symmetry: It means that the left and right halves of the body have the same design. It is found in Platyhelminthes.

(ii) Triploblastic animals: In triploblastic animals, there are three layers of cells from which differentiated tissues can be made.

(iii) Open circulatory system: In open circulatory system, blood does not flow in well-defined blood vessels. Blood is pumped by a heart into the body cavities, where tissues are surrounded by the blood.

17. Give the scientific and common name of an organism that possesses the following:

(a) Organisms that are found both on land and water.

(b) Organisms that lay eggs on land.

(c) Organisms having skeleton made of cartilage.

(d) Organisms having hair on their body.

(e) Organisms that are cold-blooded.

Ans:

(a) Frog; (b) Platypus; (c) Shark; (d) Human beings; (e) Rohu

Check Point 4

11. Write any 4 characteristics of birds.

12. Differentiate between vertebrate and invertebrate.

13. Write any 4 characters of mammals.

14. What are the differences between amphibians and reptiles?

STRUCTURAL OUTLINE

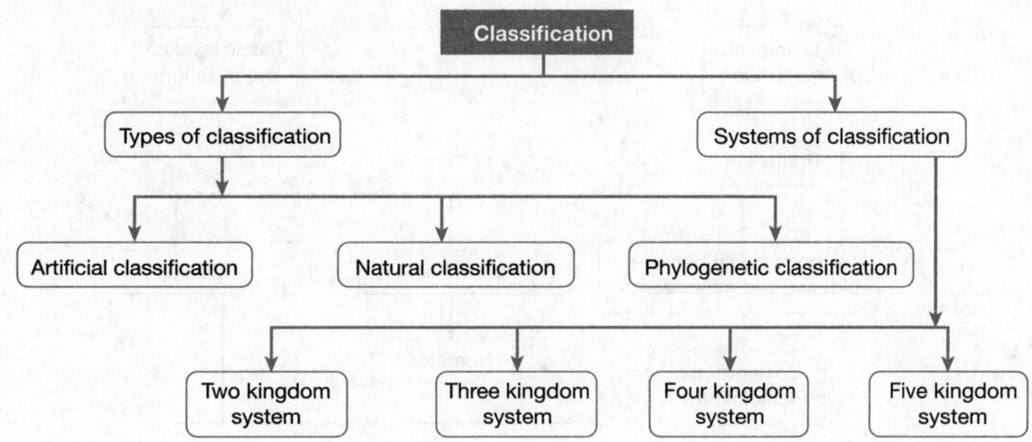

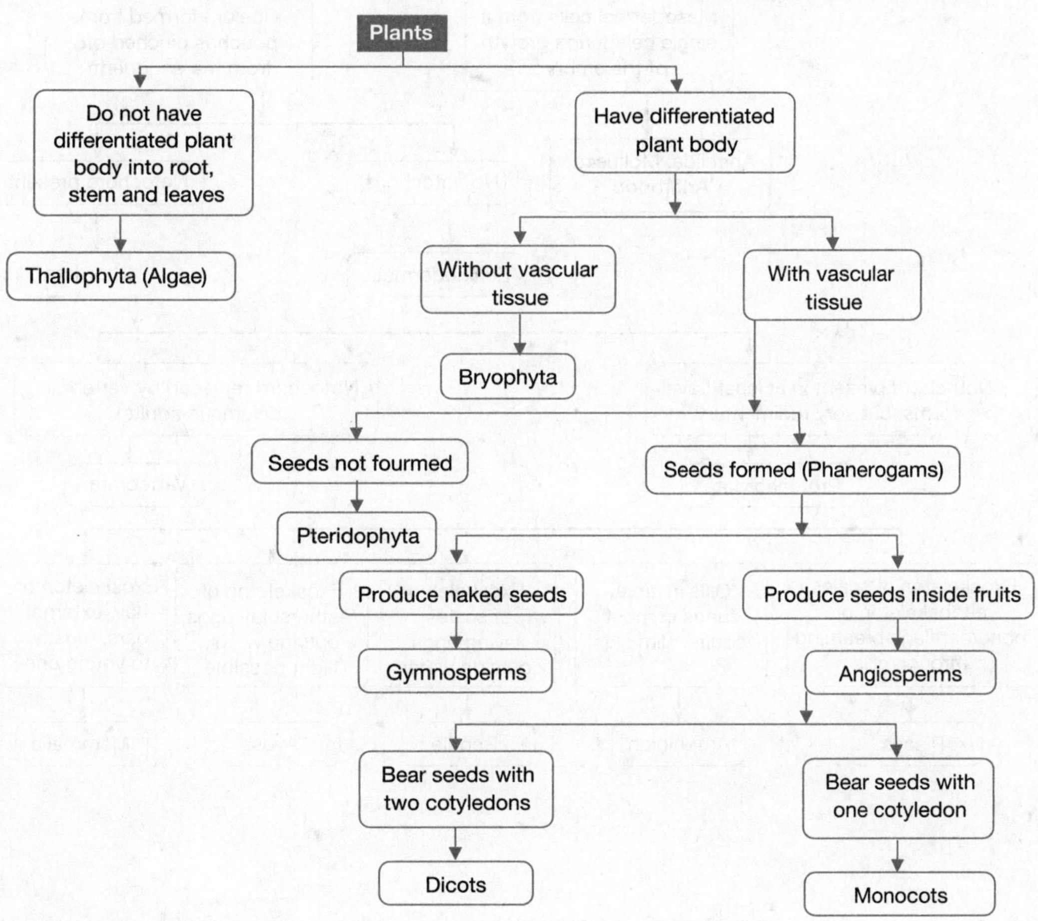

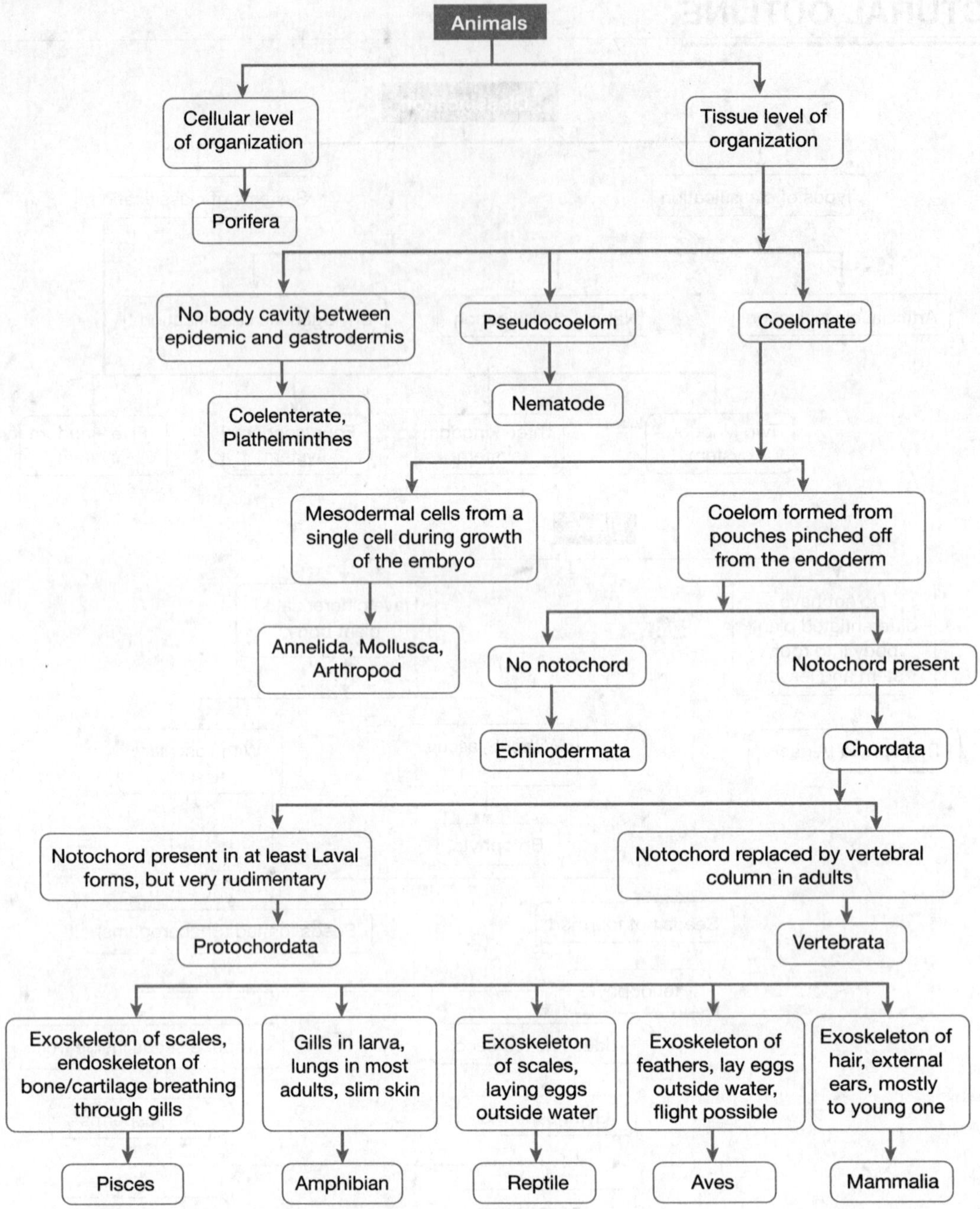
Animals
Cellular level of organization
Tissue level of organization
Porifera
No body cavity between epidemic and gastrodermis
Pseudocoelom
Coelomate
Coelenterate, Plathelminthes
Nematode
Mesodermal cells from a single cell during growth of the embryo
Coelom formed from pouches pinched off from the endoderm
Annelida, Mollusca, Arthropod
No notochord
Notochord present
Echinodermata
Chordata
Notochord present in at least Laval forms, but very rudimentary
Notochord replaced by vertebral column in adults
Protochordata
Vertebrata
Exoskeleton of scales, endoskeleton of bone/cartilage breathing through gills
Gills in larva, lungs in most adults, slim skin
Exoskeleton of scales, laying eggs outside water
Exoskeleton of feathers, lay eggs outside water, flight possible
Exoskeleton of hair, external ears, mostly to young one
Pisces
Amphibian
Reptile
Aves
Mammalia

ABRIDGEMENT

Grade 11

The Living World

- Diversity
- Nomenclature
- Systematics
- Concept of species

Biological Classification

- 2 kingdom, 3 kingdom, 4 kingdom, 5 kingdom systems
- Kingdom-Monera, Protista, Fungi, Plantae, Animalia
- Plant kingdom and basic characters of:
- Thallophyte
- Bryophyta
- Pteridophyte
- Gymnosperm
- Angiosperm

Animal kingdom and basic characters of:

- Level of organization
- Body symmetry
- Basic characteristics and classification of non-chordata
- Basic characteristics and classification of chordata

EXEMPLIFICATION

Q1. Write the examples of the organism belonging to Monera and Protista Kingdom.

Ans: Monera—Anabaena, blue-green algae

Protista—Euglena, Paramecium, Amoeba

Q2. What is lichen?

Ans: Lichen is the symbiotic association of fungi and blue-green algae.

Q3. What are gymnosperms?

Ans: The group of plants that bear naked seeds, e.g., pines, deodar.

Q4. Why the pores or holes all over the body of Porifera important?

Ans: The pores or holes present all over the body of the organisms lead to a canal system that helps in circulating water throughout the body to bring in food and oxygen.

Q5. Name the phylum of jellyfish

Ans: Coelenterates or Cnidaria.

Q6. Which are cold-blooded animal?

Ans: Those animals which show the variation in their body temperature according to the surroundings are called cold-blooded animals, e.g., fish, amphibians, reptiles.

Q7. Name a fish with skeleton made up of cartilage.

Ans: Shark.

Q8. Name the reptile with four-chambered heart.

Ans: Crocodile.

Q9. State the features of all chordates.

Ans: All chordates have the following features:

- Notochord
- Dorsal nerve chord
- Triploblastic
- Paired gill pouches

Q10. Give the characteristics of mammals.

Ans: (a) Mammals are warm-blooded animals.

(b) Four-chambered heart.

(c) Mammary glands for production of milk to nourish their younger one.

(d) Skin has hairs, sweat glands and oil glands.

(e) Most of them produce their young ones (viviparous).

KNOWLEDGE COMPENDIUM

1. Why do we classify organisms?
Ans:
For easier and convenient study, we classify organisms.

2. Give three examples of the range of variations that you see in life-forms around you.
Ans:
Small cat and big cow, Grass and banyan tree, Black crow and green parrot

3. Which do you think is a more-basic characteristic for classifying organisms?
(a) The place where they live.
(b) The kind of cells they are made of.
Why?
Ans:
Classification based on living place is more basic as there can be wide variations in organisms living in a given place.

4. What is the primary characteristic on which the first division of organisms is made?
Ans:
Nature of cell is the primary characteristics on which the first division of organisms is decided. Based on this criterion, life forms can be classified into prokaryotes or eukaryotes.

3. On what basis are plants and animal put into different categories?
Ans:
Mode of nutrition and presence or absence of cell walls.

4. Which organisms are called primitive and how are they different from the so-called advanced organisms?
Ans:
Organisms with simple cellular structure and no division of labour are called primitive organisms. Advanced organisms, like mammals, have millions of cells and there are different organs and organ system for different biological functions.

5. Will advanced organisms be the same as complex organisms? Why?
Ans:
Yes, advanced organisms mean greater degree of evolution which leads to more complexity.

6. What is the criterion for classification of organisms as belonging to kingdom Monera or Protista?
Ans:
It is the presence or absence of a well-defined nucleus. Monera has no nuclear membrane, while Protista shows well defined nucleus.

7. In which kingdom will you place an organism which is single-celled, eukaryotic and photosynthetic?
Ans:
Protista.

8. In the hierarchy of classification, which grouping will have the smallest number of organisms with a maximum of characteristics in common and which will have the largest number of organisms?
Ans:
Organisms belonging to Kingdom Monera will have the small number of organisms with a maximum of characteristics in common and kingdom Animalia will have the largest number of organisms.

9. Which division among plants has the simplest organisms?
Ans:
Thallophyta or algae.

10. How are pteridophytes different from the phanerogams?
Ans:
Pteridophytes have naked embryo and inconspicuous reproductive organ whereas phanerogams have well-differentiated reproductive organs and covered embryo.

11. How do gymnosperms and angiosperms differ from each other?
Ans:
Seeds are naked in Gymnosperms and are covered in angiosperms.

12. How do poriferan animals differ from coelenterate animals?
Ans:
- Animals from Porifera show cellular level of organization, while those from Coelenterate show tissue level of organization.
- In Porifera, there is no division of labour, while in Coelenterate some division of labour is seen.
- Porifera do not have coelom, while coelenterate have coelom.

13. How do annelid animals differ from arthropods?

Ans:

Annelids

- They have true body cavity called 'coelom'.
- Body bears lateral appendages for locomotion in the form of setae and parapodia.
- Organ differentiation occurs in a segmental fashion, with the segments lined up one after the other from head to tail.
- They breathe through body surface.
- They do not possess chitinous exoskeleton.
- They have closed type of circulatory system

Arthropods

- The body cavity is blood filled and called "haemocoel".
- Jointed legs are there for locomotion.
- These animals are also segmented but lack complete metameric segmentation.
- They possess different organs for breathing, like gills, trachea book lungs, etc.
- Chitinous exoskeleton present
- Open type of circulatory system present.

14. What are the differences between amphibians and reptiles?

Ans:

Amphibia	Reptilia
Skin is smooth and moist.	Skin is dry and cornified.
Scales are absent.	Scales are present over the body.
Digits do not possess claws.	Digits end in claws.
Heart is three chambered.	Heart is incompletely four chambered.
Fertilization is external.	Fertilization is internal.
Examples: Frog, Toad.	Examples: Lizard, Snake, Tortoise.

15. What are the differences between animals belonging to the Aves group and those in the Mammalia group

Ans:

Aves	Mammals
1. Their body is covered with their feathers.	1. Their body is covered with hair.
2. They lay eggs.	2. They give birth to their young ones.
3. Absence of mammary glands.	3. Presence of mammary glands to feed their offspring.
4. Their forelimbs are modified into wings.	4. Their forelimbs are not modified into wings.
5. Their bones are hollow and light.	5. Their bones are solid and heavy.
6. They are oviparous.	6. They are viviparous.
7. They have a beak.	7. They do not have a beak.
8. Examples: Parrots, pigeon, etc.	8. Examples: Human, dog, goat, elephants, etc.

16. What are the advantages of classifying organisms?

Ans:

Advantages of classification are as following:

- Better categorization of living beings based on common characters.
- Easier study for scientific research.
- Better understanding of human's relation and dependency on other organisms.
- Helps in cross breeding and genetic engineering for commercial purposes.

17. How would you choose between two characteristics to be used for developing a hierarchy in classification?

Ans:

Gross Character will form the basis of start of the hierarchy and fine character will form the basis of further steps of single the hierarchy. Example: Presence of vertebral column in human beings can be taken under vertebrata, presence of four limbs makes them members of Tetrapoda, presence of mammary glands keeps them under Mammalia.

18. Explain the basis for grouping organisms into five kingdoms.

Ans:

Basis of classification:

(a) Number of cells
(b) Layer of cells
(c) Presence or absence of cell wall
(d) Mode of nutrition
(e) Level of organization

19. What are the major divisions in the Plantae? What is the basis for these divisions?

Ans:

Major divisions of Kingdom plantae:

Division	Basis of Classification
Thallophyta or Algae	Thallus like body
Bryophyta	Body is divided into leaf and stem
Pteridophyta	Body is divided into root, stem and leaf
Gymnosperms	Seed bearing, naked seeds
Angiosperm	Seed bearings covered seeds

20. How are the criteria for deciding divisions in plants different from the criteria for deciding the subgroups among animals?

Ans:

In plants, body basic structure is a major criterion based on which Thallophytes are different from Bryophytes. Apart from this, absence or presence of seeds is another important criterion. Gymnosperms and angiosperms are further segregated based on if seeds are covered or not. It is clear that it is the morphological character which makes the basis for classification of plants.

In animals, classification is based on more minute structural variations. So, in place of morphology, cytology forms the basis. Animals are classified based on layers of cells, presence, or absence of coelom. Further, higher the hierarchy animals are classified based on presence or absence of smaller features, like presence or absence of four legs.

21. Explain how animals in Vertebrata are classified into further subgroups.

Ans:

Vertebrata is divided into two super classes, viz. Pisces and Tetrapoda. Animals of Pisces have streamlined body with fins and tails to assist in swimming. Animals of Tetrapoda have four limbs for locomotion.

Tetrapoda is further classified into following classes:

(a) Amphibia: They are adapted to live in water and on land. They can breathe oxygen through skin when under water.

(b) Reptilia: These are crawling animals. Their skin is hard to withstand extreme temperatures.

(c) Aves: Their forelimbs are modified into wings to assist in flying. Beaks are present and body is covered with feathers.

(d) Mammalia: Mammary glands present to nurture young ones. Skin is covered with hair. Most of the animals are viviparous.

ASSESSMENT CORNER

LEVEL 1

Fixed Response Type

Multiple Choice Questions

1. Classification reflecting the evolutionary interrelationships of organisms is called
   (A) phylogenetic classification
   (B) artificial classification
   (C) natural classification
   (D) numerical classification

2. Principles and rules of classification are studied under
   (A) Systematics
   (B) Natural classification
   (C) Nomenclature
   (D) Taxonomy.

3. Who is known as father of taxonomy?
   (A) Mendel (B) Linnaeus
   (C) Darwin (D) Crick

4. Amphibians do not have the following
   (A) Three chambered heart
   (B) Gills or lungs
   (C) Scales
   (D) Mucus glands

5. The basic unit of classification is
   (A) variety (B) species
   (C) genus (D) family

6. A branch of biology which deals with the identification, nomenclature and classification of organisms is called
   (A) Morphology (B) Ecology
   (C) Taxonomy (D) Phytogeography

7. A group of freely interbreeding organisms constitutes a
   (A) species (B) genera
   (C) family (D) class

8. Two kingdom classification was given by
   (A) Linnaeus (B) Haeckel
   (C) Copeland (D) Whittaker

9. Three kingdom classification was proposed by
   (A) Linnaeus (B) Haeckel
   (C) Whittaker (D) Lamarck

10. Five kingdom classification was proposed by
    (A) Linnaeus (B) Whittaker
    (C) John Ray (D) Lamarck Plantae

11. Mesoglea is characteristic of
    (A) platyhelminthes (B) aschelminthes
    (C) cnidaria (D) mollusca

12. Organ system grade of body organization is found in
    (A) Sponges (B) Protozoa
    (C) Arthropodes (D) Platyhelminthes

13. Polymorphism is exhibited by
    (A) Hydra (B) Physalia
    (C) Octopus (D) Crab

14. Which of the following is not a criterion for classification of living organisms?
    (A) Body design of the organism
    (B) Ability to produce one's own food
    (C) Membrane bound nucleus and cell organelles
    (D) Height of the plant

15. Platyhelminthes are called
    (A) round worms (B) flat worms
    (C) blind worms (D) none of the above

16. In Platyhelminthes, the excretory organs are
    (A) nephridia
    (B) malpighian tubules
    (C) flame cells (solenocytes)
    (D) green glands

17. Which is an exclusive chordate character?
    (A) True coelom (B) Pharyngeal gill slits
    (C) Bilateral symmetry (D) Triploblastic

18. Which of the following is not the basic feature of Chordata?
    (A) Pharyngeal gills slits
    (B) Presence of contractile vacuole
    (C) Post anal tail
    (D) Dorsal nerve cord

19. The most important character of Chordata is
    (A) Dorsal hollow nervous system
    (B) Vertebral column
    (C) Kidneys
    (D) None of the above

20. Herdmania is member of
    (A) Hemichordata (B) Urochordata
    (C) Cephalochordata (D) Vertebrata

21. Which one of following belongs to hemichordate?
    (A) Doliolum (B) Pyrosoma
    (C) Balanoglossus (D) All of the above

22. Anabaena belongs to
(A) Kingdom Monera (B) Kingdom Protista
(C) Kingdom fungi (D) Kingdom Animila

23. Platyhelminthes are
(A) coelomates (B) pseudocoelomates
(C) haemocoelomates (D) acoelomates

24. The common name for Ascaris is
(A) shipworm (B) pinworm
(C) tapeworm (D) round worm

25. Metamerism is characteristic feature of
(A) Chordata (B) Annelida
(C) Mollusca (D) Nematoda

26. The excretory organs of Annelida are
(A) nephridia (B) statocysts
(C) archeocytes (D) none of the above

27. Which one is mismatched?
(A) Flagella – Euglena
(B) Pseudopodia – Amoeba
(C) Cilia – Paramecium
(D) Flagella – Plasmodium

28. The 'Origin of Species' is written by
(A) Linnaeus
(B) Darwin
(C) Hackel
(D) Whittaker

29. Choanocytes are unique to
(A) Protozoa
(B) Porifera
(C) Mollusca
(D) Echinodermata

30. Cnidaria is characterised by
(A) nematoblasts
(B) coelenteron
(C) tissue level of organization
(D) all of the above

Fill in the Blanks

1. Prokaryotes are grouped in Kingdom ________.
2. Chemical nature of chitin is ________.
3. Lichens are indicator of ________ pollution.
4. Venus flower basket is common name for ________.
5. In echinoderms, water vascular system helps in __________ and ________.
6. Notochord is replaced by _________ in adult vertebrates.
7. Pinus and Cycas belong to ___________.
8. Funaria is a _________.
9. __________ are called as amphibians of the plant kingdom.
10. _________ proposed the binomial system of nomenclature.

True/False

1. Whittaker proposed five kingdom classification.
2. Hornworts and liverworts are pteridophytes.
3. Lichen is dual organism which shows association of algae and fungi.
4. Algae has well developed vascular system.
5. Spongocoel is found in protozoa.
6. Non-flowering plants are called cryptogamae.
7. The phylum Echinodermata organisms have water vascular system.
8. Funaria is a moss.
9. Birds are oviparous.
10. Four kingdom system is given by Carl Woese.

Match Type Questions

1. Match the following I and II.

Column I	Column II
(i) Plant cell	(a) Cyanobacteria
(ii) BGA	(b) Breast
(iii) Mycoplasma	(c) Prokaryote
(iv) Mammals	(d) Cell wall

2. Match the following I and II.

Column I	Column II
(i) Insecta	(a) Mammals
(ii) Radula	(b) Sensory Organ of ollusca
(iii) Snake	(c) Largest Class
(iv) Breast	(d) Limbless

3. Match the following I and II.

Column I	Column II
(i) Pore Bearing Animals	(a) Arthropoda
(ii) Diploblastic	(b) Coelenterate
(iii) Metameric Segmentation	(c) Porifera
(iv) Jointed Legs	(d) Annelida

Assertion and Reason Type Questions

Instructions: In the following questions, an Assertion (A) is given followed by Reason (R). Mark your responses from the following options.

(A) Both assertion and reason are true and reason is the correct explanation of assertion.

(B) Both assertion and reason are true and reason is not the correct explanation of assertion.

(C) Assertion is true but reason is false

(D) Assertion is false but reason is true

1. **Assertion:** Blue green algae follow autotrophic way to get food.
   Reason: Blue green algae make its own food in presence of sunlight and with the help of water and carbon dioxide

2. **Assertion:** A Riccia is the example of Bryophyta.
   Reason: Bryophyta is the amphibians of the plant kingdom.

3. **Assertion:** Some Platyhelminthes are generally called flatworms.
   Reason: The body of platyhelminths is flattened dorsoventrally.

4. **Assertion:** Arthropods having open circular system present in the body.
   Reason: Prawns is the example of arthropods.

5. **Assertion:** Aves are warm blooded organism.
   Reason: Sparrow is the example of Aves.

6. **Assertion:** Seeds are the result of sexual reproduction process in plants.
   Reason: Pteridophyte is generally known as amphibians of the plant kingdom.

7. **Assertion:** Fish are cold-blooded animals.
   Reason: Fish hearts have two auricles and two ventricles.

8. **Assertion:** Platyhelminthes are commonly called flatworms.
   Reason: Plathelminths are elongated, dorsoventrally flattened animals.

9. **Assertion:** Classification helps us in exploring the diversity of life forms.
   Reason: Classification helps to establish the relationship among various groups of organisms.

10. **Assertion:** Tube feet are characteristic organs of Echinodermata.
    Reason: Tube feet plays an important role in reproduction.

Comprehension Type Questions

Passage 1: Diversity is occurrence of various forms of living beings which differ from one another in external appearance, size, color, pattern, internal structure, nutrition, behavior etc. There are 1.7–1.8 million organisms ranging in size from microscopic bacteria to blue whale.

1. Diversity is in terms of
   (A) external appearance
   (B) internal structure
   (C) both
   (D) none

2. The size of bacteria is few
   (A) Armstrong (B) micron
   (C) millimeter (D) centimeter

3. Largest mammal is
   (A) ape (B) human
   (C) blue whale (D) none

Passage 2: Binomial nomenclature was given by Carolus Linnaeus. It is the system of providing organisms with appropriate and distinct names consisting of two names, first generic and second specific. The first or generic name is also called genus. The second or specific name represents the species, for example Homo sapiens is the scientific name for human beings. Here, Homo is the generic name and sapiens is the specific name.

4. Who gave binomial nomenclature?
   (A) Theophrastus (B) Aristotle
   (C) Linnaeus

5. What is the first word according to binomial nomenclature?
   (A) genus (B) species
   (C) variety

6. What is the species name of human?
   (A) indica (B) sapiens
   (C) naja

Passage 3: Biologists, such as Ernst Haeckel (1894), Robert Whittaker (1969) and Carl Woese (1977) have tried to classify all living organisms into broad categories, called kingdoms. The classification Whittaker proposed has five kingdoms: Monera, Protista, Fungi, Plantae and Animalia, is widely used. These groups are formed on the basis of their cell structure, mode and source of nutrition and body organization. The modification Woese introduced by dividing the Monera into Archaebacteria (or Archaea) and Eubacteria (or Bacteria) is also in use. Further classification is done by naming the sub-groups at various levels as given in the following scheme:

Kingdom, Phylum (for animals)/Division (for plants), Class, Order, Family, Genus, Species

Thus, by separating organisms on the basis of a hierarchy of characteristics into smaller and smaller groups, we arrive at the basic unit of classification, which is a species. A species includes all organisms that are similar enough to breed and perpetuate.

7. Who proposed Five Kingdoms?
   (a) Ernst Haeckel (1894)
   (b) Robert Whittaker (1969)
   (c) Carl Woese (1977)
   (d) None of above

8. Which of the following kingdom is a part of five kingdom system?
   (a) Monera (b) Protista
   (c) Animalia (d) All of the above

9. Kingdom Monera divided into
   (a) Archaebacteria (b) Eubacteria
   (c) Both a and b (d) None of above

Free Response Type

Very Short Answer Type Questions

1. What is notochord?
2. Name the group in which:
   (i) Seeds are naked.
   (ii) Reproductive organs are flowers.
3. Name the basic unit of classification.
4. Name two egg laying mammals.
5. Who proposed 4 kingdom classification?
6. Which is the largest phylum of kingdom animalia?
7. You are provided with the seeds of gram, wheat, rice, pumpkin, maize and pea. Classify them whether they are monocot or dicot.
8. Herdmania is classified in which subphylum?
9. Which is the largest phylum of Animalia kingdom?

Short Answer Type Questions

1. How are the seed-bearing plants further classified?
2. What is the need of nomenclature?
3. What are phanerogams?
4. Differentiate between Chondrichthyes and Osteichthyes.
5. Describe the general characters of class Mammalia.
6. What is notochord? What is its function?
7. Write down four main features of protozoa.
8. Why do amphibians do not possess exoskeleton?
9. Write down the distinct features of Chordata.
10. What is binomial nomenclature?

Long Answer Type Questions

1. What is five kingdom classification and who proposed it? Explain in detail.
2. Write names of few thallophytes, Draw a labelled diagram of spirogyra.
3. Discuss the general characteristics of pteridophytes and write the economic importance of pteridophytes.
4. Describe about the basis of animal classification?
5. Define the terms and give one example of each:
   (a) bilateral symmetry
   (b) coelom
   (c) triploblastic

Case Based Questions

Case 1: A plant specimen showed differentiated plant body lacking vascular tissue. Water is necessary to carry on their reproductive activities.

1. The group to which it belongs is ____.
2. Write any two characteristics of this group.
3. The group comprising specialised tissue for the conduction of water in the plant body is pteridophyta. (true or false)
4. Pteridophyte is also called the amphibian of plants. (true or false)

Case 2: Anishka enters the museum and observes the animal specimens. She looks at the one animal, marked as 'whale' and calls it a type of fish.

1. Whale belongs to which class?
2. Whale and fishes belong to same class? (Yes or no)
3. List any three distinguishing features to justify your statement.
4. List out three common features in cat, rat, and bat.

Case 3: While walking along roadside, Sunil asked his father, a biology teacher, whether some small, green, non-flowering, leafy and thalloid plants, having little differentiation of body and growing along pavement are of any use to us. Father answered that these plants are small, but they play very important role in maintaining green cover on the land.

1. To which group these small thalloid, green, non-flowering plants belong?
2. In what way bryophytes are useful to us?
3. Which other groups of plants act as colonizers of barren rocks and make land suitable for growth of higher plants? Do these plants play some role in pollution monitoring?

LEVEL 2

Multiple Choice Questions

1. In which the reproductive organs are hidden?
   (A) Cryptogamae
   (B) Phanerogamae
   (C) Gymnosperms
   (D) Angiosperms

2. Which among the following has specialized tissue for conduction of water?
   (i) Thallophyta (ii) Bryophyta
   (iii) Pteridophyta (iv) Gymnosperms
   (A) (i) and (ii)
   (B) (ii) and (iii)
   (C) (iii) and (iv)
   (D) (i) and (iv)

3. Which among the following produce seeds?
   (A) Thallophyta
   (B) Bryophyta
   (C) Pteridophyta
   (D) Gymnosperms

4. Which one is a true fish?
   (A) Jellyfish (B) Starfish
   (C) Dogfish (D) Silverfish

5. Which among the following is exclusively marine?
   (A) Porifera (B) Echinodermata
   (C) Mollusca (D) Pisces

6. Which among the following have open circulatory system?
   (i) Arthropoda (ii) Mollusca
   (iii) Annelida (iv) Coelenterata
   (A) (i) and (ii) (B) (iii) and (iv)
   (C) (i) and (iii) (D) (ii) and (iv)

7. In which group of animals, coelom is filled with blood?
   (A) Arthropoda
   (B) Annelida
   (C) Nematoda
   (D) Echinodermata

8. Elephantiasis is caused by
   (A) Wuchereria
   (B) Pinworm
   (C) Planarians
   (D) Liver flukes

9. Which one is the most striking or (common) character of the vertebrates?
   (A) Presence of notochord
   (B) Presence of triploblastic condition
   (C) Presence of gill pouches
   (D) Presence of coelom

10. Which among the following have scales?
    (i) Amphibians (ii) Pisces
    (iii) Reptiles (iv) Mammals
    (A) (i) and (iii) (B) (iii) and (iv)
    (C) (ii) and (iii) (D) (i) and (ii)

11. Find out the false statement.
    (A) Aves are warm-blooded, egg laying and have four-chambered heart.
    (B) Aves have feather covered body, fore limbs are modified as wing, and breathe through lungs.
    (C) Most of the mammals are viviparous.
    (D) Fishes, amphibians, and reptiles are oviparous.

12. Pteridophyta do not have
    (A) root
    (B) stem
    (C) flowers
    (D) leaves

13. Which phylum of animals is also called flatworms?
    (A) Porifera
    (B) Coelenterata
    (C) Platyhelminthes
    (D) Nematoda

14. What is the exclusive marine phylum?
    (A) Echinodermata
    (B) Porifera
    (C) Cnidarians
    (D) Protozoa

ASSESSMENT CORNER

15. Amphibians do not have the following:
(A) Three-chambered heart
(B) Gills or lungs
(C) Scales
(D) Mucus glands

16. Organisms without nucleus and cell organelles belong to
(i) fungi (ii) protista
(iii) cyano bacteria (iv) archae bacteria
(A) (i) and (ii) (B) (iii) and (iv)
(C) (i) and (iv) (D) (ii) and (iii)

17. Which of the following is not a criterion for classification of living organisms?
(A) Body design of the organism
(B) Ability to produce one's own food
(C) Membrane bound nucleus and cell organelles
(D) Height of the plant

18. The mode of nutrition in fungi
(A) only saprotrophic
(B) saprotrophic or parasitic
(C) only parasitic
(D) none of above

19. The locomotory organs of Echinodermata are
(A) tube feet
(B) muscular feet
(C) jointed legs
(D) parapodia

20. Corals are
(A) Poriferans attached to some solid support
(B) Cnidarians, that are solitary living
(C) Poriferans present at the seabed
(D) Cnidarians that live in colonies

Higher Order Thinking Skills (HOTS)

1. Label a, b, c and d, given in the figure below. Give the function of (b).

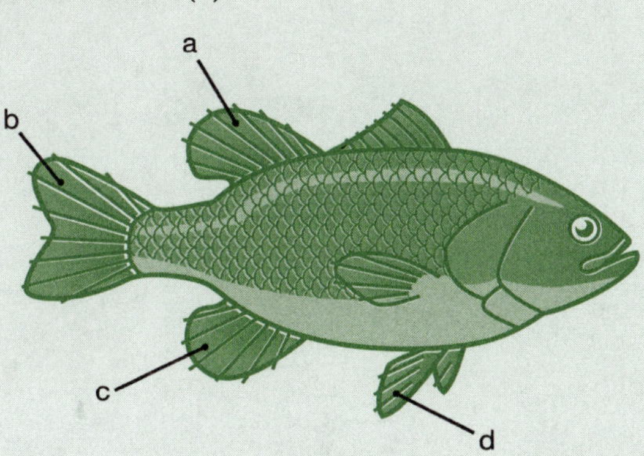

2. Fill in the boxes given in figure with appropriate characteristics/plant groups.

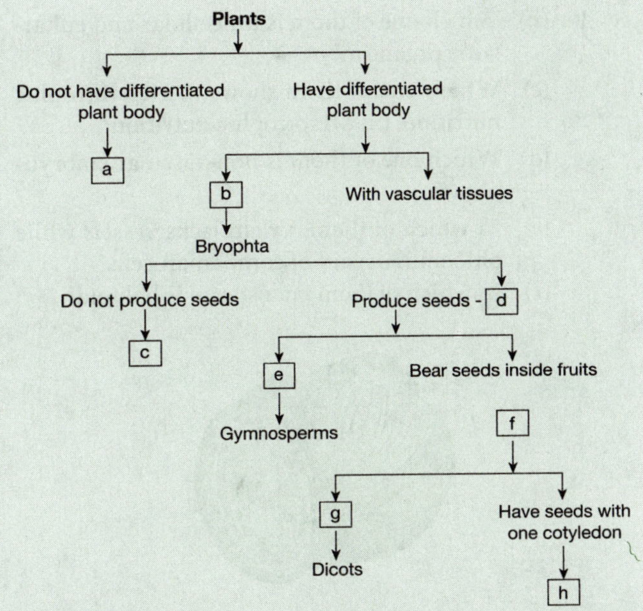

3. Characteristic features of a plant 'P' are given below, read them carefully and choose the correct option.
i. Plant 'P' produces flowers
ii. Leaves of plant 'P' show parallel venation.
(a) Plant 'P' has fibrous roots
(b) Plant 'P' has a woody stem
(c) Plants 'P' has white colored flowers
(d) Plant 'P' has seeds with two cotyledons

4. (a) Identify figures A to F.

(b) Which one of them is unicellular and eukaryotic organism?

(c) Which one of them shows (i) Heterotrophic nutrition, (ii) Mixotrophic nutrition?

(d) Which one of them is non-vascular embryophyte?

(e) In which of them, xylem lacks vessels while phloem is devoid of companion cells?

(f) In which of them endosperm is halpoid?

5.

(a) Identify the figure and write down the phylum to which it belongs.

(b) Which type of

(i) Locomotory organ is present in it.

(ii) Circulatory system is present in it.

(c) Which type of symmetry is present?

6. (a) Label W, X, Y and Z.

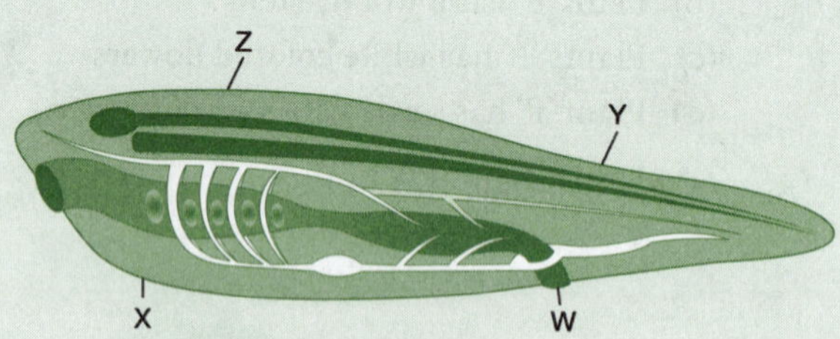

(b) Identify the above diagram.

(c) Name the phylum in which notochord is present.

(d) Name the subphylum in which notochord is present throughout life.

7. (a) Identify figure A to D.

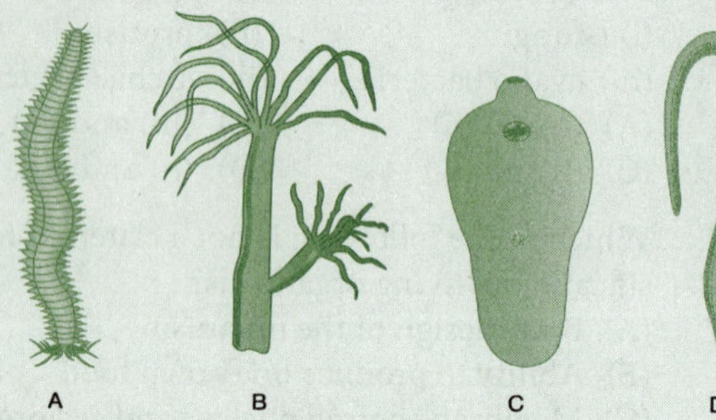

(b) Which one belongs to

1. Platyhelminthes
2. Arthropoda
3. Annelida

(c) Which one of them has

1. Tissue level organization
2. Primitive organ level organization

(d) Which one of them has

1. Flame cells as excretory organs
2. Nephridia as excretory organs

(e) Which one of them has poison claw?

(f) Which one of them is

1. Diploblastic
2. Triploblastic

ARCHIVE CORNER

1. Following are some characteristics of the three divisions of Kingdom Plantae: Bryophyta, Pteridophyta and Thallophyte.
1. Sex organs are unicellular
2. Non-vascular
3. Lack true leaves and roots
4. Embryo formed after fertilization
5. Photoautotrophs
6. Examples are Polytrichum, Funaria
7. Sporophyte is parasitic over gametophyte
8. Examples are Hydrodictyon, Laminaria

Select the option which shows the correct characteristics of the respective divisions.

	Bryophyta	Pteridophyta	Thallophyta
(A)	2, 3, 4, 6, 7	3, 4, 5, 6	1, 2, 3, 6, 7
(B)	2, 3, 4, 5, 6	3, 4, 6	1, 2, 3, 6, 7, 8
(C)	2, 3, 4, 5, 6, 7	4, 5	1, 2, 3, 5, 7, 8
(D)	2, 3, 4, 5, 6, 8	3, 4, 6	1, 2, 3, 6, 7

2. Select the incorrect statement regarding the given organisms.

(i) (ii) (iii) (iv) (v)

(A) Organism (i) possesses choanocytes whereas organism (v) possesses water vascular system.
(B) Organism (ii) is diploblastic animal whereas organism (iii) is triploblastic animal.
(C) Organisms (iii), (iv) and (v) are eucoelomates.
(D) Organisms (iv) and (v) possess notochord at some stage of their life.

3. Refer to the given dichotomous key and select the incorrect option regarding organisms P, Q, R and S.

I.	(a)	Animals with cellular level of body organization.	- P
	(b)	Animals with tissue/organ/ organ system level of body organization.	- Go to II
II.	(a)	Animals possessing bilateral symmetry.	- Go to III (a)
	(b)	Animals possessing radial symmetry.	- Go to III (b)
III.	(a)	True coelom is present.	- Go to IV (a)
	(b)	True coelom is absent.	- Go to IV (b)
IV.	(a)	Notochord is present.	- Q
	(b)	Notochord is absent.	- Go to V
V.	(a)	It is represented by medusa form.	- R
	(b)	It is represented by polyp form.	- S

(A) Body of organism P could contain numerous small pores called ostia and a large opening called osculum on top.
(B) Organism Q could possess gill slits at some stage of its life.
(C) The body of organism S could be differentiated into head, visceral mass and ventral foot.
(D) Organism R could possess nematocysts.

4. Riddhi drew a classification chart as shown.

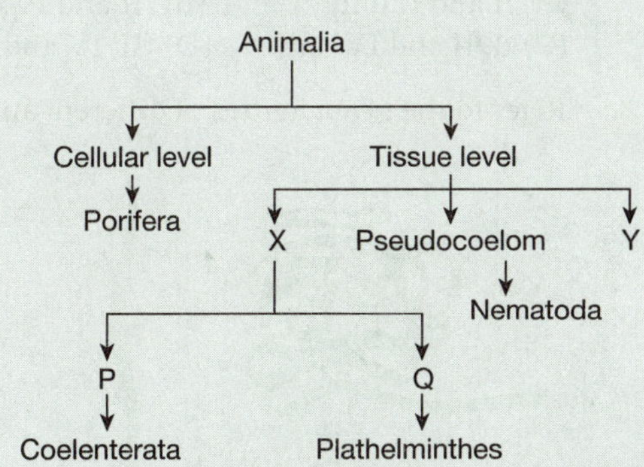

Now, select the option that correctly identifies the characters X, Y, P and Q.
(A) X is eucoelomic body cavity.
(B) P is bilateral body symmetry.
(C) Q is radial body symmetry.
(D) Y is coelomic cavity lined by mesoderm.

ARCHIVE CORNER

5. Identify M-P in the given flow chart and select the correct statement regarding them.

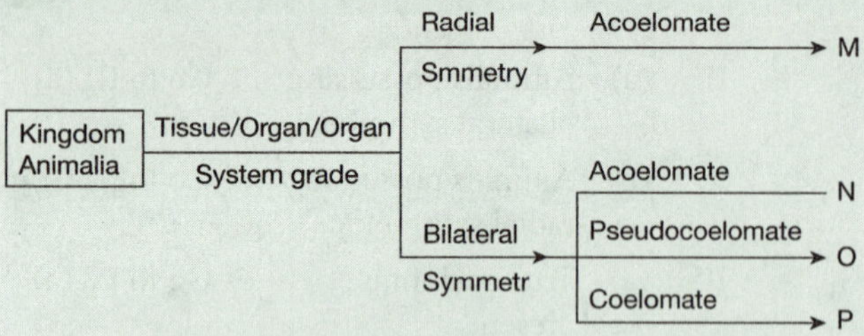

(A) M could be Obelia whereas N could be Sycon.
(B) N could be Fasciola whereas O could be Ancylostoma.
(C) M could be Pheretima whereas P could be Chiton.
(D) P could be Taenia whereas O could be Ascaris.

6. Select the option which correctly identifies P - T.

Phylum/ Class	Excretory organ	Circulatory system	Respiratory organ
Arthropoda	P	Q	Book lungs/ Gills/Tracheal system
R	Nephridia	Closed	Skin
S	Nephridia	Open	T

	P	Q	R	S	T
A.	Green gland	Closed	Mollusca	Annelida	Tracheal system
B.	Malpighian tubule	Open	Annelida	Mollusca	Ctenidia
C.	Antennary gland	Open	Porifera	Amphibia	Lungs
D.	Nephridia	Closed	Mollusca	Annelida	Lungs

7. The given table represents differences between bryophytes and pteridophytes. Identify the correct ones.

	Bryophytes	Pteridophytes
I.	Main plant body is sporophytic (diploid).	Main plant body is gametophytic (haploid).
II.	Plant body is either thalloid or foliose, however, true stem, leaves and roots are absent.	Plant body is differentiated into true roots, stem and leaves.
III.	Plant is fixed to the substratum by roots.	Plant is fixed to the substratum by rhizoids.
IV.	Sporophyte is parasitic over gametophytic plant body.	It has small, independent gametophyte.
V.	These are non-vascular plants.	These are vascular plants.

(A) I and II only (B) II and IV only
(C) I, II and IV only (D) II, IV and V only

8. Refer to the given figures of different animals.

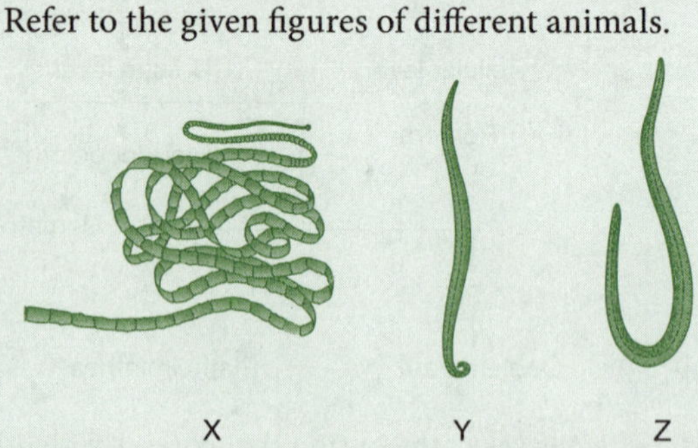

Read the characteristics given below and select the option that correctly matches these animals with their characteristics stated.

(i) Coelom absent
(ii) Pseudocoelom present
(iii) True coelom present
(iv) Triploblastic animal
(v) Flame cells as excretory organs
(vi) Body metamerically segmented
(vii) Nephridia are excretory organs

(A) X-(i, vi, vii), Y-(ii, iv, vi), Z-(iii, v, vi)
(B) X-(i, iv, v), Y-(ii, iv), Z-(iii, iv, vi, vii)
(C) X-(ii, iv, vi), Y-(i, v, vii), Z-(iii, iv, v)
(D) X-(iii, vi), Y-(ii, iv, vii), Z-(i, v)

9. Identify a member of porifera
(A) Spongila (B) Euglena
(C) Penicillium (D) Hydra

10. Refer to the given figures of two plants X and Y with their parts labelled as P, Q, R and S.

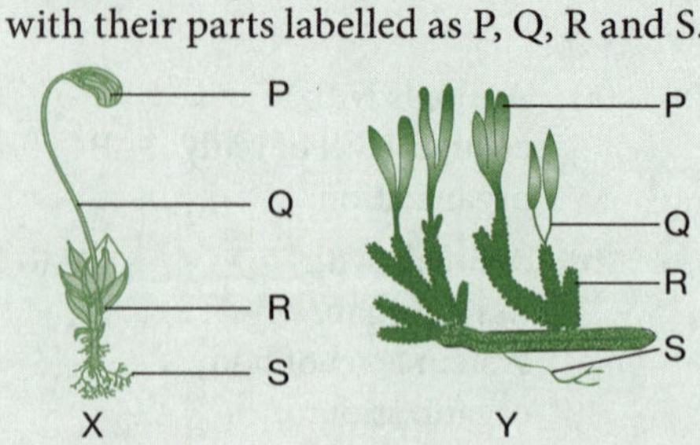

Select the correct option regarding them.

(A) Plant body of both X and Y is diploid sporophyte swhere P is the spore producing part.

(B) Q represents true stem, R represents true leaves whereas S represents true roots in both X and Y.

(C) Seed setting is absent in both plants X and Y; and they reproduce through spores.

(D) All parts of plant Y possess vascular tissues whereas vascular tissues are present only in part P of plant X.

11. Select the pair that shows the same relationship as the animals in the box.

Amoeba : Paramecium

(A) Rhizopus : Chlamydomonas

(B) Candida : Saccharomyces

(C) Pteridium : Fasciola

(D) Albugo : Adiantum

12. Select the option that correctly identifies organisms P, Q, R, S and T.

	P	Q	R	S	T
A.	Euspongia	Hydra	Hirudinaria	Fasciola	Periplaneta
B.	Euplectella	Obelia	Dugesia	Pheretima	Palaemon
C.	Sycon	Taenia	Adamsia	Scolopendra	Musca
D.	Aurelia	Schistosoma	Ascaris	Nereis	Palamnaeus

13. Which of the following is incorrect regarding organisms P, Q R, S and T? NSO 2017-18

(A) P possesses endoskeleton of calcareous spicules whereas Q is always aquatic.

(B) R could be a parasite which attaches to the body of host through hooks and suckers whereas S possesses metanephridia for excretion.

(C) T sheds off its chitinous exoskeleton periodically during its growth which is referred to as moulting.

(D) None of these

ARCHIVE CORNER

ANSWER KEYS

Level 1

Fixed Response Type

Multiple Choice Questions

1. A	2. A	3. B	4. C	5. B	6. C	7. A	8. A	9. B
10. B	11. A	12. C	13. B	14. D	15. D	16. B	17. B	18. D
19. D	20. C	21. C	22. A	23. B	24. D	25. B	26. C	27. B
28. B	29. B	30. B						

Fill in the Blanks

1. Monera
2. Carbohydrate
3. SO_2
4. Euplectella
5. Movement, respiration
6. Vertebral column
7. Gymnosperms
8. Moss
9. Bryophyta
10. Carolus Linnaeus

True/False

1. True	2. True	3. True	4. False	5. False	6. True	7. True	8. True	9. True
10. False								

Match Type Questions

1. (i)-(d), (ii)-(a), (iii)-(c), (iv)-(b)
2. (i)-(c), (ii)-(b), (iii)-(d), (iv)-(a)
3. (i)-(c), (ii)-(b), (iii)-(d), (iv)-(a)

Assertion and Reason Type Questions

1. A	2. B	3. A	4. B	5. B	6. C	7. C	8. A	9. B
10. C								

Comprehension Type Questions

Passage 1

1. C 2. B 3. C

Passage 3

4. C 5. A 6. B

Level 2

Multiple Choice Questions

1. A	2. C	3. D	4. C	5. B	6. A	7. A	8. A	9. A
10. C	11. C	12. C	13. C	14. A	15. C	16. B	17. D	18. B
19. A	20. D							

Archive Corner

1. C	2. D	3. C	4. D	5. B	6. B	7. D	8. B	9. A
10. C	11. B	12. B	13. D					

CHAPTER 4

Why do We Fall Ill

Learning Outcomes

At the end of this chapter, you would be able to:

- define health.
- describe disease.
- classify the types of diseases.
- discuss the means of spreading.
- discuss the principle of treatment and prevention.

Geekspeak

- Disease
- Incubation
- Health
- Acute
- Chronic
- Communicable
- Congenital
- Signs
- Symptoms
- Addiction
- Agent
- Prophylaxis
- Prevention
- Treatment
- Pathogen
- Transmission
- Immunization
- Antibodies
- Antigens

Introduction

All organisms, whether plants or animals, require food (nutrition) for their survival, maintenance, growth and development. Nutrition is required in specific amounts. A proper diet leads to good health and proper mental development. "Health is wealth" is exactly what it means. There are various which influence health. These factors exist both in individuals and in the societies in which they live. The internal factors are basically the genetic make-up of an individual, external factors is the environment to which an individual is exposed.

Health

A person is considered healthy if:

- They have no symptoms of illness or anxiety.
- They have no physical deformity.
- They have no mental problems and social tensions.
- They have no psychological tensions.
- All body organs are functioning properly.
- They have purposeful life.
- They have sufficient balanced diet.

The most widely accepted definition is that of the World Health Organization (1947):
"Health is a state of physical, mental and social well-being, not merely the absence of disease or infirmity."

Significance of Health:

- Health is **"a healthy body with a healthy mind and a healthy attitude".**
- Good health makes you more productive at work. Improving human performance by doing good.
- Health contributes to its own progress, to the progress of communities and to the progress of nations as a whole.
- Health also makes people happy and healthy. It allows a person to have the initiative to improve.
- Being healthy is a condition for us to exist meaningfully in this world.

Basic Conditions for Good Health: Balanced diet, personal hygiene, clean surroundings, clean food and water, clean air, exercise and relaxation, no addictions, good economic conditions.

Community and Personal Health:

- Personal health is a state of complete physical, mental and social well-being. For personal health and community health, one should keep the environment clean.
- Community health comprise of maintaining, improving and protecting the health of entire community. Good economic condition, social equality and harmony, a good civic sense all will lead to a better community health. WHO is doing remarkable work in community health.

Difference between Personal Health and Community Health is discussed in Table 4.1.

Table 4.1 Difference Between Personal Health and Community Health

Personal Health	Community Health
The state of physical, mental and social wellbeing of an individual is called personal health.	It is maintenance, protection and improvement of health of the whole community.
Only the individual maintains his /her health.	The whole community remains healthy.
An individual can maintain his health by: (a) Eating balanced diet. (b) Observing personal and domestic hygiene. (c) Consuming clean food, clean water, and clean air. (d) Proper exercise, relaxation, and good habits.	Community health can be achieved by: (a) Provision for treated and safe drinking water. (b) Proper disposal of sewage and wastes. (c) Providing medical facilities. (d) Control of communicable diseases. (e) health education.

What is a Disease?

A disease can also be defined as a disorder or deviation in the physical, physiological or any other function of the body or mind, caused either due to nutritional deficiency, genetic disorder, pathogenic invasion or any other reason. A great physician, **Hippocrates (460 – 359 B.C.),** was the first to look for scientific explanation for disease. He is remembered today as 'Father of Medicine'.

Distinction Between Healthy and Disease Free State: The term disease is used when finding a particular/specific cause of a discomfort. We may not be knowing the main cause of the discomfort, but still we can use the term disease (as shown in Fig. 4.1). A person may not be sick, but may be in poor health. This is especially true when it comes to social and mental health, where poor health can occur without taking the form of actual illness. On the other hand, when we think of disease, we think of the individual affected. Differences between Healthy and Disease-Free State is discussed Table 4.2.

Figure 4.1 Diseased Person

Table 4.2 Differences Between Healthy and Disease-Free State

Healthy	Disease Free
It is the state of physical, mental and social well being.	It is the state of absence of any body discomfort.
It depends on the environment, including people and society.	It depends upon the person alone.
A person can be unhealthy without being sick.	People are asymptomatic and disease-free.

Terms Related to Diseases:

Infection: The introduction of pathogens into the body is called an infection.

Incubation period: The incubation period is the time from infection to the appearance of the first symptoms of the disease.

Antibiotics: Antibiotics are chemicals that kill or stop the growth of certain types of microorganisms.

Pathogen: Disease causing microorganism is called pathogen.

Vaccines: Vaccines are suspensions of disease-causing microorganisms that have been modified by killing or weakening (weakening) them so that the suspension does not cause disease.

Keystone

Epidemiology: The study of causes and spread of disease is called epidemiology.

Etiology: Study of the cause of disease is called Etiology.

Father of Immunity: Edward Jenner (smallpox vaccination).

Keystone

Charaka first gave concept of digestive metabolism and immunity. He is known as 'Father of Ayurveda' [Ayurveda - Ayu Life, vade knowledge].

Antibodies: These are special chemicals found in the blood that act against bacteria and their secretions.

Antigen: Antigens are proteins or other harmful chemicals that are present on surface of invaders.

Manifestation of Diseases:

Manifestation of disease give rise to various sign and symptoms:

Symptoms are evidence of the patient's feeling of being wrong. For example, headache, loose motions or a wound with pus are symptoms which may indicate the occurrence of discomfort. Headache may be due to examination stress, meningitis.

The **sign** gives an indication of the presence of a particular disease. The physicians will also get pathological tests done to identify the disease further. Difference between symptoms and signs are discussed in table 4.3.

Table 4.3 Difference Between Symptoms and Signs

Symptoms	Signs of disease
A symptom is s change in normal functioning of the body which is felt by patient but cannot be observed by the doctor, a patient has to tell the doctor about these e.g. stomachache, headache	A sign of a disease is a change in the bodily function or structure that can be observed, e.g., rashes, swelling of gland, change in color of skin.

Types of Diseases

The manifestation of diseases is different depending upon a number of factors. On the basis of duration, a serious disease can be acute or chronic.

On The Basis of Duration

- **Acute Disease:**
  - Acute disease is the one which has a short duration by relatively severe course.
  - Most people with acute illness can expect to return to normal health.
  - A case of cough and common cold is an example of an acute illness which lasts only for a few days.
  - Afterwards, the patient becomes well without any bad effect, loss of weight, feeling of tiredness or short of breath, but in some cases acute disease like acute liver abscess can cause death.
- **Chronic Disease:**
  - Chronic disease is the one which is long lasting is usually slow to develop, often having a major effect on health, reducing the person's ability to do work efficiently, learning in school or doing work.
  - The patient will also lose weight and feel tired all the time. Examples of chronic diseases include tuberculosis, diabetes, asthma, hypertension, kidney disease, depression, etc.

On The Basis of Origin

- **Congenital Diseases:**
  - Congenital diseases are present right from the birth. They are caused either due to genetic disorders or environmental factors during development or due to combination of these factors.
  - These diseases pass on from generation to generation, e.g., hemophilia, colour blindness, sickle cell anemia, Down's syndrome, albinism, etc.
- **Acquired Diseases:**
  - These diseases are acquired by an organism after birth and are not inheritable, i.e., do not pass on from one generation to another.

These are further classified into two categories:

- **Communicable or Infectious Diseases:** These diseases are caused by pathogens/infectious agents such as bacteria, viruses, fungi, protozoans, worms as shown in Fig 4.2, etc. Examples: Tuberculosis, malaria, diarrhoea, etc.

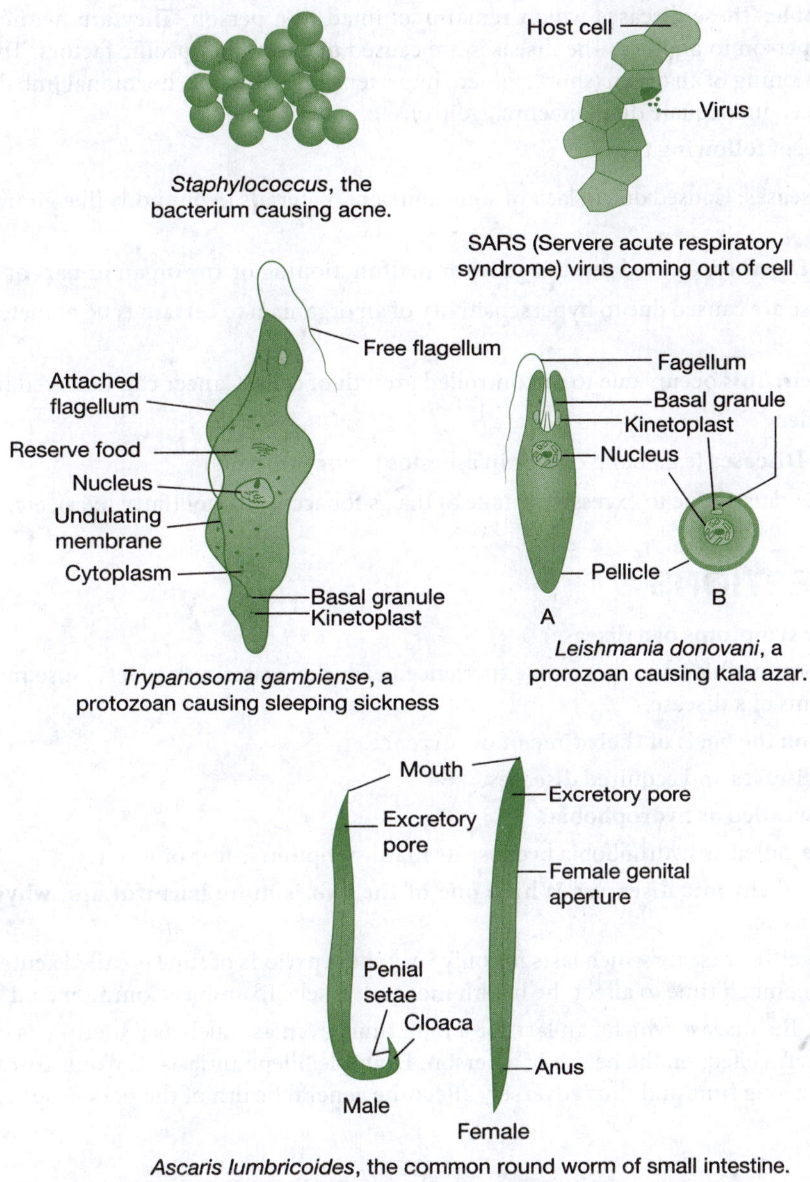

Figure 4.2 Different Types of Disease Causing Organisms

Table 4.4 Differences Between Acute and Chronic Disease

Characters	Acute Diseases	Chronic Diseases
Duration	It is of shorter duration.	It is of longer duration
Persons	Every person suffers from an acute disease at one time or the other.	Only some persons suffer from chronic diseases.
Body Damage	Being of short duration, it does not damage any organ.	It does damage the affected organ due to prolonged duration.
Recovery	The recovery is generally complete after the treatment.	The recovery is seldom complete even after treatment.
Effect	There is neither loss of weight nor feeling of weakness.	There is often a loss of weight accompanied by feeling of tiredness.
Loss	Interruption of work and loss of efficiency are of short duration. Examples: Diarrhoea, typhoid.	Interruption of work and loss of efficiency are prolonged. Example: Tuberculosis, diabetes.

- **Non-communicable:** These diseases which remain confined to a person. They are neither present at birth nor spread from one person to another. The diseases are caused due to some specific factors. They may be caused due to improper functioning of an organ (short sighted, hypertension, arthritis), hormonal imbalance (diabetes, dwarfism), allergy, cancer, inadequate diet (anaemia, goitre), etc.

  These diseases are of following types:

  - **Deficiency Diseases:** Caused due to lack of some nutrient materials in our body like vitamins, minerals, protein etc.
  - **Degenerative Diseases:** Caused due to ageing or malfunctioning of any organ or part of body.
  - **Allergies:** These are caused due to hypersensitivity of an organism to certain type of material like pollen grains, dust, etc.
  - **Cancer/Tumour:** This occurs due to uncontrolled growth of cells. Cancer can be cured in early stages.
  - **Mental Disorders**
  - **Occupational Diseases** (e.g., Lung cancer in asbestos factory workers)
  - **Addiction:** It is caused due to excessive intake of drugs tobacco, alcohol (fatty liver), etc.

❖ INTEXT QUESTIONS

1. **What is meant by symptoms of a disease?**

   Ans: The conditions in which a sick person experience headache, watering of eyes, loose motions, are collectively called the symptoms of a disease.
2. **Classify diseases on the basis of their time of occurrence.**

   Ans: Congenital diseases and acquired diseases.
3. **Why is rabies also called as hydrophobia?**

   Ans: Rabies is also called as hydrophobia because its main symptom is fear of water.
4. **What are acute and chronic diseases? Which one of the two is more harmful and why? Give an example in support of your answer.**

   Ans: Acute Disease: The disease which lasts for only very short periods of time is called acute disease. They get over soon and do not get much time to affect the health more adversely. Example: Common cold

   Chronic Disease: The disease which can last for a long time, even as much as a lifetime is called chronic disease. They have a long-term effect on the health of a person. Example: Elephantiasis. Chronic diseases are more harmful as they persist for a long time and thus adversely affect the general health of the person suffering from them.

Check Point 1

1. What is health?
2. What is a disease?
3. How will your distinguish between personal health and community health?
4. Differentiate between acute diseases and chronic diseases.

Causes of Diseases

The various causes of diseases are:

Pathogens

- They are disease causing organisms like bacteria, viruses, fungi, protozoans, worms, etc.
- The pathogens are transferred to human beings through air, contaminated food, water, soil and animals.
- Pathogens are primary cause of infectious diseases.

Lack of Nutritious Diet

- It is a second level cause of disease as absence of nutritious diet makes a person unhealthy.
- Unhealthy persons are susceptible to various diseases in comparison to healthier persons. Another contributory cause can be poor immunity which increases the *proneness* of individual to a particular disease.

Lack of Public Services

- Government should provide clean drinking water, good sewage disposal, proper garbage disposal, etc.
- If the public services are poor, there are more chances of contamination of food and water.
- Poor people, due to poverty, live in unclean surroundings where even basic amenities are lacking. These people may suffer more from diseases.

So, as it is evident from the above discussion, there are three level causes of diseases. These are infection with pathogen (1st level), lack of nutritious diet and poor immunity (2nd level) and lack of public services (3rd level). Different diseases and infectious agents are discussed in table 4.5.

Table 4.5 Different Diseases, their Causative Organism, Mode of Transmission, and Symptoms

Disease	Causative Organism	Mode of Transmission	Symptoms
Malaria	Plasmodium species	By the bite of female mosquito.	Chilliness, severe headache, rising temperature, profuse sweating.
Polio myelitis or crippling disease	Polio virus (Smallest virus)	Spread through faeces, contaminated food and water by flies.	High fever, headache, backache, rashes appear on the skin that turn into postules, on drying leave pock marks.
Hepatitis	Hepatitis virus, A, B, C, D, E and G	Hepatitis-A Oral, faecal route through contaminated food and water.	High temperature headache, fatigue, loss of appetite, nausea, vomiting, dark-yellow urine.
		Hepatitis-B Blood transfusion and through wounds, needles, razor, etc.	Malignant cancer of liver cells, hepatocellular carcinoma.
Rabies (Hydrophobia)	Rabies virus	Bite of rabied dog through the saliva.	Headache. High fever saliva, runs from mouth fear from water (hydrophobia).
AIDS	HIV	Intimate sexual contact blood transfusion, contaminated needles and syringes, organ transplantations from mothers.	Flu like illness, weight loss, fever, loss of appetite diarrhea unexplained bleeding, loss of memory.
Tuberculosis	*Mycobacterium tuberculosis*	Contact with nasal discharge, sputum of patient.	Infection of lungs followed by cough. Sputum containing blood pain in chest, loss of weight.
Typhoid	*Salmonella typhi*	Contaminated food and water.	Continued fever, slow pulse, dry coated tongue, soap-like stool.
Diarrhoea	*E. coil, Shigella sps, camphylobacter Salmonella sps.*	Contaminated food and water, oral facial route.	Frequent loose motions, vomiting dehydration.

Table 4.6 Differences Between Communicable and Non-Communicable Diseases

Communicable diseases	Non-communicable diseases
These spread from an infected person to a healthy person.	These do not spread or transmitted from infected to a healthy person.
They are caused by pathogens (e.g., bacteria, viruses, protozoans etc.)	They are caused due to deficiency of nutrients, malfunctioning of some organs of the body, allergy, abnormal growth of tissues, etc.
Example: Malaria, smallpox, cholera, tuberculosis, etc.	Examples: Cancer, heart diseases, epilepsy, marasmus, etc.

Infectious Agents

The various infectious agents are – bacteria, viruses, protozoans, helminths (worms) and fungi.

Bacteria

They are unicellular, prokaryotic, microscopic organisms. They reproduce very quickly. Some common diseases caused by bacteria are typhoid, cholera, tuberculosis, anthrax, diphtheria, tetanus, etc.

> **Competition Corner**
>
> Food poisoning by bacteria salmonella is called salmonellosis. Bacteria salmonella is present in the sick farm animals. So, the infection of bacteria *Salmonella* with causes food poisoning is contracted form the slick farm animals through their contaminated food products such as milk, eggs and meat. *Clostridium botulinum* causes food poisoning or botulism from taking persevered foods.

Viruses

They are submicroscopic organisms. They cannot reproduce by themselves because they do not have their own metabolic machinery. They utilize the metabolic machinery of the host cell and multiply. The various diseases caused by viruses are Common cold, influenza, dengue fever, AIDS, hepatitis C, mumps, adenovirus, smallpox, bacteriophage (as shown in Fig 4.3), etc.

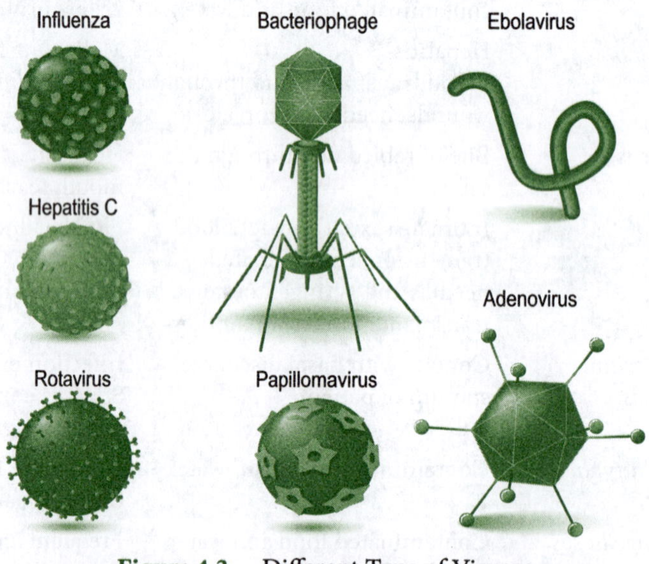

Figure 4.3. Different Type of Viruses

Protozoans

They are microscopic unicellular, eukaryotic organisms. The various diseases caused by protozoa are malaria (caused by Plasmodium), kala-azar (caused by Leishmania), etc.

Helminthes

Helminthes are multicellular worms which are mostly present in intestine.

They cause taeniasis (caused by tapeworm), ascariasis (caused by round worm), elephantiasis (caused by filaria worm, hence also known as filariasis) (as shown in Fig. 4.4), etc.

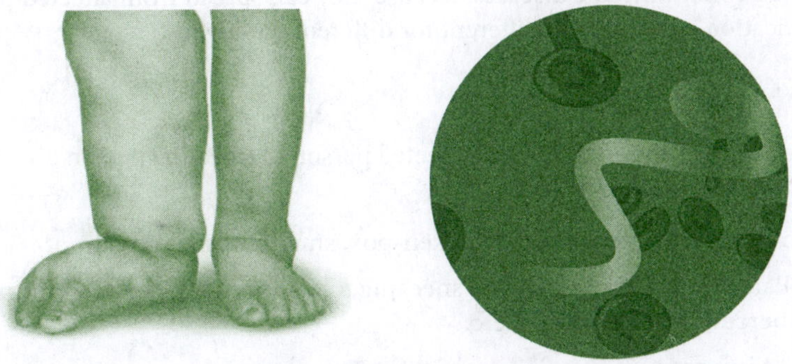

Figure 4.4 Elephantiasis (Caused by Filaria Worm)

Fungi

They are also multicellular, eukaryotic, heterotrophic organisms (as shown in Fig 4.6). They cause ring worm, athlete's foot and other skin infections (as shown in Fig 4.5).

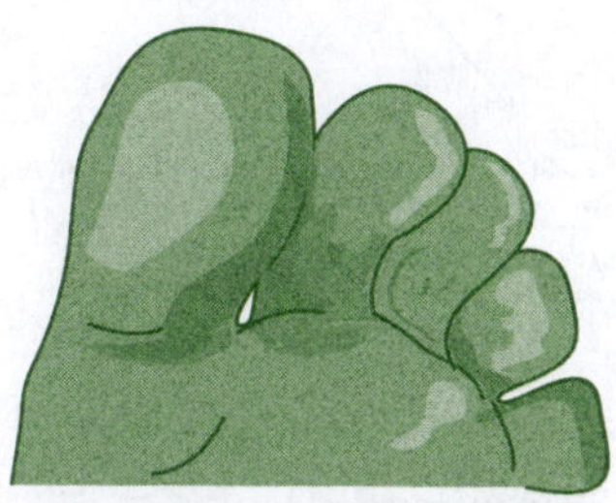

Figure 4.5 Athlete's Foot

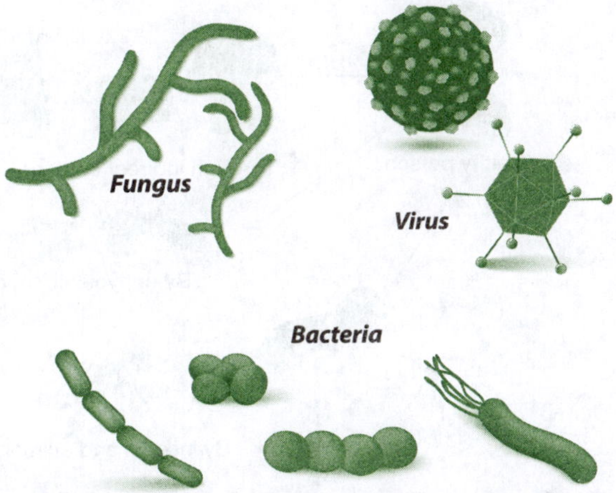

Figure 4.6 Disease Causing Organisms

Table 4.7 Different Pathogens and Disease Caused by Them

Type of Pathogens	Common Diseases Caused by Them
Viruses	Common cold, influenza, measles, mumps, polio, rabies, smallpox, chicken pox, yellow fever, AIDS, etc.
Bacteria	*Cholera, typhoid, tuberculosis, tetanus, diphtheria, pneumonia*
Rickets	Typhus fever, tick fever, etc.
Protozoa	Malaria, amoebic dysentery, sleeping sickness, etc.
Fungi	Ringworm, Athlete's foot, etc.
Worms	Filariasis, ascariasis, cysticercosis, pinworm
Mites	Scabies

Means of Spread/ Epidemiology

Infectious diseases are called communicable diseases because they can spread from affected persons to a healthy person. The means of communication or spread are different for different pathogens.

Direct Transmission

In these methods, pathogens are transmitted from an infected person to a healthy person directly without any intermediate agents (as shown in Fig 4.7). These modes include:

- **Direct contact** with an infected person e.g., chicken-pox, smallpox, measles etc.
- **Droplet infection:** Pathogens spread by way of sneezing, coughing, spitting and talking as in common cold, influenza, diphtheria, tuberculosis, pneumonia, etc.
- **Contact with soil:** As in tetanus.
- **Animal bites:** As in rabies.
- **Transplacental transmission:** From mother to foetus, e.g., German measles, syphilis, etc.

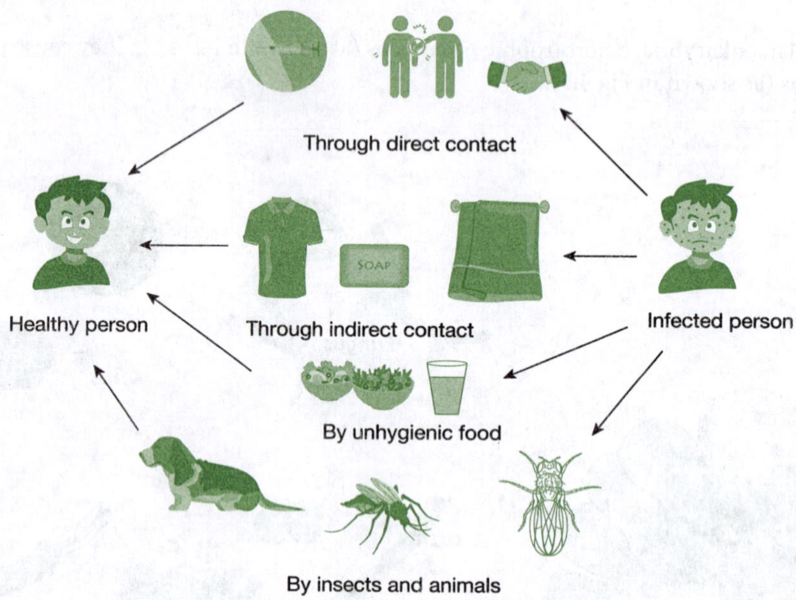

Figure 4.7 Different Mode of Diseases Transmission

Indirect Transmission

The pathogens of certain diseases enter the human body through some intermediate agents. These intermediate agents include:

- **Carriers of Vectors:** Housefly carries the pathogens of cholera, typhoid, dysentery, female Anopheles is the vector of malaria while human body louse spreads typhus.
- **Vehicle-borne Method:** Food, water, ice, blood, etc., act as vehicles for carrying pathogens in human body, e.g., cholera, typhoid, AIDS, etc.
- **Air-borne Method:** As in epidemic typhus pathogens reach the human body through air and dust.
- **Fomite-borne Method:** Contaminated articles such as garments, handkerchief, towels, utensils, toys, door handles, taps, soaps, surgical instruments, etc., can also transfer pathogens to a human body.
- **Unclean Hands:** They may transfer pathogens of large number of diseases to our body.

Competition Corner

- **Disinfection:** In this process, only active form of bacteria is killed.
- **Sterilization:** In this process, all form of pathogens including spores are killed.
- **Pathogenicity:** Pathogens can harm their hosts in a number of ways such as by:
- Destruction of body tissues and
- Release of toxins or poisons which may be endotoxins.

After entering into the body, the pathogens multiply till they produce enough toxins to make the symptoms of the disease appear. Secretion of Histamine occurs from mast cells in response to a common allergen.

Effects of Diseases

Body goes through several changes, when it gets affected by a disease, these effects are specific to the individual.

Organ or Tissue Specific Effects

Microorganisms enters the body through different points like nose, mouth, sex organs, etc., which decides the organ or tissue that microorganism invades.

At the same time the signs and symptoms of an infectious diseases also depends upon the tissue being invaded. Example: If bacteria causing tuberculosis enters through nose, it invades respiratory passage and lungs and its symptoms are cough and breathlessness, but in some cases they may infect other organs also.

Common Effects

This category includes effects like inflammation in which swelling, reddening and pain in infected area and increase in body temperature occurs.

These effects arise due to the active involvement of immune system to provide defence to body by producing some specific chemicals from WBC's, against that microbe and this is not confined to a particular organ or tissue but seen in whole body.

Severity of Effects

It directly depends upon the no. of microorganisms. If microbes are smaller in number their effects are minor and can be overcome by our immune system in a lesser time but if the number of microorganisms inside the body is very high the effects are more severe and long lasting.

Competition Corner

- **Immunization:** It is the process of stimulating the body to produce antibodies by artificial means. It can be done with the help of vaccines.
- **Endemic disease**: The disease that is constantly present to a greater or lesser degree in people of a certain class or in people living in a particular location.
- **Epidemic disease**: An epidemic disease is the rapid spread of infectious disease to a large number of people in a given population within a short period of time, usually two weeks or less.
- **Pandemic**: A pandemic is the worldwide spread of a new disease. An influenza pandemic occurs when a new influenza virus emerges and spreads around the world, and most people do not have immunity.
- **Virulence:** It is the ability of an agent of infection to produce disease. The virulence of a microorganism is a measure of the severity of the diseases it causes.

Treatment and Prevention of Diseases

Infectious diseases can be treated based on the symptoms and infecting agents. The treatment of diseases can be done using immunization and pathogen specific drugs. Prevention of infectious diseases is better than curing it, as it is a precautionary measure.

Treatment of Infectious Diseases

The basic concept behind the treatment process is to target the biochemical pathways occurring inside an organism. For this certain drug like antibiotics are prepared to alter or stop the biochemical reaction of the microbes at some stage to stop them to produce infections, toxins or to kill them or to check their further growth and multiplication.

There are two ways in which these diseases are treated they are :

Reducing the Symptoms: By this, infection is not cured but some of the symptoms like fever, pain, aches, inflammation can be reduced to make the patient full comfortable. This is done by medicines like pain killers, etc.

Killing Infectious Agents: This can be done by targeting the biochemical pathways of infectious agents using specific drugs.

Specific Methods

These methods are disease specific. Specific prevention is provided by the immune system when it produces some specific molecules called antibodies to fight against specific invading microbes or their products.

When we suffer from a mild form of disease, our immune system forms antibodies against the invading antigens. At the second infection of that disease, the immune system responds faster to destroy the antigens as there are antibodies that already recognize them. As a result, we don't suffer from the severe form of the disease. For example, if we have had mild chickenpox once, we will not suffer from its severe form later. This forms the basis of immunization.

- **Immunization:** It is the process of stimulating the body to produce antibodies by artificial means. It can be done with the help of vaccines.
  Vaccines: It is a preparation of weakened - infectious agents or their products that can be injected or given orally to prevent specific diseases. This doesn't actually cause the disease but this would prevent any subsequent exposure to the infecting microbes from turning into actual disease. Now-a-days, vaccines are available against tetanus diphtheria, whooping cough, polio, chickenpox, measles, mumps, typhoid, hepatitis and many other diseases. Many of these vaccines are given to children under the public health programme of childhood immunization.
- **Drugs:** Usually medicines are used to kill the microbes. It aims at directing / blocking the biochemical pathways used by these pathogens.
  Antibiotics: Antibiotics are chemicals that kill or stop the growth of certain kinds of microbes. They help our body to fight against diseases.

Competition Corner

The development of antibiotics began with the discovery of penicillin by Sir Alexander Fleming in 1928. Fleming notice that an agar plate inoculated with bacterium Staphylococcus aureus had become contaminated with a mould. He further noticed the presence of a clear zone in the agar plate in which breakdown of the bacterial cells had occurred. Detailed studies led to the isolation of an inhibitory substance from the mould. As the mould was identified as Penicillium, Fleming called the antibiotic penicillin. Soon other antibiotics were isolated. Some well-known antibiotics are streptomycin, gramicidin and tetracycline. The antibiotics have been obtained from either bacteria or fungi.

- Protozoan infections are treated by different types of drugs.
- Antifungal drugs are useful against all types of fungi.
- Vermicides are used for overcoming worm infection.

Prevention of Infectious Diseases/Prophylaxis

Prevention of spread of communicable diseases is called as prophylaxis. Preventive measures are the precautionary steps to check the transmission of communicable diseases (as shown in Fig 4.8).

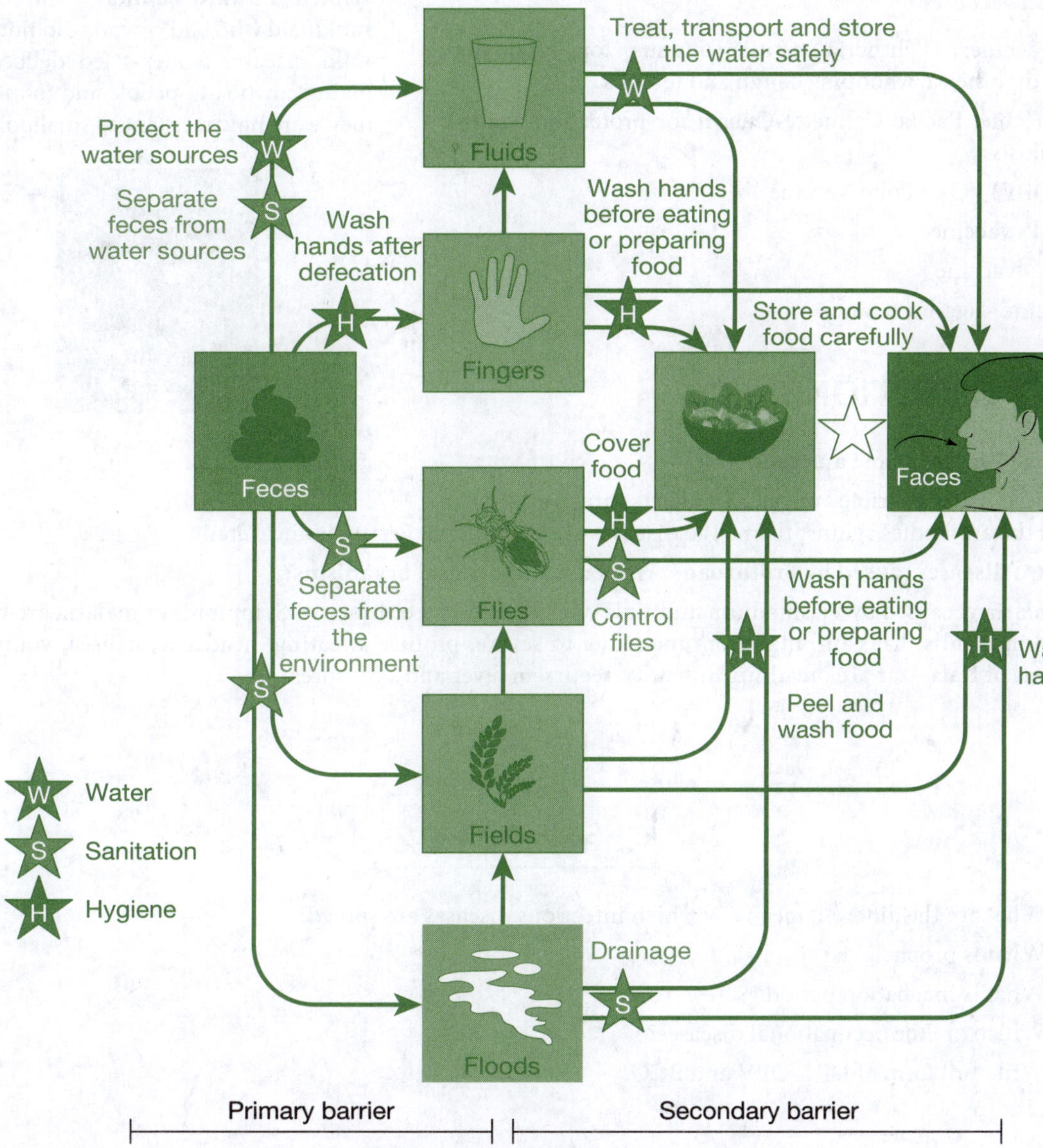

Figure 4.8 Transmission of Communicable Diseases

Diseases can be prevented by:

- Health education
- Isolation of patients from healthy persons
- Proper sanitation
- Eradication of vectors and carriers
- Sterilization of articles used by the patients
- Immunization (vaccination)
- Provision of safe water supply

- Proper disposal of excreta
- Personal hygiene
- Community hygiene

Some common vaccines:

- DPT vaccine: Diphtheria-pertussis-tetanus for protection against diphtheria, whooping cough and tetanus
- BCG vaccine: Bacille Calmette-Guerin for protection against tuberculosis
- Polio (OPV) - Oral Polio Vaccine
- Typhoid - vaccine
- Measles - vaccine
- TT vaccine - against tetanus

Keystone

Two centuries ago, an English physician named **Edward Jenner**, realized that milkmaid who had cowpox did not catch mild disease. Jenner tried deliberately giving cowpox to people and found that they were now resistant to smallpox.

❖ INTEXT QUESTIONS

5. **Why is DPT called triple antigen?**

   Ans: DPT is called as triple antigen as it affects three antigens to produce the antibodies against them. The diseases are Diphtheria, Pertussis and Tetanus.

6. **Name two diseases caused by Protozoans. What are their causal organisms?**

   Ans: Malaria is caused by Plasmodium and Kala-azar caused by Leishmania. Symptoms of malaria are high fever and shaking chills that can range from moderate to severe, profuse sweating, headache, nausea, vomiting, etc. Symptoms of Kala-azar are breathing difficulty, recurrent fever and skin sores.

Check Point 2

5. What are the different means by which infectious diseases are spread?
6. What is prophylaxis?
7. What is incubation period?
8. Which are the occupational diseases?
9. Write full form of DPT, OPV and BCG.

Keystone

Inflammation: An active immune system recruits many cells towards affected tissue to kill of the diseases causing microbes. This recruitment process is called inflammation. As part of this process, there are local effects such swelling and pain, and general effects such as fever.

Peptic ulcer: it is caused by bacteria Helicobacter pylori. It was discovered by two Australians Marshalland Warren and received Nobel prize for physiology and medicine in 20005.

Pulse polio programme: The aim of this programme it to eradicate polio from our country. It was first held in country In December 1995, Polio vaccine called Oral Polio Vaccine (OPV) is given to children orally (through the mouth), as per the National immunization Schedule (NIS).

STRUCTURAL OUTLINE

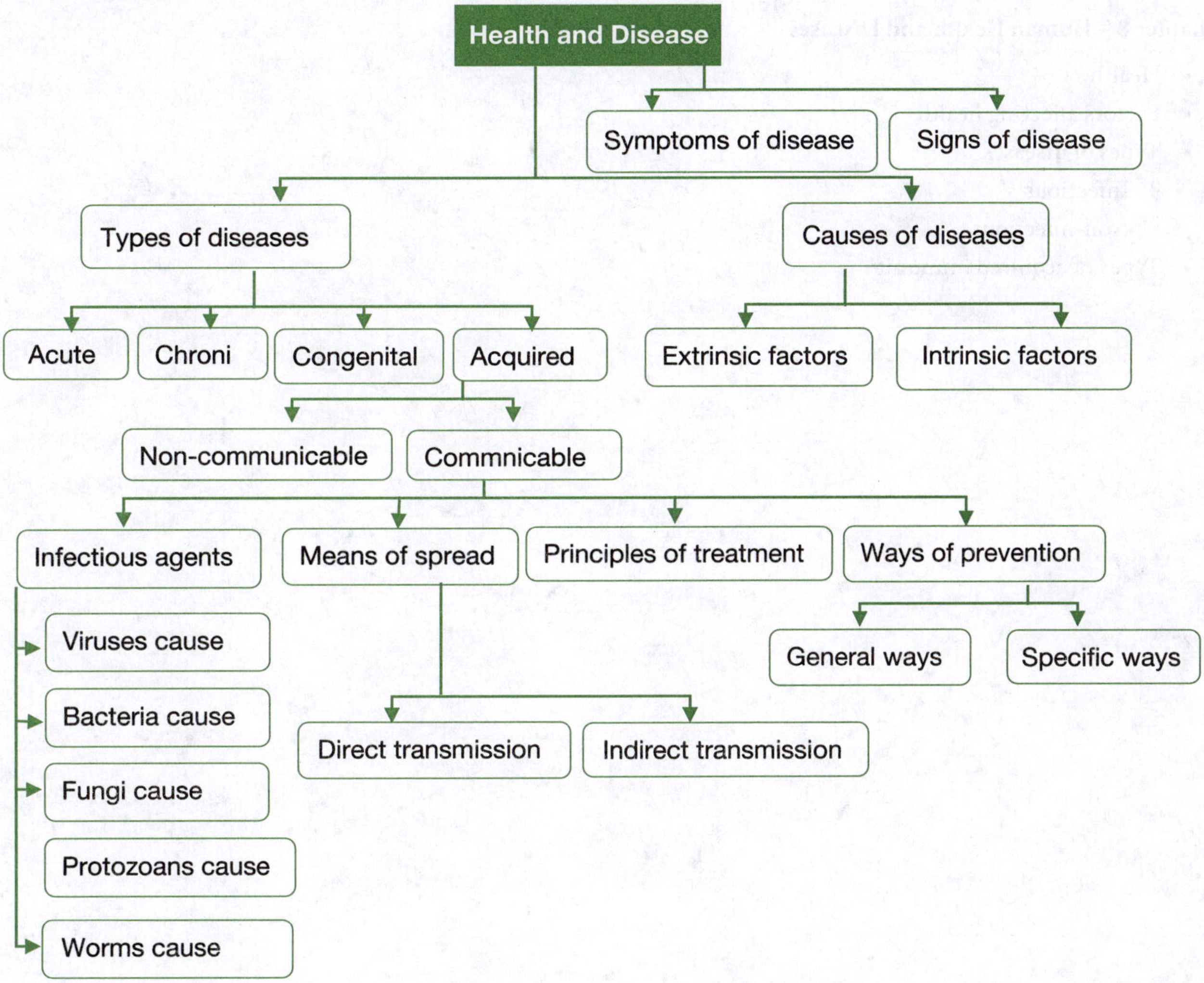

ABRIDGEMENT

Class 12

Chapter 8 – Human Health and Diseases

- Health
- Factors affecting health
- Types of diseases
    - Infectious
    - Non-infectious
- Types of acquired immunity

EXEMPLIFICATION

Q1. (i) Name two diseases caused by Protozoa.

(ii) What are their causal organisms?

Ans: (i) Sleeping sickness caused by Trypanosoma and malaria by Plasmodium.

(ii) Kala-azar caused by Leishmania.

Q2. What is the mechanism of action of antibiotics?

Ans: Antibiotics are chemical substances obtained from some microbes, which stop the growth of specific kind of pathogens. They block certain biochemical pathways important for the lifecycle of pathogen. For example, penicillin does not allow cell wall formation in some bacteria. It blocks chemical reaction required for cell wall formation.

Q3. Describe degenerative diseases.

Ans: Degenerative diseases are caused due to malfunctioning of body organs or degeneration of tissues in old age. It is a type of non-communicable disease. Example: Kidney failure is due to improper functioning of kidneys, cancer is due to uncontrolled growth of tissues in any part of the body, etc

Q4. Name the fat-soluble vitamins.

Ans: Vitamin A, D, E and K are fat soluble.

Q5. Write four common symptoms of malaria.

Ans:

- Sudden appearance of fever with pain and sensation of cold shivering.
- Body temperature rises up to 106°F and patient becomes burning hot. He or she experiences intense headache, faster breathing rate and heartbeat.
- Fever later comes down with profuse sweating. This occurs either daily at a particular time or is repeated every third or fourth day depending upon the species of the parasite.
- Enlargement of spleen and anaemia occurs.

Q6. Name the infectious disease that leads to immunodeficiency. Give the scientific name of the pathogen causing the disease and mention the body organs it primarily affects.

Ans: AIDS is an infectious disease that leads to immune deficiency and wasting of body parts. It is caused by Human Immunodeficiency Virus (HIV). HIV attacks helper T-lymphocytes, thus causing cell-mediated immunodeficiency, which makes the body more prone to various infections.

Q7. What are the causes and symptoms of goitre?

Ans: Goitre is caused due to deficiency of iodine in the diet.

Symptoms of goitre are as follows:

- Abnormal growth of thyroid gland situated in the front part of the neck.
- Increase in body weight due to accumulation of fat and retention of water in the body.
- Increased rate of spontaneous abortion and still birth.
- Disorder in nervous system. Iodine deficiency in childhood causes reduced functioning of the thyroid gland resulting in retarded growth.

Q8. Becoming exposed to or infected with an infectious microbe does not necessarily mean developing noticeable disease. Explain.

Ans: Because of strong immune system, our body is normally fighting off microbes. We have cells which are specialized to kill the pathogenic microbes. These cells are active when infecting microbes enter the body and if they are successful in removing the pathogen, we remain disease-free. So even if we are exposed to infectious microbes, it is not necessary that we suffer from diseases.

Q9. Why is the immune system essential for our health?

Ans: Immune system is essential as it helps our body to fight against disease causing microbes. It protects our body by secreting chemicals called antibodies or other substances which protect us from harmful microbes.

Q10. Name any three diseases transmitted through vectors.

Ans: Filariasis, Dengue, Chikungunya, Malaria, Kala-azar

KNOWLEDGE COMPENDIUM

KNOWLEDGE COMPENDIUM

1. State any two conditions for good health
Ans:
Two conditions essential for good health are:
(i) State of physical, mental, and social well-being.
(ii) Better surroundings or environment.

2. State any two conditions essential for being free of disease.
Ans:
The two conditions essential for being free of disease are:
(i) Personal and domestic hygiene.
(ii) Clean environment and surroundings.

3. Are the answers to the above questions necessarily the same or different? Why?
Ans:
The answer to the above questions is different because a person may be free of disease, but his mental, social, or economic health may not be good.

4. List any three reasons why you would think that you are sick and ought to see a doctor. If only one of these symptoms were present, would you still go to the doctor? Why or why not?
Ans:
The 3 reasons why one would think that he is sick are—(i) headache, (ii) cold and cough, (iii) loose-motions.
This indicates that there may be a disease but does not indicate what the disease is. So, one would still visit the doctor for the treatment and to know the cause of above symptom. Even in case of single symptom one needs to go to the doctor to get proper treatment.

5. In which of the following case do you think the long-term effects on your health are likely to be most unpleasant?
If you get jaundice
If you get lice
If you get acne
Why?
Ans:
In the above cases, lice and acne are acute problems of our health which can be cured in short duration. But jaundice is the disease that can have most unpleasant effect on our health as it affects the most important organ of our body, i.e., liver. This disease is a chronic one.

6. Why are we normally advised to take bland and nourishing food when we are sick?
Ans:
We are advised to take bland and nourishing food when we are sick because our body needs energy to release cells to overcome the infection, the wear and tear of body organ. The nourishing food provides nutrients to our body that will further provide energy and make new cells. No spices in the food makes its digestion process faster, does not release acids in the body that can interfere in the treatment and cure.

7. What are the different means by which infectious diseases are spread?
Ans:
The different means by which infectious diseases spread are:
(a) Through air: They are also called air-borne diseases. The air carries bacteria, virus and the diseases that can be caused are: common cold, influenza, tuberculosis, etc.
(b) Through food and water: When one eats/drinks contaminated food/water, that contains bacteria, virus, worm, etc., it can cause diseases like cholera typhoid, hepatitis.
(c) Through contact: Many diseases spread by contact of infected person with the healthy person. Example, fungal infections, skin diseases, scabies, etc.
(d) By sexual contact: Many diseases can be transmitted, for example, syphilis, AIDS.
(e) By body fluids: Fluids like blood, semen, mother's milk, when infected, can also cause diseases, for example, AIDS.
(f) Vectors: The organism that spreads a disease by carrying pathogens from one place to another is called vector, for example, mosquitoes are vectors that carry pathogens like protozoa.

8. What precautions can you take in your school to reduce the incidence of infectious diseases?
Ans:
The precautions that one can take in school to reduce the incidence of infectious diseases are
(a) By using handkerchief while coughing sneezing.
(b) Washing hands before eating tiffins.
(c) Staying at home if anyone suffers from infectious diseases.

(d) Getting vaccinated before the infection affects.

(e) Keeping the school surroundings clean, checking for stagnant water.

9. What is immunization?

Ans:

When the body attains immunity against any disease, due to vaccination. This process is called immunization.

10. What are the immunization programmes available at the nearest health centre in your locality? Which of these diseases are the major health problems in your area?

Ans:

The immunization programmes available at the nearest health care centres are:

1. Child immunization programme starts from 0 to 12 years.
2. Polio eradication programme
3. H_1N_1 screening programme

Age	Immunization
Infant	Polio, B.C.G
6 weeks—9 weeks	D.P.T, tetanus
9-12 months	booster doses, chicken-pox, hepatitis A & B, etc.

In major areas, tuberculosis cases are reported in a large number which is a major concern.

11. State any two conditions for good health.

Ans:

Two conditions essential for good health are:

(i) State of physical, mental and social well-being.

(ii) Better surroundings or environment.

12. State any two conditions essential for being free of disease.

Ans:

The two conditions essential for being free of disease are:

(i) Personal and domestic hygiene.

(ii) Clean environment and surroundings.

13. Are the answers to the above questions necessarily the same or different? Why?

Ans:

The answer to the above questions is different because a person may be free of disease but his mental, social or economic health may not be good.

14. List any three reasons why you would think that you are sick and ought to see a doctor. If only one of these symptoms were present, would you still go to the doctor? Why or why not?

Ans:

The 3 reasons why one would think that he is sick are—(i) headache, (ii) cold and cough, (iii) loose-motions.

This indicates that there may be a disease but does not indicate what the disease is. So, one would still visit the doctor for the treatment and to know the cause of above symptom. Even in case of single symptom one needs to go to the doctor to get proper treatment.

15. In which of the following case do you think the long-term effects on your health are likely to be most unpleasant?

If you get jaundice

If you get lice

If you get acne.

Why.

Ans:

In the above cases, lice and acne are acute problems of our health which can be cured in short duration. But jaundice is the disease that can have most unpleasant effect on our health as it affects the most important organ of our body i.e., liver. This disease is a chronic one.

16. Why are we normally advised to take bland and nourishing food when we are sick?

Ans:

We are advised to take bland and nourishing food when we are sick because our body needs energy to release cells to overcome the infection, the wear and tear of body organ. The nourishing food provides nutrients to our body that will further provide energy and make new cells. No spices in the food makes its digestion process faster, does not release acids in the body that can interfere in the treatment and cure.

17. What are the different means by which infectious diseases are spread?

Ans:

The different means by which infectious diseases spread are:

(a) Through air: They are also called air-borne diseases. The air carries bacteria, virus and the diseases that can be caused are common cold, influenza, tuberculosis, etc.

(b) Through food and water: When one eats/drinks contaminated food/water, that contains bacteria, virus, worm, etc., it can cause diseases like cholera typhoid, hepatitis.

(c) Through contact: Many diseases spread by contact of infected person with the healthy person, for example, fungal infections, skin diseases, scabies, etc.

(d) By sexual contact: Many diseases can be transmitted, for example, syphilis, AIDS.
(e) By body fluids: Fluids like blood, semen, mother's milk, when infected, can also cause diseases, for example, AIDS.
(f) Vectors: The organism that spreads a disease by carrying pathogens from one place to another is called vector, for example, mosquitoes are vectors that carry pathogens like protozoa.

18. What precautions can you take in your school to reduce the incidence of infectious diseases?

Ans:

The precautions that one can take in school to reduce the incidence of infectious diseases are

(a) By using handkerchief while coughing sneezing.
(b) Washing hands before eating tiffins.
(c) Staying at home if anyone suffers from infectious diseases.
(d) Getting vaccinated before the infection affects.
(e) Keeping the school surroundings clean, checking for stagnant water.

19. What is immunization?

Ans:

When the body attains immunity against any disease, due to vaccination. This process is called immunization.

20. What are the immunization programmes available at the nearest health centre in your locality? Which of these diseases are the major health problems in your area?

Ans:

The immunization programmes available at the nearest health care centres are:

1. Child immunization programme starts from 0 to 12 years.
2. Polio eradication programme
3. H_1N_1 screening programme

Age	Immunization
Infant	Polio, B.C.G
6 weeks—9 weeks	D.P.T, tetanus
9-12 months	booster doses, chicken-pox, hepatitis A, B etc.

In major areas tuberculosis cases are reported in a large number which is a major concern.

21. How many times did you fall ill in the last one year? What were the illnesses?

(a) Think of one change you could make in your habits in order to avoid any of/ most of the above illnesses.
(b) Think of one change you would wish for in your surroundings in order to avoid any of/ most of the above illness.

Ans:

The illness was 2-3 times, common-cold, occurred in a year.

(a) One change I would make in my habits in order to avoid the above illness is that I would take proper diet rich in vitamin C and would avoid too cold food.
(b) The surroundings should be neat, and clean,

22. A doctor/nurse/health worker is exposed to more sick people than others in the community. Find out how she/he avoids getting sick herself/himself.

Ans:

A doctor/nurse/health worker when exposed to sick people they keep their nose and mouth covered, take care of hygiene, wash hands with soap before drinking water or eating food. They use mask, gloves, etc., to avoid the direct contact with the person suffering from infectious diseases.

23. Conduct a survey in your neighbourhood to find out what the three most common diseases are. Suggest three steps that could be taken by your local authorities to bring down the incidence of these diseases.

Ans:

Common-diseases in neighbourhood	Steps to bring down the diseases spread
1. Malaria	1. Clean surrounding
2. Typhoid	2. Clean drinking water
3. Cough and cold	3. Childhood immunization

24. A baby is not able to tell his/her caretakers that she/he is sick. What would help us to find out

(a) that the baby is sick?
(a) what is the sickness?

Ans:

(a) The symptoms like body temperature, fever, cough, cold, loose-motions, non-stop crying improper or no food intake, etc., would help up to find that the baby is sick.
(b) The symptoms could help us to find out the sickness of the body.

25. Under which of the following conditions is a person most likely to fall sick?

(a) When she is recovering from malaria.
(b) When she has recovered from malaria and is taking care of someone suffering from chicken-pox.

(c) When she is on a four-day fast after recovering from malaria and is taking care of someone suffering from chicken-pox.

Why?

Ans:

(c) When she is on a four-day fast after recovering from malaria and is taking care of someone suffering from chicken-pox.

As the person is not taking proper diet which is required for her proper health and healing of body, her chances of getting chicken-pox also high as her body's immunity has lowered.

ASSESSMENT CORNER

Level 1

Fixed Response Type

Multiple Choice Questions

1. Which one of the following is a communicable disease?
   (A) Leucoderma (white patches on the skin)
   (B) Diabetes mellitus
   (C) Beri-beri
   (D) Cholera

2. The form of cancer called 'carcinoma' is associated with
   (A) lymph cells (B) mesodermal cells
   (C) blood cells (D) epithelial cells

3. The familiar disease Amoebiasis is caused by
   (A) Entamoeba histolytica
   (B) Taenia solium
   (C) Ascaris lumbricoides
   (D) Wuchereria bancrofti

4. The disease that affects our lungs is
   (A) AIDS
   (B) Rabies
   (C) Polio
   (D) Tuberculosis

5. Saline is given to a person suffering with cholera because it
   (A) causes lysis of bacterial cell wall
   (B) helps to produce antibodies
   (C) causes severe diarrhoea leading to loss of salts
   (D) both B and C are correct

6. Which one of the following is a deficiency disease caused due to lack of iron in the body?
   (A) Tuberculosis (B) Tetanus
   (C) Anaemia (D) Colour blindness

7. The group of diseases spread by housefly is
   (A) Malaria, Cholera, Scabies
   (B) Rabies, Rickets, Diarrhoea
   (C) Typhoid, Dysentry, Cholera
   (D) Ringworm, Scurvy, Vomiting

8. The mosquito that spreads malaria in man is named
   (A) Male Anopheles
   (B) Female Anopheles
   (C) Culex
   (D) Female Aedes

9. Many children in our country suffer from Kwashiorkor. This can be prevented by giving children food rich in
   (A) carbohydrates (B) fats
   (C) proteins (D) minerals

10. The BCG vaccine is given for the immunity against
    (A) Hepatitis (B) Jaundice
    (C) Tuberculosis (D) Malaria

11. Which one of the following diseases is caused by virus?
    (A) Tuberculosis (B) Smallpox
    (C) Cholera (D) Diphtheria

12. The deficiency of vitamin D causes
    (A) beri-beri (B) rickets
    (C) anaemia (D) goitre

13. Hydrophobia is caused by
    (A) acute virus (B) bacteria
    (C) rabies virus (D) tubercle

14. Disease transmitted by dog is
    (A) plague (B) T.B.
    (C) scurvy (D) rabies

15. Malaria is caused due to
    (A) Protozoa
    (B) Anopheles mosquito
    (C) Both a and b
    (D) None of these

16. In order to prevent spreading of a communicable disease like cholera, it is necessary to
    (A) control the population of mosquitoes
    (B) dry up all ponds in the neighbourhood
    (C) educate people to drink boiled water and not to eat exposed food
    (D) prevent others from coming in contact with the diseased person

17. Plasmodium is an example of
    (A) Virus (B) Bacteria
    (C) Protozoa (D) Worm

18. Antibodies are produced by
    (A) RBCs (B) platelets
    (C) lymphocytes (D) saliva

19. Examples of bacterial diseases are
    (A) Smallpox, Typhoid, Tuberculosis
    (B) Typhoid, Tuberculosis, Tetanus

(C) Polio, Smallpox, Whooping cough
(D) Diphtheria, Smallpox, Typhoid

20. Diarrhea, cholera, typhoid are the diseases that have one thing in common that is
(A) All of them are caused by bacteria
(B) All of them is transmitted by contaminated food and water
(C) All of them are cured by antibiotics
(D) All of the above

21. Worms are responsible for which of the following diseases?
(A) Elephantiasis (B) Anthrax
(C) Flu (D) Kala Azar

22. HIV virus when active in body, mainly attacks on
(A) Lungs (B) Liver
(C) Heart (D) Immune System

23. Which one of the following is not a sexually transmitted disease?
(A) Gonorhoea (B) Syphilis
(C) AIDS (D) Typhoid

24. Antibiotics work against
(A) bacteria (B) virus
(C) dengue (D) elephantiasis

25. Which of the following follows a general principle of flowing the immune system by putting particular infection into the body?
(A) AIDS (B) Vaccination
(C) Antibiotic (D) Antiseptic

26. The word 'vaccine' was first coined by
(A) Koch (B) Pasteur
(C) Jenner (D) Kohler

27. Given below are the pairs of disease and causal pathogen. Which one of these is not a matching pair?
(A) Kala azar - Leishmania
(B) Sleeping sickness - Trypanosoma
(C) Malaria - Salmonella
(D) Acne - Staphylococci

28. The causative agent of the disease 'sleeping sickness' in human beings is an
(A) intracellular parasite found in RBC.
(B) extracellular parasite found in blood plasma
(C) intracellular parasite found in WBC.
(D) extracellular parasite found on the surface of platelets.

29. Health is
(A) Complete physical well-being
(B) Mental well-being
(C) Social well-being
(D) All of the above

30. Remain healthy means
(A) Free of infection by pathogen
(B) Tension free mental status
(C) Living in a population free environment
(D) All of the above

Fill in the Blanks

1. The literal meaning of disease is ______ ease.
2. Acute disease are for ______ periods
3. _________ disease continues for many days and causes _________ on body.
4. Tuberculosis is a ______ disease.
5. Disease that can be transmitted from one individual to another are called communicable or ______ disease
6. An animal that spreads as disease is called a ______.
7. ______ disease continues for a few days and causes no longer term effect on body.
8. Disease present from the birth is called ______.
9. ______ is defined as physical, mental and social well-being and comfort.
10. The duration between infection and appearance of symptoms is called ______.

True/False

1. Cholera is a communicable disease.
2. AIDS can be transmitted through blood transfusion.
3. Antibiotics are produced by bacteria and fungi.
4. Influenza is transmitted through the air.
5. Ringworm is caused by fungi.
6. Diabetes is an infectious disease.
7. Typhoid is caused by a virus named Mycobacterium tuberculosis.
8. Diseases which are present since birth are called congenital disease.
9. Elephantiasis disease can have short term effect on health.
10. Acquire diseases are developed after birth.

Match Type Questions

1. Match the following I and II.

Column I	Column II
(i) Virus	(a) Kala azar
(ii) Worm	(b) AIDS
(iii) Bacteria	(c) Multicellular
(iv) Protozoa	(d) Cholera

2 Match the following I and II.

Column I	Column II
(i) Health	(a) Tuberculosis
(ii) Antibodies	(b) Immunity
(iii) AIDS	(c) State of normal functioning
(iv) BCG	(d) Sexually transmitted disease

Assertion and Reason Type Questions

Instructions: In the following questions, an Assertion (A) is given followed by a Reason (R). Mark your responses from the following options.

(A) Both Assertion and Reason are true and Reason is the correct explanation of 'Assertion'
(B) Both Assertion and Reason are true and Reason is not the correct explanation of 'Assertion'
(C) Assertion is true but Reason is false
(D) Assertion is false but Reason is true
(E) Both Assertion and Reason are false.

1. **Assertion:** Virus can't be treated with antibiotics.
   Reason: They uses host machinery and are living only inside host cell.
2. **Assertion:** Tuberculosis is a bacterial disease.
   Reason: Tuberculosis is mainly transmitted by droplet infection.
3. **Assertion:** Communicable diseases are called infectious diseases.
   Reason: Cancer is a communicable disease.
4. **Assertion:** It is okay to sit near a person suffering from cold.
   Reason: Cold is a communicable disease.
5. **Assertion:** A person suffering from AIDS cannot fight even very minor infections.
   Reason: Casual organism of AIDS is HIV.
6. **Assertion:** Tuberculosis is an acute disease.
   Reason: Disease that lasts for a short period is called acute disease.
7. **Assertion:** Malaria is caused due to Plasmodium and kala-azar is caused due to Leishmania.
   Reason: They both are protozoans.
8. **Assertion:** Elephantiasis is a chronic disease.
   Reason: It lasts for a long time and has a long-term effect on health.
9. **Assertion:** Dengue can be treated by taking antibiotics.
   Reason: Antibiotics block the biochemical life processes of viruses.
10. **Assertion:** Majority of children in many parts of India are already immune to hepatitis A by the time they are five years old.
    Reason: Children are exposed to the virus through water.

Comprehension Type Questions

Passage 1: Many disease-causing organisms are spread through the air. This occurs through little droplets thrown out by infected person when he sneezes or coughs. Anyone standing near who inhales these droplets, has high chance of infection.

1. The most common method of spread of respiratory disease is
   (A) Air (B) Food
   (C) Water (D) All of these
2. Chance of respiratory infection decrease when distance is
   (A) More (B) Less
   (C) Uncertain (D) None of these

Passage 2: The digestive system has the stomach and intestines, and it helps to digest food taken in from outside the body. The musculoskeletal system, which is made up of bones and muscles, holds the body parts together and helps the body move. When there is a disease, either the functioning of one or more systems of the body will change for the worse. These changes give rise to symptoms and signs of disease. Symptoms of disease are the things we feel as being 'wrong'. Such as headache, cough, loose motions, a wound with pus these are all symptoms. These indicate that there may be a disease, but they don't indicate what the disease is. For example, a headache may just stress or very rarely it may mean meningitis, or any one of a dozen different diseases.

3. Which of the following is the function of musculoskeletal system?
   (A) Digest food taken in from outside the body
   (B) Holds the body parts together
   (C) Helps the body move
   (D) Both (B) and (C)

4. Which of the following is the function of digestive system?
   (A) Digestion of food
   (B) Holds the body parts together
   (C) Helps the body move
   (D) Both b and c

5. Diseases that last for only very short periods of time are termed as
   (A) Chronic Diseases
   (B) Symptoms
   (C) Acute Diseases
   (D) Congenital diseases

Passage 3: Microbes can be classified into different categories. They are viruses, bacteria, fungi or protozoa. Each of these groups of organisms will have some essential biochemical life process which is peculiar to that group. Similarly, there are drugs that kill protozoa such as the malarial parasite. One reason why making anti-viral medicines is harder than making anti-bacterial medicines is that viruses have few biochemical mechanisms of their own. They enter our cells and use our machinery for their life processes. This means that there are relatively few virus-specific targets to aim at. Despite this limitation, there are now effective anti-viral drugs, for example, the drugs that keep HIV infection under control.

6. Which of the following are the classes of microbes?
   (A) Viruses (B) Bacteria
   (C) Fungi (D) All of the above

7. Identify correct statement given below.
   Statement 1 – Microbes are classified into: viruses, bacteria, fungi or protozoa.
   Statement 2 – Making anti-viral medicines is harder than making anti-bacterial medicines.
   Statement 3 – Malarial parasite is bacteria.
   Statement 4 – HIV is caused due to fungi.
   (A) Both 1 and 2 (B) Both 2and 3
   (C) Only 4 (D) None of above

8. Malarial parasite is ______.
   (A) Bacteria (B) Fungi
   (C) Virus (D) Protozoa

Free Response Type

Very Short Answer Type Questions

1. Name the disease caused by protozoa.
2. Name two diseases caused by Protozoans.
3. Define communicable and non - communicable diseases.
4. Name four disease caused by bacteria.
5. How is AIDS spread?
6. What is deficiency disease?
7. What are their causal organisms?
8. Why are children vaccinated for cholera?
9. Write two common symptoms of malaria.
10. Defined degenerative diseases?

Short Answer Type Questions

1. What is the difference between community health and personal health?
2. Define communicable disease and give three examples.
3. Why is immune system essential for our health?
4. Give any four factors necessary for a healthy person.
5. Define the following terms:
   (i) vector (ii) disease
6. Write the difference between signs and symptoms.
7. Classify the following diseases as infectious or non-infectious.
   (A) AIDS
   (B) Tuberculosis
   (C) Cholera
   (D) High blood pressure
   (E) Heart disease
   (F) Pneumonia
   (G) Cancer
8. Why is immune system essential for our health?
9. Write short note on pulse polio program.
10. Give two examples for each of the following:
    (A) Acute diseases
    (B) Chronic diseases
    (C) Infectious diseases
    (D) Non-infectious diseases

Long Answer Type Questions

1. Write in detail about the treatment of infectious diseases.
2. Describe influenza with its symptoms and prevention.

3. Discuss the causes, symptoms, preventive measures and treatment of AIDS.
4. Differentiate between personal health and community health.
5. Write in detail on specific method of treatment and prevention of diseases.

Case Based Questions

Case 1: Sita was bitten by a stray dog. After some days her nature gets irritated, she started fearing water.

1. Name the disease.
2. Is there any vaccine available?
3. Is there any plan of your local authority for the control of this disease?

Case 2: Recently, our school organised health check-up camp. Eminent doctors visited our school. Doctor Vinit, leader of the team, gave us tips about essential conditions of keeping good health, extrinsic and intrinsic causes of diseases as well as types of diseases. Later, students at the school were examined by the doctors. Next day, our class teacher asked us to answer the following questions:

1. List at least three conditions essential for good health.
2. How can we keep our surroundings clean? Mention atleast two ways.
3. How would you define a 'disease'?

Case 3: Few days back, there was some news about increased incidences of malaria in nearby villages of our city. The Chief Medical Office of the district asked the biologists and their team to conduct thorough survey of the area and take necessary steps. The survey revealed that public health services were in very poor shape. As a result, lot of garbage and water had accumulated at places which provided ideal sites of breeding of mosquitoes and other disease carrying agents. Recall what you have studied about diseases in the class and answer following questions:

1. Name causative agent of malaria. Which insect vector spreads it?
2. Which step the biologists immediately took to check the disease?
3. Name the most common antimalarial drug being used. From where is it extracted?

Case 4: An HIV infected employee was dismissed from service by the employer. The colleagues of the employee in the office intervened and convinced the boss of the company to reinstate the services of the employee as HIV is not transmitted by mere physical contact. They told the employer that such person should not be made a victim of social stigma on contracting the disease.

1. Name the disease which the employee was suffering from.
2. How does the disease get transmitted from one person to another?
3. What values are shown by the colleagues of the employee?

Level 2

Multiple Choice Questions

1. A carrier is a human being that
(A) functions as a reservoir of infection
(B) possesses pathogen but is not harmed
(C) Communicable diseases
(D) Both (B) & (C)

2. Malaria is a
(A) Infectious diseases
(B) Non-infectious diseases
(C) Communicable diseases
(D) Both (B) and (C)

3. Specific defence mechanism against disease comprises
(A) physical barrier
(B) lysozyme
(C) phagocytes
(D) immune system

4. Malaria is a -
(A) Infectious diseases
(B) Non-infectious diseases
(C) A specific protein or polysaccharide present on its coat
(D) Both (A) and (B)

5. Pathogens are destroyed by
(A) kidneys
(B) liver
(C) adipose tissue
(D) lymphatic tissues

6. A non-infectious unnatural and unusual reaction to a substance or condition is
(A) immunity (B) allergy
(C) infection (D) toxin

7. AIDS is caused by
(A) Bacteria (B) Fungi
(C) HIV (D) Allergy

8. Which of these is not a chronic disease?
(A) Tuberculosis (B) Asthma
(C) Common cold (D) None of these

9. AIDS day is on
(A) May 1 (B) December 20
(C) June 1 (D) December 1

10. Antibodies are
(A) lipids (B) genes
(C) proteins (D) carbohydrates

11. Which of the following statements is correct?
(A) Degenerative diseases are non-communicable.
(B) Allergy is caused by droplet infection.
(C) Cholera is a viral disease.
(D) AIDS can be prevented by vaccination.

12. Remain healthy means
(A) free of infection by pathogen
(B) tension free mental status
(C) living in a pollution free environment
(D) All of the above

13. Diseases occurring due to infected articles of a patient are called
(A) Air borne (B) Water borne
(C) Fomite borne (D) Food borne

14. World health day is on
(A) 1st May (B) 7th April
(C) 30th June (D) 5th December

15. Specific defence mechanism against disease comprises -
(A) Physical barrier (B) Lysozyme
(C) Phagocytes (D) Immune system

16. Pulse polio programme is organied in our country for
(A) curing polio
(B) eradicating polio
(C) spreading polio
(D) none of the above

17. Community health aims at
(A) better health and family planning
(B) better hygiene and clean environment
(C) removing communicable diseases
(D) all of the above

18. Head quarter of World Health Organisation (WHO) is located at
(A) New York (B) Geneva
(C) London (D) Paris

19. Droplet infection is a mode of
(A) direct transmission
(B) indirect transmission
(C) pathogen spread through mosquitoes
(D) fomite transmission

20. Which one of the following is not a viral disease?
(A) Dengue (B) AIDS
(C) Typhoid (D) Influenza

Higher Order Thinking Skills (HOTS)

1. (A) Identify the figure.

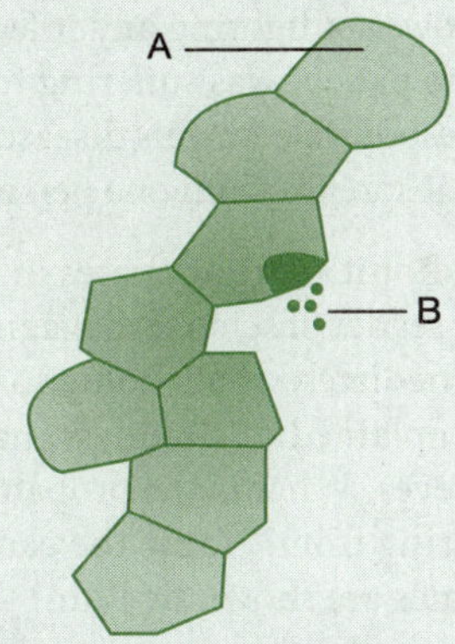

(B) What do A and B depict?

2. What is correct? Give reason.
(A) A person strolling in the lawn of his house is relaxing or doing exercise.
(B) Wearing socks and full sleeves at night will prevent the attack from dengue.
(C) Regular use of ORS cures diarrhoea.

3. Name a disease in which
(A) Antibiotic has no role.
(B) Kissing does not spread the disease while sexual contact transfers the same.
(C) Mass scale immunization is going on.
(D) Virus, bacterium and protozoan can be causal agent.

4. The antigen present in the pathogen is:
(A) A specific protein involve metabolism
(B) Polysaccharide synthesized by it in the host
(C) A specific protein or polysaccharide present on its coat
(D) None of the above

5. A doctor/nurse/health-worker is exposed to more sick people than others in the community. Find out how she/he avoids getting sick herself/himself.

6. A baby is not able to tell her/his caretakers that she/he is sick. What would help us to find out:
(A) that the baby is sick?
(B) what is the sickness?

ASSESSMENT CORNER

7. A child is suffering from fever but the doctor cannot immediately pinpoint the ailment on the basis of this one symptom. Explain why. Also, mention another two such general symptoms.

8. Why are kids and elderly people more vulnerable to cold/flu?

9. Why do people staying in air-conditioned homes/ offices catch cold more often?

10. It was diagnosed that the body of a patient had lost his power of fighting any infection. Name the disease the patient was suffering from. Which microbe is responsible for this disease? Give two ways by which it spreads from one person to another.

11. Ram and Rohit are roommates in the hostel. Ram is an avid reader of science magazines and articles. Ram immediately took Rohit to a doctor when Rohit complained of tiredness, nausea, vomiting and pale eyes. What is the probable disease Rohit was suffering from? Name the causative microbe. What values are shown by Ram?

12. Aarti and arjun were parents of a newborn child but they were afraid to take their child for vaccination as someone told them that the vaccine contains harmful germs. However, when they consulted Dr. Seema, she listened to them patiently and then cleared their doubts about vaccines. She told them that the vaccines only contain dead germs or inactivated germs which do not cause the disease. How do the dead germs in vaccines protect from diseases? What are the values shown by Dr. Seema?

13. Megha's told her that he had been feeling tired, breathless, had persistent cough and blood was coming out in his sputum. She told him that these are symptoms of an infectious disease and advised him to consult a doctor. She also took him for diagnostic tests prescribed by the doctor. The helps were diagnosed as suffering from an infectious disease. He took the medicines prescribed by the doctor and got cured of the disease.
   (A) Name the most likely disease and microbe from which the help suffered?
   (B) How does the disease get transmitted?
   (C) What are the values depicted by Megha?

14. The municipality of an area advised the residents of the area to eliminate the breeding grounds of mosquitoes and use mosquito repellents in homes to avoid a disease which results in chills and recurring fever in patients. The children of the area formed teams which inspected the surrounding areas and put few drops of oil or petrol on stagnant water pools of the area.
   (A) Name the disease, causative organism and the vector of the disease which was spreading in the area.
   (B) How do the drops of petrol or oil on stagnant water prevent the spread of the disease?
   (C) What are the values shown by the students?

15. Government has recently taken series of steps to minimise cigarette smoking and tobacco chewing by people as these are injurious to health.
   (A) List atleast three steps taken by government to aware people about harmful effects of cigarette smoking and tobacco chewing.
   (B) What is passive smoking?
   (C) List atleast one chromic disease that occurs due to continuous use of tobacco.

ARCHIVE CORNER

1. Match column I with column II and column III and select the correct option from the given codes.

Column I (Disease)	Column II (Causative agent)	Column III (Mode of transmission)
P. Cholera	A. Bacteria	1. Contaminated water
Q. Chicken pox	B. Virus	2. Wound
R. Polio	C. Protozoa	3. Air
S. Amoebic dysentery		4. Direct contact
		5. Contaminated food

	P	Q	R	S
A.	B, 1	B, 3, 4	A, 2	A, 1
B.	A, 1	C, 5	B, 2, 4	C, 1, 5
C.	A, 1, 5	B, 3, 4	B, 1, 3	C, 1, 5
D.	B, 1	B, 2, 4	A, 1, 3	C, 1, 5

2. Read the given statements and select the correct one.
   (A) Acute diseases persist for a long time hence cause prolonged ill health.
   (B) Acquired diseases are physiological abnormalities present since birth.
   (C) Cleft palate is caused due to environmental factors whereas haemophilia is caused due to gene mutation.
   (D) AIDS and German measles cannot be transferred to baby from infected mothers.

3. Refer to the given Venn diagram.

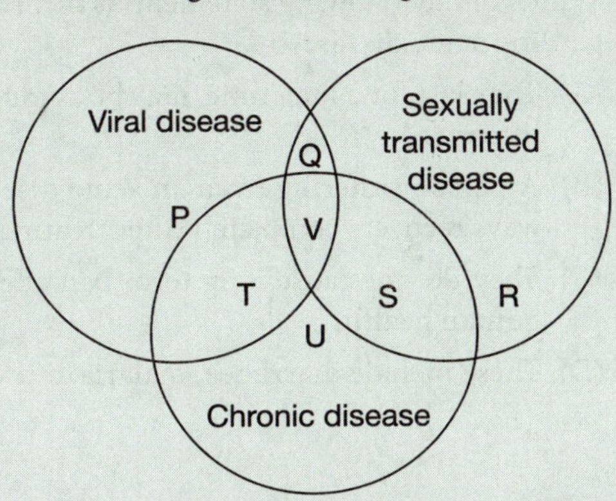

Tuberculosis (X) and AIDS (Y) can be placed at which alphabets respectively?

	X	Y
A.	U	V
B.	P	S
C.	Q	V
D.	T	S

4. Study the following table and select the correct option for p, q, r, s and t.

Disease	Causative organism	Mode of transmission
Measles	P	Air
Q	Bacterium	Water/Food
Dengue	R	S
Malaria	T	Mosquito

   (A) P-Virus, q-Hepatitis-B, r-Protozoan, s-Mosquito, t-Protozoan
   (B) P-Bacterium, q-Cholera, r-Virus, s-Mosquito, t-Protozoan
   (C) P-Virus, q-Cholera, r-Virus, s-Mosquito, t-Protozoan
   (D) P-Virus, q-Typhoid, r-Protozoan, s-Air, t-Bacterium

5. Refer to the given Venn diagram and select the option that correctly identifies X and Y.

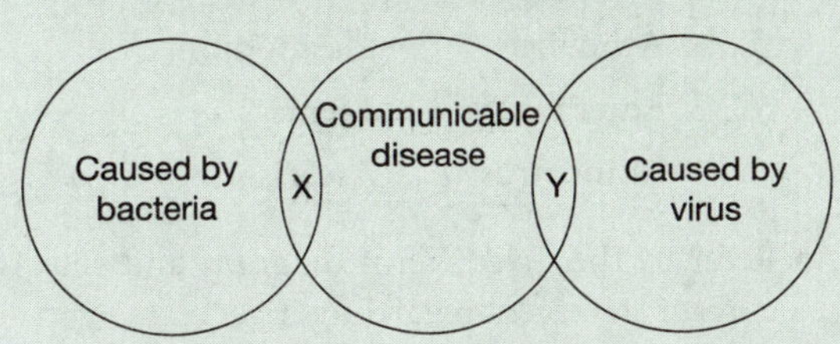

	X	Y
(A)	Malaria	Cholera
(B)	Anthrax	Dengue
(C)	AIDS	Acne
(D)	Elephantiasis	Whooping cough

6. Read the given statements and select the option that correctly identifies them as true (T) and false (F) ones.
   (A) Quinine is an antimalarial drug obtained from bark of chinchona tree.
   (B) Tuberculosis causing organism enters via nose and usually resides in the pancreas.
   (C) HIV virus upon entering the human body spreads to all lymph nodes.
   (D) Virus causing Hepatitis, damage the liver cells resulting in jaundice.

ARCHIVE CORNER

	(i)	(ii)	(iii)	(iv)
(A)	F	F	T	T
(B)	F	T	T	T
(C)	T	F	T	T
(D)	T	T	T	F

7. The given graph shows the pathogen load in the body of a person during the period of sickness. Now select the correct statement regarding this.

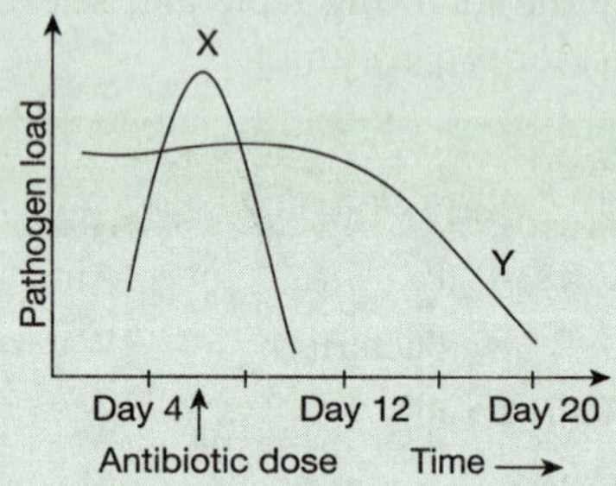

(A) The person is suffering from two pathogenic infections simultaneously.
(B) X could be a viral infection that decreased rapidly after antibiotic treatment.
(C) Both X and Y are different bacterial infections where recovery in case of X is due to body's immunity whereas that in case of Y is due to antibiotic treatment.
(D) Both X and Y are viral infections which decreased due to body's immunity and antibiotic treatment had no role in it.

8. Select the correct match of the deficiency disease and related nutrient.
(A) Vitamin E – Scurvy
(B) Iodine – Marasmus
(C) Protein – Cheilosis
(D) Vitamin D – Osteomalacia

9. Study the given table carefully and select the option that correctly fills the blanks.

Disease	Causative organism
Mumps	P
Elephantiasis	Q
R	Bacillus anthracis
Ringworm	S

	P	Q	R	S
A.	Rubelavirus	Wuchereria bancrofti	Anthrax	Epidermophyton
B.	Arbovirus	Plasmodium	Tetanus	Trichophyton
C.	Enterovirus	Taenia	Diphtheria	Microsporum
D.	Rhinovirus	Ascaris	Typhoid	Leishmania

10. Refer to the given Venn diagram and select the correct statement regarding it

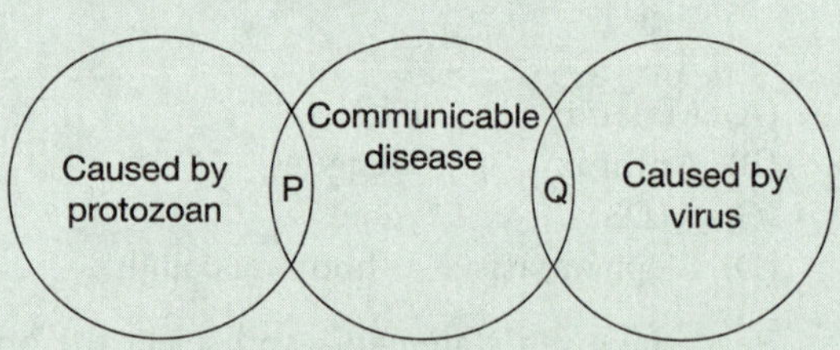

(A) P could be caused by the bite of tse-tse fly whereas Q could be caused by Vibrio cholerae.
(B) P could be characterised by uncontrolled cell divisions whereas Q could be treated by drug obtained from bark of cinchona tree.
(C) P could be African sleeping sickness whereas Q could be Kala-azar.
(D) P could be malaria whereas Q could be dengue.

11. Which of the following statements is incorrect regarding acute diseases?
(A) They last for a long time, may be as much as a lifetime.
(B) A person suffering from an acute disease always recovers completely after treatment.
(C) They do not cause long term bad effects on human health.
(D) These include diarrhoea, malaria, etc.

ARCHIVE CORNER

12. Refer to the given table and select the correct option.

Disease	Non-communicable	Spreads through contaminated food and water	Spreads through direct contact
P	×	√	×
Q	×	×	√
R	√	×	×

	P	*Q*	*R*
A.	Tuberculosis	Whooping cough	Measles
B.	Hepatitis-B	Pneumonia	Malaria
C.	AIDS	Cholera	Dengue
D.	Typhoid	Chickenpox	Goitre

13. Read the given statements, each with one or two blanks and select the option that correctly fills any four of them.
    (i) __P__ causes ulcers in stomach and duodenum.
    (ii) __Q__ diseases last for only short period of time but are severe.
    (iii) __R__ is caused by hypersecretion of thyroid hormone whereas __S__ is caused by hyposecretion of thyroid hormone.
    (iv) Dengue fever causing microbes are transmitted through bite of infected __T__ whereas sleeping sickness causing microbes are transmitted through bite of infected __U__.
    (A) P-Salmonella typhi, R-Myxoedema, T-Sandfly, U-Anopheles mosquito
    (B) Q-Acute, S-Grave's disease, T-Tsetse fly, U-Sandfly
    (C) P-Helicobacter pylori, Q-Acute S-Myxoedema, T-Aedes mosquito
    (D) Q-Chronic, R-Grave's disease, T-Aedes mosquito, U-Sandfly

14. Refer to the given box containing names of some human diseases and select the incorrect statement regarding it.
    Diphtheria, Tetanus, Malaria, Addison's disease, Anthrax, Sleeping sickness, Poliomyelitis, Kala-azar, Hepatitis-B, Cretinism
    (A) The given box contains two protozoan diseases and four bacterial diseases where all the protozoan diseases are vector borne.
    (B) Out of the two hormonal disorders listed in the given box, one occurs due to hypersecretion of thyroid hormone.
    (C) The given box contains two viral diseases and three bacterial diseases.
    (D) Both A and B

15. Read the given passage.
    Charulata contracted chickenpox few days back and soon recovered from the infection. She got immune to any subsequent infection of chickenpox virus. Her younger brother Ajeet is just two months old and is mother fed. He has received some immunity from his mother via milk.
    Which of the following is correct regarding Charulata and Ajeet's immunity?
    (A) Charulata's immune system has developed its own antibodies when encountered the pathogen or antigen, however Ajeet has received preformed antibodies from his mother.
    (B) Ajeet's immunity is long lasting but Charulata's immunity is for a brief period only.
    (C) Charulata is also immune to diseases like measles and polio, however Ajeet is immune to most of the pathogenic diseases.
    (D) Ajeet's immunity may cause some side effects in his body, however Charulata's immunity has no side effects.

16. Pulse polio immunization programme was launched with an aim to eradicate polio disease. It involves simultaneous administration of polio drops (polio vaccine) to the high risk population on a single day throughout the nation. What is the basic objective of pulse polio immunization programme?
    (A) To immunise those children who are not earlier immunised or are partially immunised.
    (B) To boost the immunity of children already immunised.
    (C) To eradicate the polio-causing virus from the world.
    (D) All of these

17. Which of the following statements regarding the carbon cycle is correct?
    (A) Respiration is the first step of the carbon cycle as it converts abiotic carbon to organic carbon.
    (B) At least some carbon is removed from carbon cycle when dead animals and plants become fossilised and form fossil fuels.
    (C) All living organisms return carbon to the abiotic environment by respiration.
    (D) Tropical rainforests act as major carbon sinks of the carbon cycle due to their ability

to liberate carbon dioxide into the environment when trees die and are decomposed.

18. Which of the following statements is correct regarding chronic diseases?
   (A) They last for a long time, may be as much as a lifetime.
   (B) A person suffering from a chronic disease always recovers completely after treatment.
   (C) They do not cause long term bad effects on human health.
   (D) These include Alzheimer's disease, cholera, arthritis, cancer, etc.

19. Read the given statements and select the option that correctly fill the blanks in any two of them.
   (a) Entamoeba histolytica causes _____(i)_____ and Entamoeba gingivalis causes _____(ii)_____.
   (b) _____(i)_____ bacteria can fix atmospheric nitrogen into nitrates.
   (c) _____(i)_____ and _____(ii)_____ are common bacteria that cause denitrification.
   (A) (a)-(i) Amoebiasis, (ii) Food poisoning (c)-(i) Rhizobium, (ii) Thiobacillus
   (B) (b)-(i) Rhizobium, (c)-(i) Thiobacillus, (ii) Pseudomonas
   (C) (a)-(i) Amoebiasis, (ii) Pyorrhoea (b)-(i) Thiobacillus,
   (D) (a)-(i) Pyorrhoea, (ii) Amoebiasis (c)-(i) Nitrosomonas, (ii) Pseudomonas

20. Refer to the given dichotomous key and select the incorrect option regarding it.

I.	(a) Disease is present since birth.	- P
	(b) Disease develops after birth.	- Go to II
II.	(a) It is a communicable disease.	- Go to III
	(b) It is a non-communicable disease.	-Go to IV
III.	(a) It spreads through direct contact.	- Q
	(b) It spreads through vector.	- R
IV.	(a) It occurs due to deficiency of nutrients.	- S
	(b) It occurs due to deficiency of a hormone.	- T

   (A) P could be cleft palate, R could be elephantiasis and T could be goitre.
   (B) Q could be rhinitis, R could be sleeping sickness and S could be night blindness.
   (C) P could be Down's syndrome, Q could be measles and R could be malaria.
   (D) Q could be kala-azar, R could be haemophilia and S could be cretinism.

21. Refer to the given Venn diagram and select the correct option regarding P and Q.

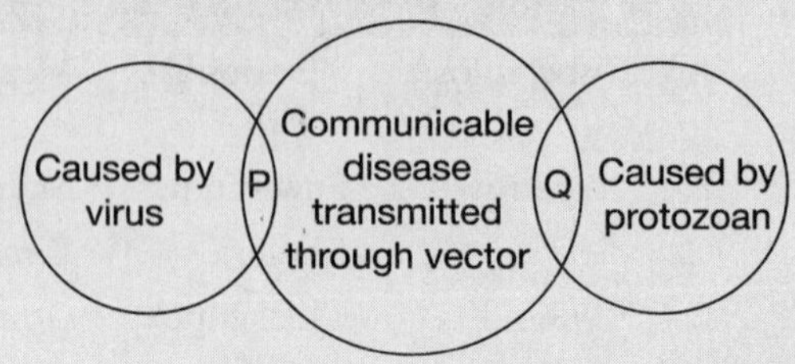

   (A) Q could be a disease that is commonly treated by a drug obtained from bark of Cinchona tree.
   (B) P could be a fever which is transmitted by the bite of Aedes aegypti mosquito that bites during daytime.
   (C) P could be a disease characterised by severe joint pain and sudden onset of high fever whereas Q could be dum-dum fever or sleeping sickness.
   (D) All of these

22. The given graph shows the pathogen load in the body of a person during the period of sickness. Now select the correct option regarding this.

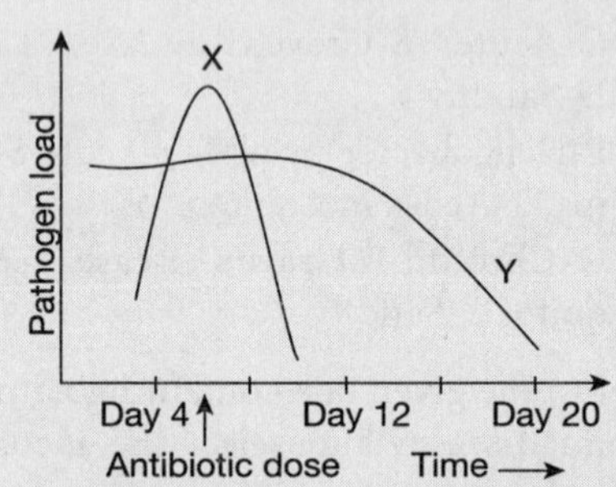

   (A) The person is suffering from two pathogenic infections simultaneously.
   (B) X could be a viral infection that decreased rapidly after antibiotic treatment.
   (C) Both X and Y are different bacterial infections where recovery in case of X is due to body's immunity whereas that in case of Y is due to antibiotic treatment.
   (D) Both X and Y are viral infections which decreased due to body's immunity and antibiotic treatment had no role in it.

23. Refer to the given box containing names of some human diseases and select incorrect statement regarding it.

Chikungunya,	Rabies,	Yellow fever,
Gonorrhoea,	Malaria,	Trypanosomiasis,
Dengue,	Kala azar,	Tetanus,
Genital herpes		

(A) The given box contains five viral diseases out of which four are vector borne and one is sexually transmitted.
(B) The given box contains two protozoan diseases and three bacterial diseases where all the protozoan diseases are vector borne.
(C) Out of the two bacterial diseases listed in the given box, one is sexually transmitted while DPT vaccine is available for the other.
(D) Female Aedes aegypti serves as a vector for three of the diseases listed in the box.

24. Which of the following correctly exemplifies acquisition of active immunity by a person?
(A) A person who has recovered from an attack of mumps, develops natural active immunity.
(B) When ready-made antibodies are directly injected into a person's body to protect him against foreign agents, then he acquires artificial active immunity.
(C) When a person is vaccinated for a disease then he acquires natural active immunity for that disease.
(D) When antibody is transferred from mother to the foetus through placenta then the developing baby acquires artificial active immunity

ANSWER KEYS

Level 1

Fixed Response Type

Multiple Choice Questions

1. D 2. D 3. B 4. D 5. C 6. C 7. C 8. B 9. C
10. C 11. B 12. A 13. C 14. D 15. C 16. C 17. C 18. C
19. A 20. D 21. C 22. A 23. D 24. D 25. A 26. B 27. C
28. C 29. D 30. D

Fill in the Blanks

1. Disturbed
2. Short
3. Chronic, long-term effect
4. Bacterial
5. Infectious
6. Vector
7. Acute
8. Congenital
9. Health
10. Incubation period

True/False

1. False 2. True 3. True 4. True 5. True 6. False 7. False 8. True 9. False
10. True

Match Type Questions

1. (i)-(b), (ii)-(c), (iii)-(d), (iv)-(a)
2. (i)-(c), (ii)-(b), (iii)-(d), (iv)-(a)

Assertion and Reason Type Questions

1. A 2. B 3. C 4. D 5. B 6. D 7. A 8. A 9. E
10. A

Comprehension Type Questions

Passage 1
1. A 2. A

Passage 2
3. D 4. A 5. C

Passage 3
6. D 7. A 8. D

Level 2

Multiple Choice Questions

1. D 2. D 3. D 4. D 5. D 6. B 7. C 8. C 9. D
10. C 11. A 12. D 13. C 14. B 15. D 16. B 17. D 18. B
19. B 20. C

Archive Corner

1. C	2. C	3. A	4. C	5. B	6. C	7. A	8. D	9. A
10. D	11. A	12. D	13. A	14. D	15. A	16. D	17. C	18. A
19. B	20. D	21. D	22. A	23. B	24. A			

CHAPTER 5

Natural Resources

Learning Outcomes

At the end of this chapter, you would be able to:

- classify natural resources.
- discuss air, winds, atmosphere, rain, air pollution and its effects.
- discuss water, importance, water pollution and its effects.
- explain soil formation, types, soil pollution, soil erosion.
- describe biogeochemical cycles – water cycle, nitrogen cycle, carbon cycle, global warming, greenhouse effect.
- explain oxygen cycle, ozone layer and its depletion.
- discuss the management of natural resources.

Geekspeak

- Resources
- Hail
- Sleet
- Snow
- Eutrophication
- Biomagnification
- Humification
- Pollution
- Erosion
- Ammonification
- Fixation
- Nitrification

Introduction

Natural Resources indicates the potential wealth of a country. The variety of substances that man gets from earth and nature to meet his basic needs are called natural resources. The word resource means a source of supplying a material generally held in reserve.

Natural resources are both living and non-living. Some of these resources are found in abundance, while others are found in limited quantities and that too in some restricted parts of our land. For this reason, the natural resources have to be wisely used. However, in reality it is not so. They are being used indiscriminately.

Types of Natural Resources

Natural resources are the assets that we receive from nature, they are of numerous kinds, Resources can be classified based on on factors, which we will discuss.

Physical resources: E.g., Air, water, soil, minerals, coal, etc.

Biological resources: E.g., Microorganisms, plants and animals.

Based on Availability

Natural resources can be categorized based on its availability into following types:

Inexhaustible Natural Resources

- Resources that are in unlimited quantity.
- Resources that are not likely to be exhausted by human activity or their use.
- Examples: Air, water, and solar radiations.

Exhaustible Natural Resources

- Resources that are in limited quantity.
- Resources that are likely to be exhausted by human activities.

Exhaustible natural resources are of two types:

- **Renewable:** They can replenish themselves by recycling and replacement within a reasonable time. They are not likely to be exhausted. Examples: soil, forests and wildlife.
- **Non-Renewable:** They cannot replenish themselves by recycling and replacement. They may be exhausted. Examples: minerals, fossil fuels.

Based on Origin

Natural resources can be categorized based on its origin into following types-

Biotic

These are obtained from the biosphere. Forest and forest products, crops, birds, animal, fish and other marine life forms are examples of biotic resources. Coal and mineral oil also belong to the category since they originate from organic matter. Some biotic resources like forest and livestock are renewable.

Abiotic

These are non-renewable. Resources composed of non-living inorganic matter. Land, water and minerals like iron, copper, lead and gold are abiotic resources.

Based on Chemical Nature

Natural resources can be classified based on chemical nature into three types, that are:

Inorganic Resources

Air, water and metallic minerals.

Organic Resources

Plants, animals, microorganisms and fossil fuels.

Mixed Resources

Inorganic as well as organic, e.g., soil.

Based on Distribution

Natural resources can be classified based on distribution into two types, that are:

National Resources

All the resources within the boundaries of a country are called national resources. Examples: minerals, roads, rails, within the boundary of the country are national resources.

International Resources

The resources which belong to all the countries of the world. Examples: water, seas and oceans, etc.

The Breath of Life – Air

Air is a mixture of gases which is odorless, tasteless and invisible. Air also holds water vapour and dust particles. It is essential for the survival of human beings and also of microbes, plants and animals. In atmosphere, about 95% of the total air is present up to the height of about 20km, above earth above earth's surface. The remaining 5% of air is present in rest of atmosphere up to about 280 km, height.

Composition of air:

Nitrogen (N_2) – 78%
Oxygen (O_2) – 21%
Argon (Ar) – .93%
Carbon Dioxide (CO_2) – .03%
Other Gases – 0.02% (Neon, Helium, Xenon, Ammonia, Hydrogen)

Besides these gaseous components air also possesses water vapour, industrial gases, dust, smoke particles, microorganisms, pollen grains, fungal spores, etc.

Different Zones of Atmosphere or Air

Atmosphere consists of several regions (as shown in Fig. 5.1) which differ in their properties, these layers are:

Troposphere

It is the basal part that extends about 8–16 km above the earth's surface (upto 8 km on poles). In this layer important climatic events occur like cloud formation, lightning, thundering etc. In this region, air temperature gradually decreases with height. Its upper limit is called **Tropopause.**

> **Keystone**
>
> Venus and Mars atmosphere is 95–97% CO_2

Stratosphere

It lies next to troposphere and is up to 50 km high. In this layer temperature rises. There is a formation of ozone layer in this region which can absorb the harmful ultraviolet rays coming from sun.

Mesosphere

It lies next to stratosphere and is up to 80 km in height. Temperature decreases in this region.

Ionosphere

It lies up to 400 km above earth's surface. In this layer, gaseous components become ionized due to sun's energy and remain there as ions.

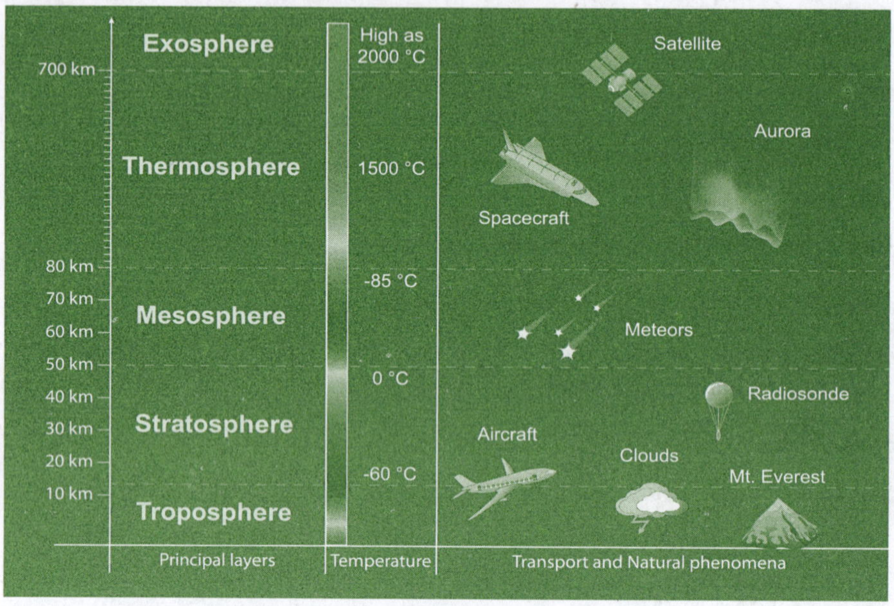

Figure 5.1 Different Regions of Atmosphere

Different regions of atmosphere have been discussed in the Table 5.1.

Table 5.1 Different Regions of Atmosphere

Region	Range of distance	Density of air	Importance
Troposphere	11 kms from the surface of earth	Highest	Most of the atmospheric air is present here. It is a medium for locomotion of flying animals, helps in dispersal of seeds and fruits; region of cloud formation.
Stratosphere	50 kms from the surface of earth	Less than troposphere	Contains ozone layer that traps most of uv rays and cosmic rays of the sun.
Mesosphere	80 kms from the surface of earth	Low	______
Thermosphere	100 kms upwards	Extremely low	Reflect radio waves back to earth, artificial satellites are present here.

Role of Air or Atmosphere

- Air or Atmosphere serves several important purposes like:
- It acts as medium for movement of insects, birds, etc.
- It protects the life on earth from harmful ultra violet rays.
- It is a source of oxygen, carbon dioxide and nitrogen required for various metabolic activities of living beings.
- It helps in dispersal of spores, pollen grains, etc.
- It maintains temperature on earth required for life.
- It transmits sound for communication.

- Ionosphere reflects the radio waves back to earth for long distance communication due to presence of ions and free electrons.
- Burning (combustion) takes place in presence of oxygen and produces carbon dioxide.
- Specific climatic conditions and water cycle is maintained due to circulation of air.
- Eukaryotic cells and many prokaryotic cells require O_2 for breakdown of glucose to get energy through respiration. They release CO_2.

The Role of Atmosphere in Climate Control

Climate is an average weather of an area. Temperature, light and rainfall are important factors that determine climate of an area. Atmosphere plays a crucial role in its control:

- It acts like a blanket covering the whole earth.
- It keeps the temperature of earth steady.
- It acts as bad conductor of heat thus prevents the sudden increase in temperature during the day as well as slows down the escape of heat into the outer space during night. The temperature range on the surface of moon –190°C to 110°C.

Movement of Air

When the solar radiation falls on the earth, some are absorbed and majority of these are reflected back or reradiated by the land and water bodies. These solar radiations heat up the atmosphere from below resulting convection currents in the air. Since the land gets heated faster than the water, the air over land also gets heated faster than the air over water bodies.

Hot air on land rises upwards and produces an area of the low air pressure. Air from region of high pressure will move towards this region of low-pressure producing breeze or wind.

Wind: Air in motion is called wind. Speed of wind can be determined by (as shown in Fig. 5.2):

- Heating of air.
- Formation of water vapour.
- Atmosphere can be heated from below by radiations, such radiations are reflected back.
- Convection currents appear in air on being heated.

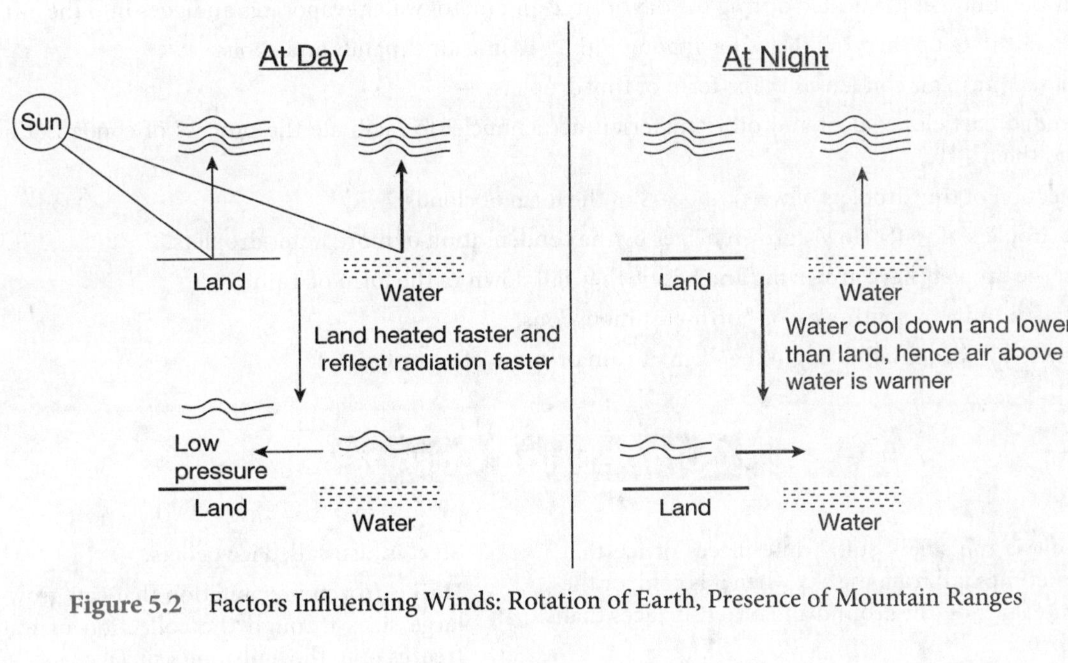

Figure 5.2 Factors Influencing Winds: Rotation of Earth, Presence of Mountain Ranges

Testing Room 1

Aim: To demonstrate that air currents are caused by the uneven heating of air.

Requirements: Beaker or wide-mouthed bottle, candle, matchstick, incense stick.

Procedure: Place a candle in a beaker or wide-mouthed bottle and lit it Now, light an incense stick and bring it to the edge of the mouth of the beaker or bottle. Observe the direction of flow of smoke. Now, keep the incense stick a little above the candle and note the direction of flow of smoke. Keep the incense stick in other regions above the beaker or bottle and again note the direction of smoke.

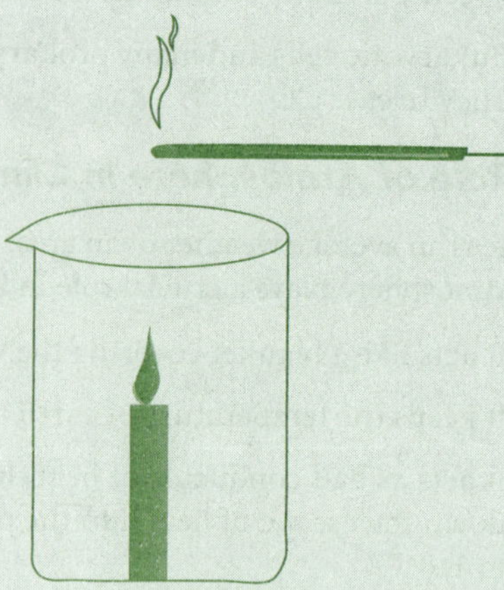

Observations and Conclusion:

- You will notice that the direction of flow of smoke is different when the incense stick is kept at the edge of the mouth of the beaker or bottle, a little above the candle and in different regions above the beaker or bottle.
- When the incense stick is kept at the edge of the mouth of the beaker or bottle, the smoke will flow towards the candle and then above.
- When the incense stick is kept a little above the candle, the direction of flow of smoke will be upwards.
- When the incense stick is placed at different regions above the beaker or bottle, the direction of flow of smoke will be towards the candle and then upwards.
- It is so because the patterns revealed by the smoke show us the directions in which the hot and cold air move.
- The air above the burning candle gets heated and therefore rises, creating a low pressure below.
- Therefore, air from adjacent cold areas moves towards this low-pressure zone.

Rain

- When water bodies are heated during the day, a large amount of water evaporates and goes into the air.
- The hot air rises up carrying the water vapour with it. Rising air expands and cools.
- Water vapour in air condenses in the form of tiny droplets.
- Suspended particles of dust and other materials act as nuclei to facilitate the process of condensation of water around them.
- A collection of tiny droplets of water appears in the form of clouds.
- These droplets of water slowly grown bigger by the condensation of more water droplets.
- When the droplets have grown big and heavy, they fall down in the form of 'rain'.
- Rainfall in India by south-west or north-east monsoons.
- Big and heavy drops fall down in the form of **rain** or **snow, sleet** or **hail**.

Competition Corner

- **Snow** is the small, soft, white pieces of ice that sometimes fall from the sky when it is cold, or the white layer on the ground and other surfaces that it forms.
- **Sleet** is also called ice pellets.
- **Hail** is frozen precipitation that can grow to very large sizes through the collection of water that freezes onto the hailstone's surface.

Testing Room 2

Aim: To collect information from newspapers and weather reports about rainfall patterns across the country and construct a rain gauge.

Requirements: Daily newspapers, graph, pencil, rubber, etc.

Procedure: Read the newspapers daily or alternatively listen to the weather reports on television. Record the relevant information about rainfall patterns across the country daily in your note book. Prepare the rain-gauge.

Observations and Conclusion: You will notice that rainfall patterns in different regions/cities/towns are not uniform throughout the year. Different regions or cities or towns get varied amount of rainfall in specific months of the year only. In large parts of India, rains are mostly brought by the south-west or north-east monsoons. You will also observe the month in which your city/town/village get the maximum rainfall. Similarly, you will observe the month in which your state or union territory get the maximum rainfall. Rain is not always accompanied by thunders and lightening. However, it is generally accompanied by thunders and lightening in monsoon months.

❖ INTEXT QUESTIONS

1. **What are renewable resources?**

   Ans: Resources which can replenish themselves by quick recycling are called renewable resources. For example, forests and wildlife.

2. **In which zone of atmosphere is ozone layer present?**

   Ans: Stratosphere

3. **What are clouds?**

   Ans: Clouds are collection of tiny particles of liquid or solid water occurring in the atmosphere above the Earth's surface.

4. **What is smog?**

   Ans: The suspended particles like unburnt carbon particles and hydrocarbons mix with smoke and fog in the atmosphere, especially in the cold weather to form smog which results in a lowered visibility.

Check Point 1

1. How is Venus and Mars atmosphere different from earth?
2. How does the atmosphere act as a blanket?
3. What causes wind?
4. Describe the role of atmosphere in climate control.

Pollution

Any undesirable change in physical, chemical or biological characteristics in the air, water and land which is harmful to the men directly or indirectly through animals, plants, industrial units or raw materials is called as pollution. Pollution is manmade. But it can also be natural.

Pollutants

Any material or act of man, or nature which leads to pollution is called as pollutants. The pollution is usually brought about by the addition to the environment of waste products of human activity. When the waste products are not efficiently assimilated, decomposed or otherwise removed by natural, biological and physical processes (recycling) and the system is unable to utilize them properly, so that the balance of the system breaks down. Therefore, such type of pollutants can stimulate or inhibit the biological reactions or change in their capacity. Therefore, changes also take place in the ecosystem. The amount, number and type of pollutants are increasing with the growth of the population. Pollutants can be divided into primary and secondary pollutants, same has been discussed in Table 5.2.

Table 5.2 Difference Between Primary and Secondary Pollutants

Primary pollutants	Secondary pollutants
Pollutants which persist in the environment in the form it is produced.	Pollutant formed from a primary one through change or reaction. $(NO)_x$ and hydrocarbons react photochemically to produce pan (peroxyacetyl nitrate) and O_3.
These include particulate matter, CO, CO_2, SO_2, $(NO)_x$ and hydrocarbons	Photochemical smog, O_3 and peroxy acetyl nitrate are secondary pollutants.
These are less toxic.	These are more toxic than the primary pollutants and this phenomenon is called synergism.

Air Pollution

Air pollution is caused due to the addition of the unwanted substances or gases. The atmospheric pollution is mainly caused by the activities of man and concentrated to the inhabited and the industrial complexes in cities. There are two main categories of air pollutants.

- **Gaseous:** The gaseous materials include various gases and vapours of volatile substances or the compound with a boiling point below 200ºC.
- **Particulate:** Dust particles, carbon particles, particles of other metals, etc.

Major air Pollutants and Their Effects

- **Carbon monoxide (CO) :** This is the main air pollutant. Carbon monoxide is highly toxic and it is colourless and odourless in nature. It combines with hemoglobin of the blood and blocks the transportation of oxygen. Thus, it impairs respiration and it causes death.
- **Unburnt hydrocarbons:** Out of them 3, 4 – benzopyrene is the main pollutant. This causes cancer in lungs.
- **Ethylene:** The falling of leaves without particular reason, falling buds, etc., effects are seen in plants are due to ethylene.
- **Oxides of nitrogen:** These oxides of nitrogen form photochemical smog in the atmosphere and release ozone. Ozone causes harm to mucilaginous membrane. The oxide pollutants of nitrogen are nitric oxide (NO), and nitrogen di oxide (NO_2). These oxides and ozone are very harmful for the plants.

  The entry of these pollutants causes various diseases in animals like respiratory trouble such as emphysema, bronchitis, swelling of lungs and lung cancer, etc.
- **Smoke:** Many constituents are present in smoke such as Sulphur dioxide (SO_2), Sulphur trioxide (SO_3), Sulphuric acid (H_2SO_4), Ozone (O_3), Carbon dioxide (CO_2), PAN (peroxyacetyl nitrate), Arsenic and Fluoride etc. The distribution area of lichen and mosses are the indicators of SO_2 pollution because lichen and mosses cannot grow in the industrial regions or the regions containing SO_2 pollutants. The higher concentration of ozone produces harmful effects. Ozone layer absorbs UV rays which are harmful for the living beings.
- **Aerosol:** The aerosol like CFC (Chorofluorocarbon) released into the atmosphere from the refrigerators, air conditioners and jet planes, deplete or reduce the ozone layer. This thin layer of ozone is also known as ozone hole results in the increase in temperature of the earth.

Secondary Effect of Air Pollution

Secondary effects of Air pollution are discussed below.

Greenhouse Effect

Usually, carbon dioxide is not considered as pollutant, but its higher concentration forms the thick layer above the earth surface which checks the radiation of the heat from the earth surface. Because of this the temperature of the earth surface increases. This is called as 'greenhouse effect' (as shown in Fig. 5.3).

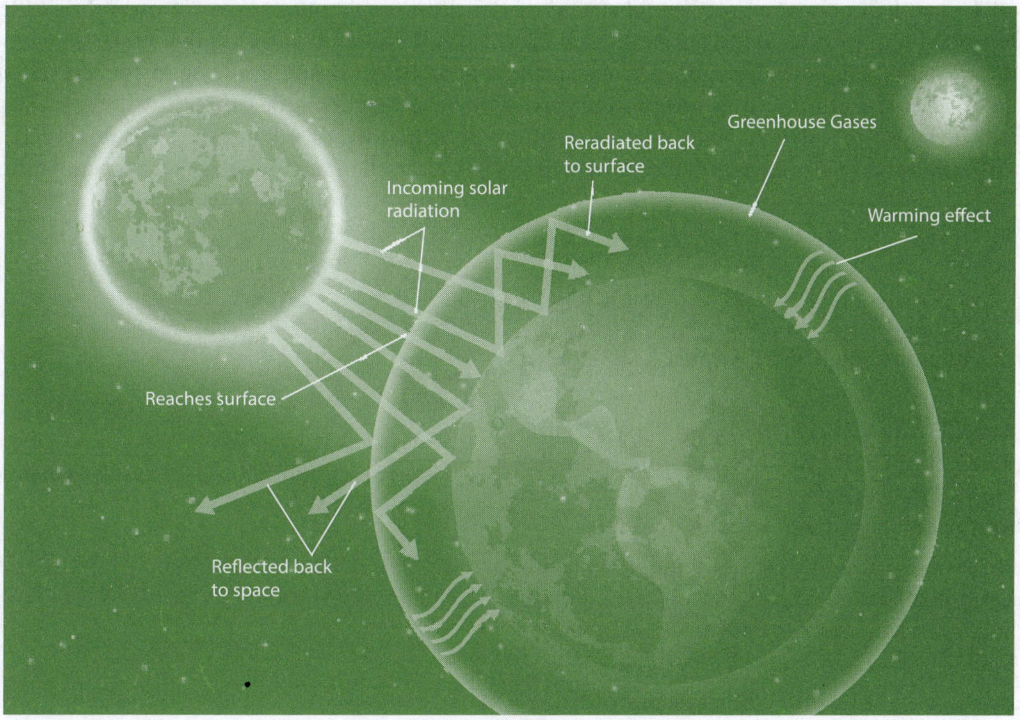

Figure 5.3 Greenhouse Effect

The various greenhouse gases are CO_2 (Warming effect 60%), CH_4 (warming effect 20%), chlorofluorocarbon or CFCs (14%) and nitrous oxide (N_2O 6%). Even 2–3° C rise in temperature will lead to melting of glaciers and ice caps of polar regions and consequently causes floods in rivers, rise in sea level and changes in cycle of rain. Islands may be emerged in sea water.

Global Warming

Global warming is the increase in average global temperature due to increase in amount of GHGs in earth's atmosphere.

Consequences of global warming:

- **Increase in the sea level:** Global warming will melt polar ice caps. If all the ice on the earth will melt water would be added to surface of all oceans. Thus, low lying coastal cities like Shanghai, Kolkata, Bangkok, Dhaka, Venice, etc., will be inundated.
- **Increase in global temperature:** If present input of GHGs will be continued, the earth's global
- temperature will rise.
- **Effect on agriculture:** Grain production will be reduced. India's annual monsoon rains may even cease together. One third of global forest might be swept away. Deserts are likely to increase chances of hurricanes, cyclones and floods will be more.
- **Increased temperature and humidity** caused by global warming will lead to spread of diseases like malaria, filariasis, etc., due to spread of vectors. Incidences of respiratory and skin diseases are likely to increase.

Testing Room 3

Aim: To study about various greenhouse gases and the consequences of global warming.

Requirements: Daily newspapers, books and periodicals.

Procedure: Read the newspapers, books and periodicals daily and alternatively listen to news on television. Record relevant information about various greenhouse gases and also about consequences of global warming.

Observations and Conclusion: You would notice that various greenhouse gases are carbon dioxide, methane, chlorofluorocarbons, nitrous oxide, ozone (present in troposphere) and water vapors. Of these, carbon dioxide alone contributes 60% to global warming. Consequences of global warming. Increase in concentration of carbon dioxide and other greenhouse gases leads to increase of environmental temperature. It will make the polar ice to melt resulting in rise in sea level. Thus, coastal regions will be flooded or might even get submerged. Increase in temperature of the earth due to greenhouse effect will also result in changes in weather and precipitation patterns.

Acid Rain

- The term was coined by **Robert August** (1872). pH of normal rain is 5.6 – 6.5.
- The most acidic rain has occurred over West Virginia USA with a pH of 1.5. Acids from atmosphere are deposited over earth in two forms, wet and dry. **Wet deposition** occurs through rain, snow and fog.
- Dry deposition is settling down of windblown acidic gases and particles over trees, various articles and soil. About 50% of acidity is passed to earth as dry deposition.

Keystone

Acid rain is rainfall and other forms of precipitation with a pH of less than 5.

$$2SO_2 + O_2 \rightarrow 2SO_3 ; SO_3 + H_2O \rightarrow H_2SO_4$$
$$2NO + [O] \rightarrow N_2O_5 ; N_2O_5 + H_2O \rightarrow 2HNO_3$$

- Rainfall will wash it down from trees and other articles. Acid rain is caused by large scale emission of acidic gases into the atmosphere from thermal power plants, industries and automobiles (as shown in Fig. 5.4)
- The common ones are sulphur dioxide, nitrogen oxides $(NO)_x$, volatile organic carbons (VOCs) and hydrogen chloride.
- $(NO)_x$ are also produced in atmosphere through lightning.
- Sulphur dioxide and nitrogen oxides are changed in the atmosphere into sulphuric acid and nitric acid by combining with oxygen and water.

Figure 5.4 Acid Rain Formation

Effect of Acid Rain

- Acid rain damages plants by direct effect on foliage and growing points (e.g., chlorosis, necrosis, defoliation, dieback.)
- It causes leaching of essential minerals of soil. Toxic minerals left in the soil further kill the plants.
- 50% of natural forests have been destroyed by acid rain in Germany, Sweden, north east, USA, Romania, Poland, etc.
- Acid rain has also ruined fresh water reservoirs of most industrialized countries.
- Acidity dissolves toxic metals like Hg, Pb, Zn, Al. Both acidity and toxic metals kill all types of aquatic life except some algae and fungi.
- Acid rain corrodes metals, marble, painted surfaces, slate, stone, etc. The phenomenon is called **stone leprosy.**

Ozone Depletion

- Between 20 and 26 km above the sea level it occurs ozone layer and the part of atmosphere containing it is called ozonosphere (Stratosphere).
- This layer is established due to an equilibrium between photo dissociation of ozone by UV – radiations and regeneration of ozone.
- The thickness of this ozonosphere averages 5 km.
- The ozone layer acts as a shield and absorbs the harmful UV–radiations of the sunlight so protect the earth's biota from the harmful effects of strong UV–radiations. So, this layer is very important for the survival and existence of life on earth.

Causes of Thinning of Ozone Layer: The decline in spring layer thickness is called ozone hole. Ozone hole is largest over Antarctica and was just short of 27 million square km during September 2003.

Main chemicals responsible for destruction of ozone layer is chlorofluorocarbons (CFCs), halogens (used in fire extinguishers) methane and nitrous oxide. Out of these, most damaging is the effect of CFCs which are a group of synthetic chemicals and are used as coolants in refrigerators and air conditioners; as cleaning solvents, propellants and sterilant, etc. These CFCs produce "active chlorine" (Cl and ClO' radicals) in the presence of UV radiations. These active chlorine radicals catalytically destroy ozone and convert it into oxygen.

$$CFCI_3 \xrightarrow{UV-C} CFCI_2 + CI$$
$$CFCL_2 \xrightarrow{UV-C} CFCL + CI$$
$$CI + O_2 \rightarrow CIO + O_2CIO + O_2 \rightarrow CI + 2O_2$$

Nitrous oxide: It is produced by industrial processes, forest fires, solid waste disposal, spraying of insecticides and pesticides, etc. Methane and nitrous oxide also cause ozone destruction.

Effects of Ozone Depletion: The thinning of ozone layer results in an increase in the UV radiations (in the range of 290 – 320 nm) reaching the earth's surface (as shown in Fig. 5.5). It is estimated that a 5 per cent loss of ozone results in a 10 per cent increase in UV radiations.

These UV radiations:

- Increase incidences of cataract and skin cancer.
- Decrease the functioning of immune system due to killing of melanin – producing cells of the skin.
- inhibit photosynthesis in most of phytoplankton so adversely affect the food chains of aquatic ecosystems.
- Damage nucleic acids of the living organisms.

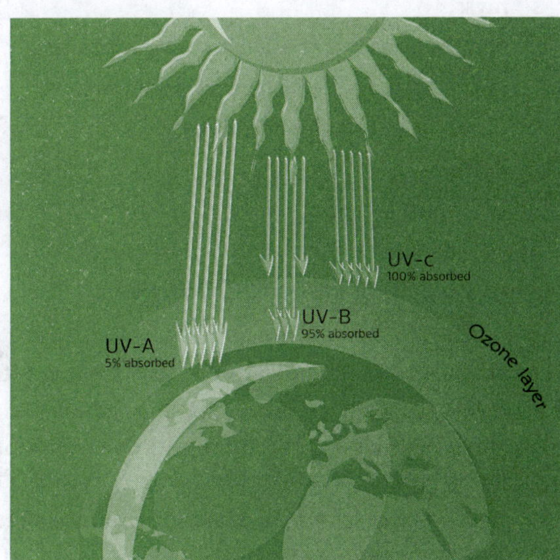

Figure 5.5 Ultraviolet Radiation

Measures to Control Air Pollution: Barium compounds should be mixed with petrol which reduce the smoke.

It is also very essential to check the quality of gases released from the factories. Industries should not be established at one place. The smoke should be released into the atmosphere after filtration and purification (by cyclone collector or electrostatic precipitators).

Testing Room 4

Aim: To study about ozone depleting substances and ozone hole. How the change in size of ozone hole would affect life on earth?

Requirements: Daily newspapers, books and periodicals.

Procedure: Read the newspapers, books and periodicals daily or alternatively listen to special news programmes on television. Record relevant information about ozone shield in the atmosphere, ozone depleting substances (ODS) and about changes in the size of ozone hole over the years and its effect on life on earth.

Observations and Conclusion: You will notice that high concentration of ozone about 18-50 km above in the stratosphere forms an ozone shield. It absorbs harmful UV radiations of the sun and prevent them from reaching the surface of the earth.

$$O_2 + O^- \xrightleftharpoons{\text{UV radiations}} O_3$$

Ozone is being depleted by air pollutants produced due to human activities. The chemicals that deplete ozone layer are called ozone depleting substances (ODS). Chlorofluorocarbons (CFCs) are mainly responsible for ozone depletion. Other ozone depleting substances include nitrogen oxides and hydrocarbons. Continuous depletion of ozone layer by ozone depleting substances has decreased the thickness of ozone layer at certain regions. Such regions are called Ozone holes. Ozone hole was first discovered over Antarctica.

❖ INTEXT QUESTIONS

5. **How is ozone layer useful to us?**

   Ans: Ozone is present in the upper layers of the atmosphere (stratosphere). Before reaching the Earth, the sunrays pass through the stratosphere. The ozone layer present there absorbs the harmful UV rays present in the sunrays and prevent them from reaching the Earth. Thus, it protects the entire planet from disastrous effects of UV rays.

6. **Name the major industrial air pollutants.**

   Ans: The major industrial air pollutants are:
   - SO_2, CO_2, oxides of nitrogen
   - H_2
   - Fumes of acids
   - Dust
   - Particles of unburnt hydrocarbons
   - Lead

7. **What is photochemical smog and what are its effects?**

   Ans: Oxides of nitrogen combine chemically in sunlight and produce hydrocarbons, peroxyacetal nitrate (PAN), and ozone which are commonly known as photochemical smog. This is very harmful and makes eyes watery, affects the growth of plants by checking the rate of photosynthesis and increases the rate of transpiration.

8. **Name the gases which cause greenhouse effect.**

   Ans: Greenhouse effect is caused by carbon dioxide, chlorofluorocarbons (CFCs), nitrogen oxide and methane.

Check Point 2

5. Give any two examples of primary pollutant.
6. State the harmful effects of ultraviolet rays.
7. Define stone leprosy.
8. Write down any two effect of ozone depletion.

Water

It is a renewable resource which is essential for sustenance of life. It covers 3/4th of the earth's surface. Of the total water present in hydrosphere 97% is present in oceans which is not utilizable by living beings. Only 3% water is fresh water. Among this 3%, 02.0% in Ice caps, 0.68% in Ground Water, 0.009% in Freshwater lakes, 0.009% in Salt lakes and 0.0019% in Atmosphere is present.

Types of Water Resources

Water is one of the most abundant resource on this planet earth, they can be of following types:

Freshwater Resource: It consists of ponds, lakes, large rivers. it can be recycled. It is essential for life on earth as well as for survival. It can be obtained by three different types of natural resources.

- **Rainwater:** India receives 3 trillion m3 of water from rainfall or precipitation. Its intensity is different in different zones, on this basis zones are classified as :
  - **Wet zone:** With very high rainfall
  - **Intermediate zone:** With heavy rainfall
  - **Semi-arid zone:** With moderate rainfall
  - **Arid zone:** With low rainfall.
- **Surface water:** There are major river systems with plenty of lakes and ponds, etc.
- **Ground water:** It is the water which percolate into the ground. There is a certain level below the soil surface where the rocks are saturated with water and this level is known as the zone of saturation.

The upper level of the zone of saturation is called the water table. However, **the vertical distance from the surface of a region to the water table is called the water level.**

Saltwater Resource: In consists of oceans, seas, etc. It cannot be used by living beings for drinking.

Role of Water or Hydrosphere

- Water is the main constituent of protoplasm.
- It is the universal solvent. Through which mineral salts are transported from one part of the plant to the other.
- Various metabolic reactions take place in the medium containing water.
- It acts as a reactant in numerous metabolic reactions.
- During photosynthesis, water releases oxygen.
- Turgidity of the growing cells is maintained with water.
- Various movements of plant organs like movements in sensitive plant (touch-me-not) are controlled by water.
- The growth of the cells during elongation phase mainly depends upon absorption of water.

- Metabolic end product of respiration is water.
- It acts as a temperature buffer as its specific heat is highest (only exception - liquid ammonia).
- It shows the properties of cohesion and adhesion which account for the capillary action of water.

Testing Room 5

Aim: To study various water-harvesting techniques being employed by municipal corporations to improve the availability of water for use.

Requirements: Daily newspapers, books and periodicals.

Procedure: Read the newspapers, books and periodicals daily. Record relevant information regarding water-harvesting and its techniques being employed by various municipal corporations in our country to improve the availability of water for use.

Observations and conclusion: Water-harvesting essentially includes collection and storage of rain water and unused water going waste from roofs or from a surface catchment for future use. The water is generally stored in rain water tanks or reservoirs or directed into mechanisms which recharge ground water. Traditionally, rain water harvesting has been practiced in arid and semiarid areas or in other areas where water table is very low. There are many-fold reasons of rain water harvesting in urban areas. These include: promotion of water supply for the city requirement, increasing soil moisture level for urban greenery, increasing ground water table through artificial recharge, mitigating urban flooding and improving the quality of ground water.

Water Pollution

The water pollution is caused by the addition of organic and inorganic chemicals as well as the biological materials which change the physical and chemical properties of water. This harmful process is called as water pollution. The water pollution is caused by many sources such as sewage matter, industrial wastage, agricultural wastage, domestic wastage, hot water of thermal plants and nuclear reactors etc. Water pollution can be caused by the following man-made sources:

Household Detergents

The household detergents include the compounds of phosphate, nitrate, ammonium and alkylbenzene sulphonate, etc. harmful substances which are gathered in water. Alkyl benzene sulphonate (ABS) is not degradable, so that its concentration increases which is harmful for aquatic life.

Control measures: For the control of this pollution lime, ferric chloride, etc., are used to precipitate the phosphate. Zirconium is considered best for this purpose.

Sewage

- Sewage contains highest number of organic materials and biological materials.
- These organic materials increase the number of decomposers like bacteria and fungus.
- The acceleration of microbial activity increases the BOD of water.
- BOD (Biological Oxygen Demand) is very less in pure water.
- The higher BOD is the indication of water pollution, and the water of polluted reservoir cannot be utilized and produces a very bad smell spreading around the locality.
- The infection or disease also takes place.
- Daphnia and some fishes are sensitive to water pollution and show the intensity of water pollution.

Control measures:

- To control the water pollution of sewage water it should be left into reservoir after the primary and secondary treatment.

- The big particles are mainly separated in primary treatment through floatation and sedimentation.
- Microorganisms are used for secondary treatment such as oxidation chamber or activated sludge process.
- Oxidation chamber is a shallow reservoir in which the sewage is stored.
- Algae and bacteria grow very well because of the higher amount of organic materials in it
- Bacteria decomposes the organic materials and produce CO_2 which is utilized by the algae in
- photosynthesis.
- Oxygen released by photosynthesis protects the water pollution. Therefore oxidation pond is the good example of symbiosis in between algae and bacteria.
- The infectious bacteria are destroyed during the activity (reactions) in the oxidation pond. So that the simple substances are left after decomposition of organic matter.

Industrial Wastes

The wastes of industries are discharged into the running water, rivers and canals, Industrial wastes mainly contain inert suspended particles such as dust, coal, toxins like acid, base, phenols, cyanides, mercury, zinc, etc., inorganic materials like ferrous salts, sulphides, oils and other residues of organic material and hot water. The water polluted by mercury, lead etc. causes disorganization of nervous system. It means it produces insanity.

Keystone

The Minamata disease caused in Japan by eating of mercury polluted fishes. So many people died because of this disease.

Control measures: The industrial wastes and toxic components should be made pure before releasing into rivers, lakes, ponds or sea. So that the water pollution of industrial effluents can be controlled by suitable treatment to remove the pollutants.

Bioaccumulation of pesticides: Pesticides like DDT are poisonous chemicals sprayed on crops to protect them from pests and diseases. This increase in concentration of harmful non-biodegradable chemical substances in the body of living organisms at each trophic level of a food chain is called biological magnification.

Eutrophication: The discharge of sewage water and detergents in water bodies promotes excessive growth of phytoplankton (minute aquatic algae). This excessive growth causes reduction in oxygen level of water. The excessive growth of phytoplankton brings about a reduction in dissolved oxygen which affects other aquatic organisms. Consequently, potential sources of food are highly reduced.

❖ INTEXT QUESTIONS

9. State two factors, which are responsible for polluting water.

Ans: Municipal sewage and discharge from industries are responsible for polluting water.

10. Name two freshwater resources, which provide freshwater for human use.

Ans: The two freshwater resources, which provide fresh water for human use are:

(i) Groundwater

(ii) Surface water (ponds, lakes, streams, etc.)

11. What is hydrosphere?

Ans: The water available on the earth's surface as well as underground water comprise together as hydrosphere. Water covers 75% of the Earth's surface.

Check Point 3

9. Why do organism need water?

10. What is the major source of fresh water?

11. What is water table?

Soil

Lithosphere is the main life supporting system. Top layer of earth is called soil. It is the main natural resource essential for survival and development.

Structure and Formation of Soil

Soil is formed due to interaction between weathering of rocks, rain, wind, temperature (physical components) and plants, animals and microbes (biological components). It is formed by combined action of climatic factors such as temperature, rainfall, light, etc., and biotic factors such as plants and microbes on earth crust.

Constituents of Soil

Soil contains:

- Inorganic constituents of parent rocks.
- Organic products of living organisms.
- Living organisms including microorganisms.
- Air in the pores.

There are four important components of soil. They are

- Mineral matter 50 – 60%
- Organic matter 10% (living organisms and decomposed matter)
- Soil water 25 – 35 %
- Soil air 15 – 25 %

Types of Soil

On the basis of its nature and composition, soil is mainly of six types:

- **Alluvial Soil:** It is rich in loam and clay.
- **Black Soil:** It has clay.
- **Red Soil:** It is sandy to loam.
- **Mountain Soil:** It is a stony and sandy soil.
- **Desert Soil:** It is sandy.
- **Laterite Soil:** It has porous clay.

Outer most layer of earth is called **crust**. Many types of minerals are found in crust. They provide many types of nutrients to living beings.

Factors Responsible for Formation of Soil

Formation of soil is governed by several factors, such as:

Sun

Rocks get expanded due to heat produced by sun during daytime. At night, the rocks cool down and contract. Due to this unequal expansion and contraction of rocks, cracks in rocks appear. This leads to formation of smaller pieces of rocks.

Water

Due to continuous movement of rain and fast flowing river water, rock pieces collide and break down in still finer particles due to their abrasive effect.

Wind

Wind has abrasive effect on rocks. Finer rock particles are blown away and get deposited at other distant places.

Living Organisms

The step of weathering is brought about by plants and animals. Lichens are first to appear on bare rocks. They produce acids which corrode the rocky surface to produce fine particles. Now, plants like mosses can appear on it. In such type of soil, certain microbes, algae, insects and worms appear and die. Organic matter gets accumulated. Roots of some plants grow into the cervices of rocks.

Soil Pollution

- Soil is also polluted through the polluted water and air.
- These pollutants are mixed into the soil through the rainy water. Such as H_2SO_4 acid is formed by mixing of SO_2 with rainy water in the air.
- The fertilizers are used to increase yield of the crops.
- Various types of pesticides and weedicides etc. are sprayed over the crops. All these mixed with soil to produce harmful effects.
- The growth of plants inhibited or reduced due to this type of pollution and sometimes death also takes place. Excluding to this soil pollution is also caused by the disposal of house hold detergents, sewage, flowing oils, radioactive substances and hot water etc.
- The main substances of pesticides in soil pollutants are D.D.T. and weedicides 2, 4 – D (2, 4 di–chlorophenoxy acetic acid) 2, 4, 5–T (2, 4, 5, tri–chlorophenoxy acetic acid).

Control Measures

- Soil pollution can be controlled through biological degradation of waste materials.
- The various carbonic materials are of agricultural waste, cattle dung etc. Which can be minimized by the use of biogas plants which can produce energy also.
- inspite all measures pesticides and weedicides should be used in limited quantity only when they are required.
- **Bhopal Gas Tragedy** is the best example of human hazard which took the life of many persons the tank of methyl isocyanate burst during the manufacturing of **Savin insecticide** on **3 December 1984.**

Soil Erosion

Fertility of soil depends on Presence of organic matter (humus) and nutrients, Capacity of soil to retain water and air. A loamy soil is the best - suited for plant growth. The fertility of soil is threatened due to various activities of humans. The main threat to the fertility of soil is from soil erosion, which is the loss of soil due to wind or water flow.

Methods of Preventing Soil Erosion

Prevention of soil erosion can be brought about by controlling the factors which cause soil erosion. The methods would thus be as follows:

- Deforestation should be stopped, rather, trees should be planted (afforestation).
- Afforestation should be undertaken not only in areas already cut, but additional areas should be brought under plantation.
- To reduce the effect of strong wind in the fields, the boundaries of the fields should be planted with trees in two or three rows.
- To maintain the soil in its natural condition, it is advisable to grow different crops.

- Crop rotation helps to maintain the fertility of the soil. The water - holding capacity of the soil is also maintained by this method.
- Proper drainage and irrigation arrangements should be made in the fields.
- On the sloping areas in hills, strip cropping (means the planting of crops in rows or strips to check flow of water). should be practiced, thereby reducing the steepness of the slopes and checking soil erosion.

Testing Room 6

Aim: To demonstrate the role of plants in checking soil erosion.

Requirements: Two identical trays, beakers, soil, water, mustard or green gram or paddy seedlings.

Procedure: Take two identical trays A and B and fill them with soil. Plant mustard or green gram or paddy seedlings in tray A and keep tray B as such. Water both the trays regularly for a few days. Now, tilt both the trays at an angle . Make sure that both the trays are tilted at the same angle. Pour equal quantity of water gently on both the trays in such a way that the water flows out of the trays from other end . Study the amount of soil that has been carried out of the trays with water. Now, pour equal quantities of water on both the trays from a height. The water must be 3-4 times the amount that had been poured earlier. Study the amount of soil that is carried out of the trays with water.

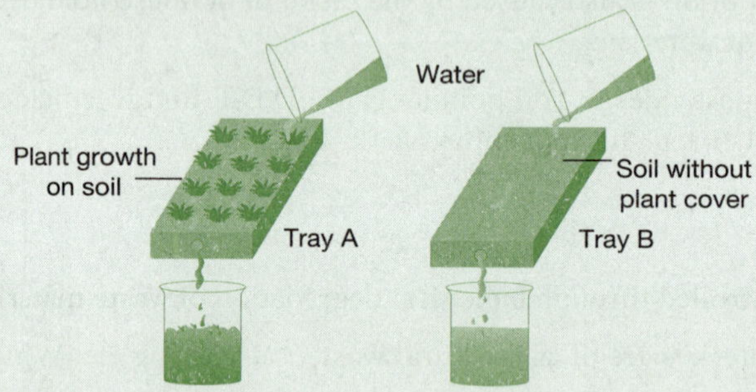

Observations and Conclusion: You will notice that in the first set of experiment, more soil will be carried out of tray B than out of tray A. In second set of experiment, when more water is poured on the trays and that too from a height, the flowing water further loosen the soil. More soil will be loosened in tray B without plants and will be carried out with water than from tray A having plants. It is so because in tray A roots of plant seedlings play important role in preventing soil erosion by binding the soil.

❖ INTEXT QUESTIONS

12. Why is replenishment of soil essential? Describe two natural ways of soil replenishment.

Ans: Some nutrients of the soil get depleted by growing the same crop year after year. So, replenishment of the soil is essential to keep it fit for further cultivation.

Two natural ways of soil replenishment are crop rotation and leaving the agricultural land uncultivated for one or two seasons so as to allow it to regain its fertility.

13. Give any two effects of soil erosion.

Ans: Two effects of soil erosion are:

(i) Desertification

(ii) Reduction in soil futility

14. In which regions is soil erosion very difficult to revert?

Ans: The regions with bare vegetation, mountains and hilly regions, soil erosion is very difficult to reverse.

Check Point 4

12. How is soil formed?

13. What is Soil erosion?

14. What are method of preventing soil erosion?

Biogeochemical Cycles

These are the cyclic pathways (Fig 5.6) through which chemical elements move from environment to organisms and back to the environment. The earth and its environment, with reference to these elements, are considered as closed system and there is no inflow of such elements from outside the earth and their amount is limited.

Two types of biogeochemical cycles are:

- Gaseous cycles
- Sedimentary cycles

Difference between gaseous and sedimentary cycles, is discussed in Table 5.3

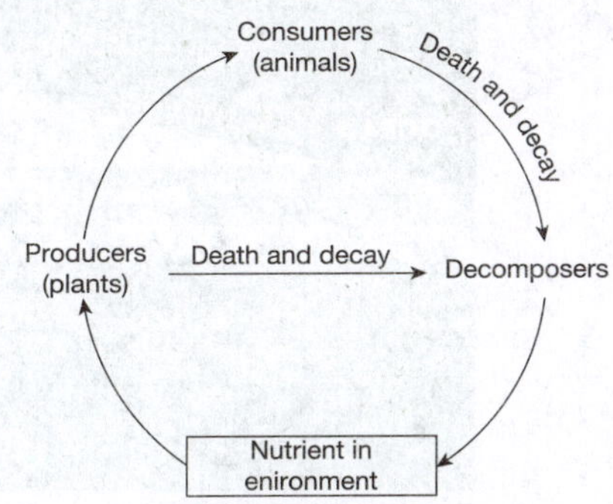

Cycling of Nutrients

Figure 5.6 Cycling of Nutrients

Table 5.3 Differences between gaseous and sedimentary cycles

Characters	Gaseous cycles	Sedimentary cycles
Reservoir pool	Air or water	Rocks
Speed	Faster	Slower
Examples	Carbon, nitrogen and oxygen cycles	Calcium, phosphorous and sulphur cycles.

Water Cycle

Water is the most abundant (60 – 90 %) component of protoplasm. It acts as a habitat for hydrophytes and many aquatic animals, a good ionizer, good solvent, temperature, buffer and perform transportation of materials. It also helps in digestion of organic compounds and in photosynthesis of plants.

Types of Water Cycles

- **Global Water Cycle:** It does not involve living organisms and involves the interchange of water between the earth's surface and the atmosphere via the processes of precipitation and evaporation (as shown in Fig. 5.7) Ocean is the biggest store house of water. Evaporation involves the conversion of liquid and solid forms of water into vapours and later form the clouds. Precipitation involves the rainfall, hail, snow, etc. Energy for global water cycle is provided by sunlight.
- **Biological Water Cycle:** It is the interchange of water between abiotic and biotic components of environment. the plants absorb water from water bodies and soil while loose most of the water by the process of transpiration, animals consume water from water bodies, or the food ingested, while release water via the processes of respiration and excretion.

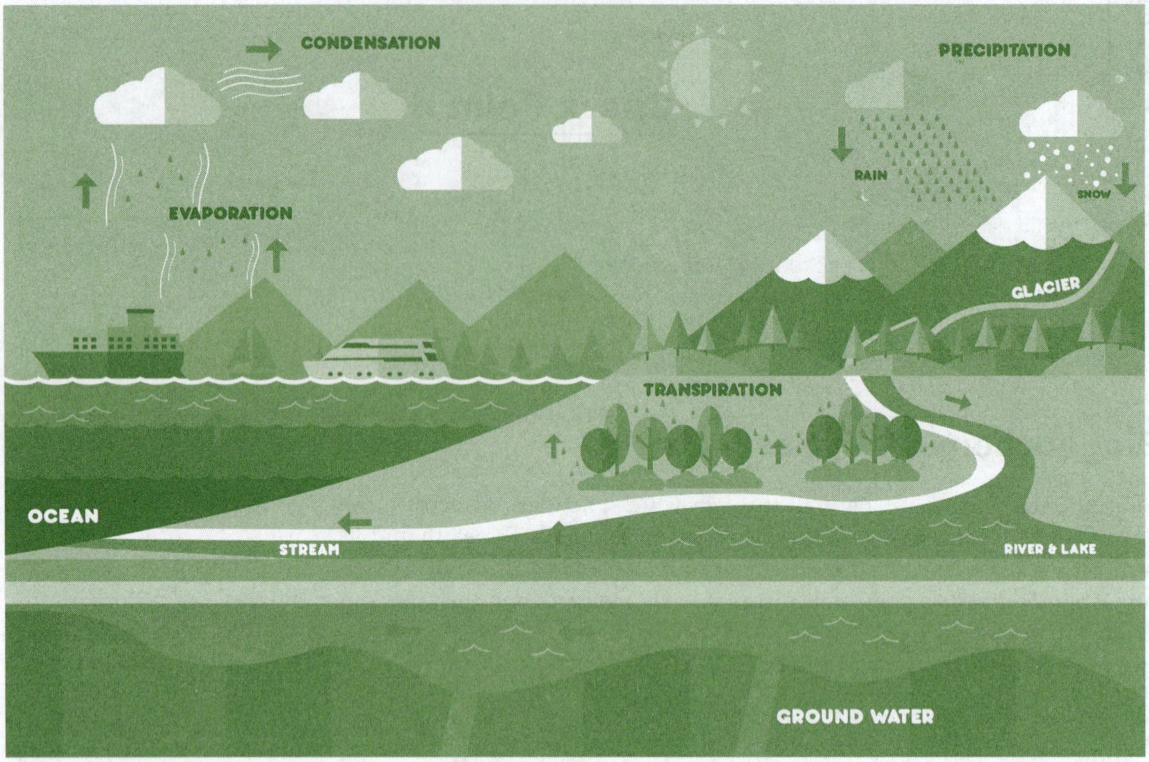

Figure 5.7 Water Cycle

Nitrogen Cycle

Nitrogen is an essential component of amino acids, proteins, enzymes and nucleic acids of the protoplasm. Reservoir pool of nitrogen is atmosphere which contains about 78.08% of nitrogen in gaseous state. But it cannot be used directly and is changed into nitrites and nitrates and then utilized (as shown in Fig. 5.8).

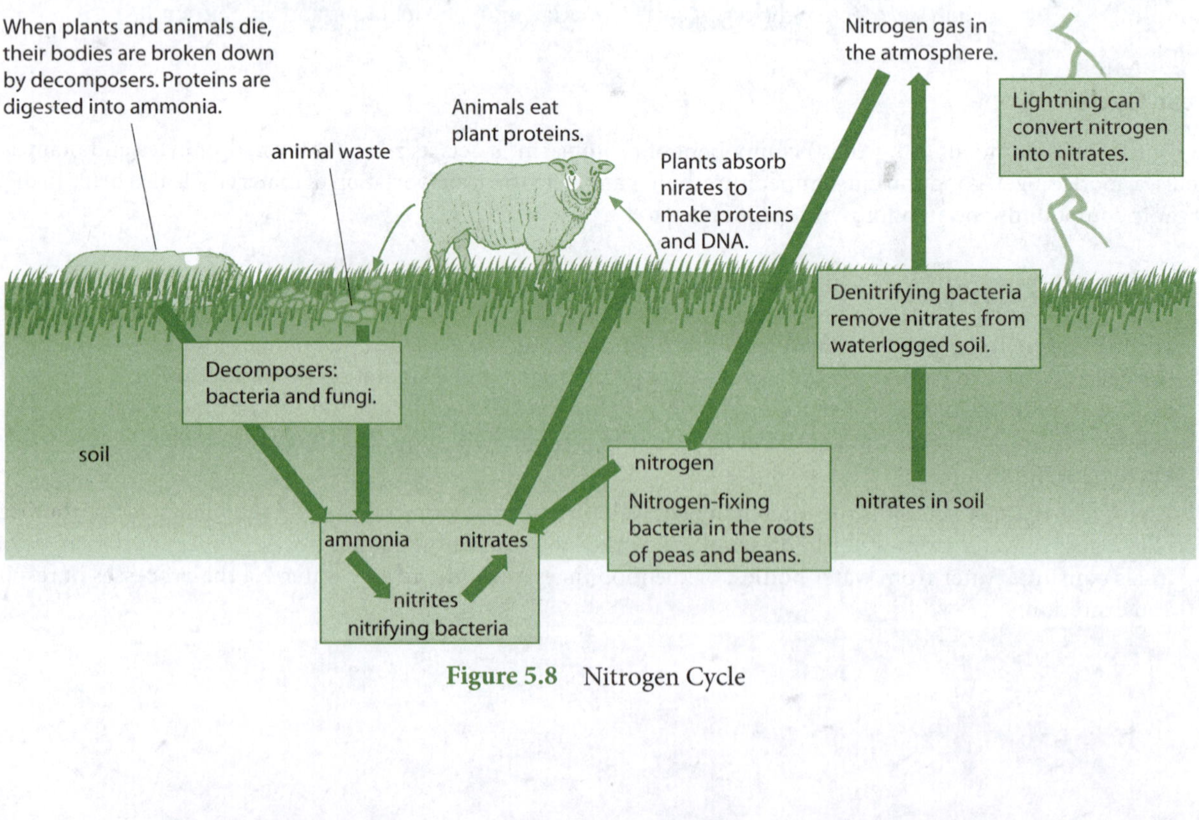

Figure 5.8 Nitrogen Cycle

Steps of Nitrogen Cycle

- **Nitrogen FIxation:** It involves the conversion of free diatomic nitrogen (N_2) into nitrites and nitrates.
- **Physical Nitrogen Fixation:** Atmospheric nitrogen fixation in the presence of photochemical and electrochemical reactions induced by thundering and lightening. Industrial nitrogen fixation in the industries at high temperature and high pressure.
- **Biological Nitrogen Fixation:** Biological nitrogen fixation occurs in the presence of certain living organisms such as:
- **Rhizobium** bacterium in the root nodules of legumes.
  - **Azotobacter** bacterium in the soil.
  - **Anabaena** (blue green algae) in water in the paddy fields.
  - **Azospirillum** bacterium in loose association with the roots of maize, sorghum, etc.
- **Ammonification:** It involves the decomposition of proteins of dead plants and animals to ammonia in the presence of ammonifying bacteria like *Bacillus ramosus.*
- **Nitrification:** It involves the oxidation of ammonia to nitrites (NO_2^-) and nitrates (NO_3^-) in the presence of nitrifying bacteria like *Nitrosomonas* (Ammonia to nitrite), *Nitrobacter* (Nitrite to nitrate), etc. Plants absorb the nitrites and nitrates from the soil through their roots and convert them into organic compounds (e.g., proteins) of protoplasm by the process called nitrogen assimilation.
- **Denitrification:** It involves reduction of ammonium compounds, nitrites and nitrates to molecular nitrogen in the presence of denitrifying bacteria like *Thiobacillus denitrificans.*

Carbon Cycle

Carbon is the basic component of all the organic compounds like carbohydrates, proteins, lipids, enzymes and nucleic acid of the protoplasm (as shown in Fig. 5.9). In atmosphere, it is present as carbon dioxide. It involves two types of processes, one involving CO_2 utilization and another involving CO_2 production. They are expressed as follows :

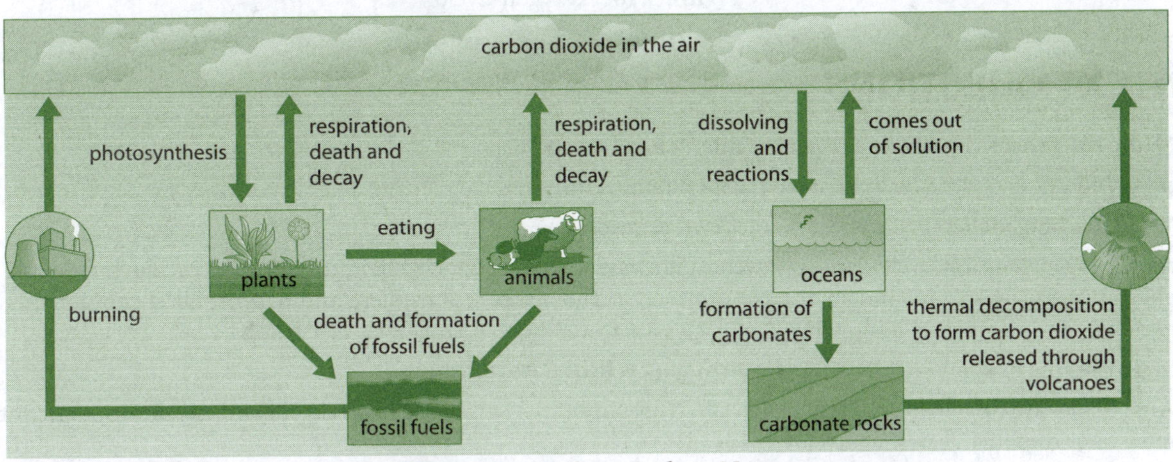

Figure 5.9 Carbon-Cycle in Nature

CO_2 Utilization

Carbon dioxide is utilized by the photosynthetic organisms like green plants, photosynthetic bacteria, diatoms and blue green algae in the process of photosynthesis, **It** occurs in the presence of chlorophyll and radiant energy of sunlight. Glucose synthesized in photosynthesis is used to synthesize other organic compounds.

CO_2 Production

- CO_2 is released during respiration of both producers and consumers.
- During decomposition of organic compounds of dead bodies.
- During burning of fossil fuels like wood, coal, petroleum, etc.
- Volcanic eruptions and hot springs.
- During weathering of rocks by acids produced by microorganisms and roots of higher plants.

Oxygen Cycle

Oxygen is present in water and forms 20% of air in atmosphere. All living beings need it for respiration. Oxygen content of atmosphere has remained constant for the last several million years. Most of O_2 is replenished by photosynthesis. During photosynthesis CO_2 is used by plants to form food along with release of oxygen (as shown in Fig 5.10). The oxides can be reduced both chemically and biologically to produce oxygen. Microbial oxidation can also occur due to burning of materials oxygen form carbon dioxide. When oxygen combines with nitrogen, it forms oxides of nitrogen, amino acids, proteins, etc.

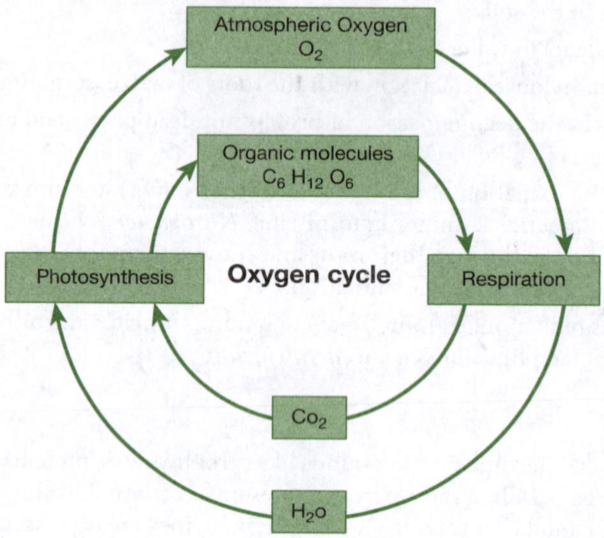

Figure 5.10 Oxygen Cycle

❖ INTEXT QUESTIONS

15. **Name the process by which oxygen is replenished in nature.**

    Ans: Oxygen is replenished in nature through photosynthesis.

16. **What are biogeochemical cycles? Names two examples.**

    Ans: Biogeochemical cycles are the cyclic pathways through which chemical substances move through biotic environment (biosphere) and abiotic environment (lithosphere, atmosphere and hydrosphere) components of the earth. A few examples of biogeochemical cycles are water cycle, nitrogen cycle, carbon cycle, oxygen cycle.

17. **State the role of symbiotic bacteria in nitrogen cycle of nature.**

    Ans: Plants are unable to take atmospheric nitrogen directly. Symbiotic bacteria convert the atmospheric nitrogen into water soluble nitrates, which are easily utilized by plants.

18. **State the process by which carbon enters in the living system.**

    Ans: Respiration is the process by which carbon enters in the living system in the form of carbon dioxide.

Check Point 5

15. Name two biologically important compounds that contain both oxygen and nitrogen.
16. What are two forms of oxygen found in the atmosphere?
17. Draw a flow chart of the following.

    (i) Carbon cycle **(ii)** Oxygen cycle **(iii)** Nitrogen cycle

STRUCTURAL OUTLINE

Type of natural resources

- Based on availability
  - In exhaustible
  - Exhaustible
    - Renewable
    - Non-renewable
- Based on origin
  - Biotic
  - Abiotic
- Based on Chemical nature
  - Inorganic
  - Organic
  - Mixed
- Based on Distribution
  - National
  - International

Natural resources

- Air
  - Atmosphere
    - Troposphere
    - Stratosphere
    - Mesosphere
    - Ionosphere
  - Role of atmosphere
    - Climate control
    - Movement of air
    - Wind
    - Rain
  - Air pollution
- Water
  - Types of water Resources
  - Role of water
  - Water pollution
- Soil
  - Soil erosion
  - Soil pollution
  - Factors of soil Formation types
  - Constituents of soil
  - Structure soil
- Biogeo-chemical cycles
  - Water cycle
  - Nitrogen cycle
  - Carbon cycle
  - Oxygen cycle

ABRIDGEMENT

Class 12th – Chapter 16: Environmental Issues

- Air pollution and its control
- Water pollution and its control
- Agrochemicals and their effects
- Solid waste management
- Radioactive waste management
- Greenhouse effect and climate change
- Ozone layer depletion
- Deforestation

EXEMPLIFICATION

Q1. Define weathering. Write the different means which cause weathering.

Ans: The process of breaking down of rocks into small, fine mineral particles is called weathering. The weathering may occur due to physical, chemical or biological means.

Q2. What are the harmful effects of air pollution?

Ans: It may cause respiratory problems like sneezing, allergy, asthma or bronchitis in some persons.

- It may cause acid rain which leads to deterioration of metals and other building material.
- It may cause global warming which leads to change in the climate of the Earth.
- Carbon monoxide may lead to many problems of respiratory system.
- Smog, which reduces the visibility as well as causes respiratory ailments.

Q3. What are the various causes of soil erosion?

Ans: Causes of soil erosion:

(i) Wind causes soil erosion by "carrying away the topsoil particles.

(ii) Rain causes soil erosion on unprotected topsoil by washing it down.

(iii) Improper farming or tilling and leaving the field fallow for long time causes soil erosion.

(iv) Frequent flooding of rivers causes soil erosion by removing the topsoil of the fields near the river banks.

(v) Deforestation also leads to soil erosion.

Q4. How can we prevent the loss of topsoil?

Ans: Loss of topsoil can be prevented by increasing the vegetational cover checking the falling of trees by preventing excessive grazing by animals.

Q5. Explain why root nodules are useful for the plants.

Ans: Root nodules contain the symbiotic bacteria, Rhizobium which convert/fix the atmospheric nitrogen into usable form i.e., nitrates 'Which are utilized by plants for the synthesis of amino acids and proteins.

Q6. Name two oxides formed by burning of fossil fuels, which are responsible for acid rain.

Ans: The oxides of nitrogen and sulphur:

(i) Sulphur dioxide and sulphur trioxide

(ii) Nitrous oxide and nitrogen dioxide

Q7. Name two gases which cause greenhouse effect.

Ans: (i) Carbon dioxide, (ii) Methane, (iii) Oxides of nitrogen

Q8. What are the three ways by which CO_2 is returned back into atmosphere?

Ans: The three ways by which CO_2 is returned back into atmosphere are:

1. By the decomposition of dead organic matter.
2. As the product of respiration by both plants and animals.
3. As the gaseous waste formed by the combustion of fuels like coal, wood, petrol and gaseous fuels.

Q9. Write three ways to prevent soil pollution.

- By judicious use of fertilizers and pesticides.
- By proper management of disposal of household waste.
- Intensive cropping, terrace farming should be practiced.

Q10. Explain the role of the sun in the formation of soil.

Ans: Sun plays an important role in the formation of soil. The rocks heat up and expand under the influence of solar radiations. At night the rocks cool down and contract. Continuous expansion and contraction and uneven heating of different parts of rock tends to break them into smaller pieces. These smaller pieces of rocks play an important role in the formation of soil.

KNOWLEDGE COMPENDIUM

1. How is our atmosphere different from the atmosphere on Venus and Mars?

Ans:
Our atmosphere is a mixture of many gases like nitrogen-oxygen, carbon dioxide, and water vapours. The atmosphere of Venus and Mars consists of carbon dioxide only. So there is no life on Venus and Mars.

2. How does the atmosphere act as a blanket?

Ans:
Air is a bad conductor of heat and our atmosphere contains air. The atmosphere acts as a protective blanket because it keeps the average temperature of the earth fairly steady during the day and even during the course of the whole year. The atmosphere prevents the sudden increase in temperature during the daylight hours and during the night, it slows down the escape of heat into outer space.

3. What causes wind?

Ans:
The energy of the sun is responsible for winds. Winds are caused due to unequal heating of atmospheric air. The air above the land gets heated and starts rising, at this time a low-pressure area is created and air over the sea moves in to this area of low pressure. The movement of air from one region to the other creates winds. Rotation of the earth, the presence of mountains ranges in the paths of winds also influence it.

4. How are clouds formed?

Ans:
When the water bodies are heated with Sun's radiation during the daytime, a large amount of water evaporates and goes into the environment. The air carrying water vapours also get heated. These hot water vapours rise up with hot air. As the air rises, it expands and cools. On cooling, the water vapours condense into tiny droplets. Dust or other suspended particles present in the air act as the 'nuclei for these droplets to form around. These droplets of water grow bigger by the condensation of more water droplets. An enormous collection of tiny droplets of water appears as clouds. When the droplets have grown big, they fall down in the form of rain.

5. List any three activities that you think would lead to air pollution.

Ans:
(i) Excessive use of fossil fuels like coal and petroleum produces oxides of nitrogen and sulpher which cause air pollution.
(ii) Forest fire, mining process, and excessive use of CFC cause air pollution.
(iii) Incomplete combustion of fuels forms unburnt carbon particles in the air. At the time of cold weather, water condenses and these particles combine with water to form smog which lowers visibility.

6. Why do organisms need water?

Ans:
Organisms need water to carry out the following activities:
(i) Photosynthesis uses water as a raw material. All cellular processes in all organisms take place in a water medium.
(ii) Water makes up 70% of the bodyweight of all living beings.
(iii) Water acts as a universal solvent and helps in transporting substances from one part of the body to other in a dissolved form.
(iv) It also helps in the digestion of food and absorption of nutrients in the blood.
(v) Water is also required by organisms for many of their activities such as drinking, cooking, washing, irrigation, production of hydel power, etc.
(vi) It helps in maintaining body temperature.

7. What is a major source of fresh water in the city/town/village where you live?

Ans:
The major source of fresh water in the city/town/village where we live is underground water and river, lakes, ponds are also the main sources of freshwater.

8. Do you know of any activity which may be polluting this water source?

Ans:
Sewage and industrial wastes are the major sources of pollution of river water.

9. How is soil formed?

Ans:
Soil is a mixture of small particles of rocks and humus. Temperature variation due to solar radiation, rainwater, winds, and living organisms influence the formation of soil.

i. The sun heats up rocks during daytime and they expand but at night rocks cool down and contract. This contraction is uneven and this leads to the formation of cracks in the rocks into smaller pieces.
ii. Flow of water through or over the rocks makes the cracks bigger. Falling/flowing water also has to erase the effect on the rocks. On freezing the water expands in rock cervices and breaks the rocks.
iii. Strong winds erode rocks and carry sand from one place to the other.
iv. Living organisms like lichens grow on the surface of rocks. They release substances that cause the rock surface to powder down and form a thin layer of soil.

10. What is soil erosion?

Ans:

The removal of the top layer of soil which is rich in humus and nutrients from its original position to another place with the help of certain factors like strong wind and fast running water, is called soil erosion.

11. What are the methods of preventing or reducing soil erosion?

Ans:

Soil erosion can be prevented or reduced by:
(i) Intense cropping and use of proper drainage canals.
(ii) Terracing on a slop field retards the flow of water and prevents soil erosion.
(iii) Planting trees and grasses.
(iv) Trees planted in lines around farmland reduce erosion.
(v) By avoiding overgrazing.

12. What are the different states in which water is found during the water cycle?

Ans:

All three states of water can be seen during the water cycle:
(i) Water vapours in the air which ultimately from clouds.
(ii) Rainwater that falls on earth and is available to us in water bodies or as underground water, dew, snow, sheet or hail.

13. Name two biologically important compounds that contain both oxygen and nitrogen.

Ans:

(i) Nucleic acids (DNA and RNA), (ii) Proteins.

14. List any three human activities which could lead to an increase in carbon dioxide content air.

Ans:

(i) Burning of fossil fuels leads to an increase in carbon dioxide.
(ii) Burning associated with agricultural practices.
(iii) Deforestation increases in CO_2 because trees absorb CO_2 and convert it into organic compounds by the process of photosynthesis.

15. What is the greenhouse effect?

Ans:

The greenhouse is a glass enclosure that is used for growing tropical plants in colder climates even in winters. The glass wall of the greenhouse allows sun rays to enter inside but heat developed inside is not allowed to go out. This makes greenhouse air warmer than the outside air and the phenomenon is called the greenhouse effect. An increase in gases like carbon dioxide in the atmosphere forms a layer around the earth that prevents the heat inside the atmosphere, and this leads to an increase the average temperature. This is called global warming. This is known as the greenhouse effect.

16. What are the two forms of oxygen found in the atmosphere?

Ans:

Molecular oxygen (O_2) and ozone (O_3).

17. Why is the atmosphere essential for life?

Ans:

The atmosphere is essential for life because:
(i) It keeps the average temperature of the earth.
(ii) It contains gases which are essential for life. Oxygen present in it is needed by living things to break down glucose molecules and get energy for their activities. Carbon dioxide in the atmosphere is used as raw material in photosynthesis.
(iii) It contains all gases that are essential for sustaining life on the earth.
(iv) Ozone layer of the atmosphere stop harmful UV radiation from the sun and prevent us from harmful effects.

18. Why is water essential for life?

Ans:

Water is essential for life because of the following reasons:
(i) Photosynthesis uses water as a raw material. All cellular processes in all organisms take place in a water medium.
(ii) Water makes up 70% of the bodyweight of all living beings.

(iii) Water acts as a universal solvent and helps in transporting substances from one part of the body to other in a dissolved form.
(iv) It also helps in the digestion of food and absorption of nutrients in the blood.
(v) Water is also required by organisms for many of their activities such as drinking, cooking, washing, irrigation, production of hydel power, etc.
(vi) It helps in maintaining body temperature.

19. How are living organisms dependent on the soil? Are organisms that live in water totally independent of soil as a resources?

Ans:

Living organisms are dependent on the soil in the following ways:

(i) Plants grow on the soil. All living organisms are dependent on plants directly or indirectly for their survival. Thus living organisms are dependent on the soil.
(ii) Number of insects, animals that build their home in the soil.
(iii) Soil provides essential nutrients to plants.
(iv) No, organisms that live in water are not totally independent of soil as a resource because many nutrients present in the soil flow in the water, which is necessary for these organisms. All water bodies have soil beds.

20. You have seen weather reports on television and in newspapers. How do you think we are able to predict the weather?

Ans:

We are able to predict the weather in the following ways:

(i) We have to obtain a detailed picture of present weather conditions in the region for which we wish to predict the weather.
(ii) Various instruments are used to record the reading viz. temperature, air, pressure, humidity, wind (speed and direction), and rainfall.
(iii) We also make visual observations like cloud cover and visibility.
(iv) All the information collected is sent to the meteorological department which prepares a weather report. This report is displayed on the maps and transmitted on television and radio and published in the newspapers.

21. We know that many human activities lead to the increasing levels of pollution of air, water bodies, and soil. Do you think that isolating these activities to specific and limited areas would help in reducing pollution?

Ans:

Yes, if the human activities are restricted and isolated to specific and limited areas would help in reducing pollution.

(i) If all the industries are established far from the residential areas, this can minimize airborne diseases.
(ii) All the sewage of a particular area is collected at one place and after proper treatment, it will be discharged into water bodies. This can prevent aquatic life to a little extent.
(iii) Wastewater from the industries must be treated before discharging in water bodies.
(iv) We should avoid the use of non-biodegradable substances like plastics, polythene.

22. Write a note on how forests influence the air, soil, and water resources?

Ans:

Forest is a large area covered thickly with trees and other plants such as shrubs and grasses. Forests are renewable natural resources. Forests influence the air, water, and soil resources in the following ways:

(i) Forest plants maintain the O_2 and CO_2 balance in the atmosphere.
(ii) They prevent the greenhouse effect.
(iii) Forest maintains the natural environment by influencing such factors as temperature, humidity, and precipitation.
(iv) Forests maintain the soil environment by affecting its composition, structure, chemical properties, water contents, etc.
(v) Roots of forests plants bind the soil and do not allow soil erosion by fast winds or fast-moving water. In this way, they help in maintaining the fertility of the soil. Many bacteria found in root nodules replenish the fertility of the soil.
(vi) Forest prevents flooding, landslides.
(vii) Forests regulate the biogeochemical cycles of water, carbon, nitrogen, oxygen, and other elements.

ASSESSMENT CORNER

LEVEL 1

Fixed Response Type

Multiple Choice Questions

1. A renewable source of energy is:
(A) petroleum (B) coal
(C) nuclear fuel (D) trees

2. Maximum air in which we breath is present at:
(A) troposphere (B) stratosphere
(C) ionosphere (D) mesosphere

3. Corrosion of statues and monuments occurs due to:
(A) Photochemical smog
(B) CO
(C) Acid rain
(D) Methane

4. Major source of mineral in soil is the
(A) parent rock from which soil is formed
(B) plants
(C) animals
(D) bacteria

5. Ozone layer is present in atmosphere in:
(A) troposphere (B) stratosphere
(C) mesosphere (D) thermosphere

6. Total earth's surface covered by water is
(A) 75% (B) 65%
(C) 85% (D) 51%

7. Plants and animals are known as:
(A) biotic resources (B) abiotic resources
(C) machines (D) none of these

8. Coal is an/a:
(A) exhaustible resource
(B) inexhaustible resource
(C) potential resource
(D) none of these

9. Ozonosphere occurs at height of:
(A) 8 – 10 km above poles
(B) 8 – 10 km above equator
(C) 20 – 26 km above the sea level
(D) 11 – 16 km above equator

10. Biosphere is made of –
(A) living beings and their remains
(B) living beings, lithosphere, hydrosphere and atmosphere
(C) living beings
(D) living beings, lithosphere and hydrosphere.

11. Which one of the following is renewable resource?
(A) Water (B) Metals
(C) Fossil fuel (D) All of these

12. CO_2 and O_2 balance in atmosphere is due to:
(A) photosynthesis (B) respiration
(C) leaf anatomy (D) photorespiration

13. Which gas is mainly responsible for the depletion of ozone layer?
(A) Oxygen (B) CFC
(C) Nitrogen dioxide (D) All of the above

14. Acid rain mainly contains:
(A) nitric acid (B) hydrochloric acid
(C) sulphuric acid (D) (A) and (C) both

15. Which gas is responsible for the global warming?
(A) O_2 (B) N_2
(C) H_2 (D) CO_2

16. Lichens indicate pollution by:
(A) O_3 (B) SO_2
(C) NO_2 (D) CO

17. Pollutant released by jet planes is:
(A) Fog (B) Aerosol
(C) Smog (D) Colloid

18. Biotic component of biosphere is not constituted by
(A) producers (B) consumers
(C) decomposer (D) air

19. The percentage of fresh water is:
(A) 3% of total water (B) 7% of total water
(C) 8% of total water (D) 21% of total water

20. Which is a consequence of water pollution?
(A) Bioaccumulation of pesticides
(B) Eutrophication
(C) Minamata disease
(D) All of the above

21. BOD increases in:
(A) Polluted water (B) Pure water
(C) Ground water (D) None of these

22. Which makes the maximum part of soil?
(A) Mineral matter (B) organic matter
(C) Soil water (D) Soil air

23. The two forms of oxygen found in the atmosphere are
(A) water and ozone
(B) water and oxygen

(C) ozone and oxygen
(D) water and carbon-dioxide

24. Which is the cause of soil erosion?
(A) Overgrazing (B) deforestation
(C) flood (D) All of the above

25. Bhopal gas tragedy is related with:
(A) Di-chlorophenoxy acetic
(B) Tri chlorophenoxy acetic acid
(C) Methyl isocyanate
(D) None of these

26. Soil erosion can be prevented by:
(A) deforestation
(B) afforestation
(C) overgrazing
(D) removal of vegetation

27. Soil is a part of:
(A) atmosphere (B) lithosphere
(C) hydrosphere (D) ionosphere

28. Which is not a gaseous cycle?
(A) Carbon (B) Nitrogen
(C) Oxygen (D) Calcium

29. Nitrobacter bacteria convert:
(A) Ammonia to nitrite (B) Nitrate to nitrite
(C) Nitrite to Nitrate (D) Nitrite to ammonia

30. Azospirillum bacteria present in:
(A) Roots of maize (B) Roots of sorghum
(C) Roots of babool (D) Both (A) and (B)

Fill in the Blanks

1. ______%of oxygen is present in earth's atmosphere.
2. The ______, ______ and ______ form the non-living or abiotic component of the biosphere.
3. Root of plant holds soil and thus ______ soil erosion.
4. Increase in amount of gases like CO_2 has led to ______.
5. Higher concentrations of ______ is one of the causes of greenhouse effect/global warming.
6. ______ is mixture of gases
7. Top soil is rich in ______.
8. ______ is the biological process by which water is lost in the form of water vapour from the aerial parts of the plants called stomata.
9. ______ gas makes up 78% of our atmosphere.
10. Water covers ______ of the Earth's surface.

True/False

1. The layer of ozone gas absorbs UV rays that come from the sun to the earth.
2. Under high temperature and pressure, dead plants get slowly converted to coal.
3. Rhizobium is a symbiotic bacterium which lives in the root nodules of leguminous plants.
4. Carbon monoxide and carbon-dioxide of air produce acid rain.
5. Topsoil is the uppermost fertile layer of soil that is rich in mineral nutrients.
6. Air forms a protective blanket around the earth and does not allow all the solar radiations to reach the Earth.
7. Resources which are present in unlimited quantity in nature are called exhaustible natural resources.
8. Winds are caused due to unequal heating of atmospheric air.
9. BOD increases in pure water.
10. soil erosion can be prevented by afforestation.

Match Type Questions

1. Match the following I and II.

Column I	Column II
(i) Greenhouse effect	(a) CFCs
(ii) Ozone depletion	(b) Legumes
(iii) Nitrogen fixation	(c) Reduce fertility of soil
(iv) Monoculture	(d) Increase in CO_2

2. Match the following I and II.

Column I	Column II
(i) Petroleum	(a) Moving air
(ii) Wind	(b) Exhaustible
(iii) Deforestation	(c) Soil erosion
(iv) Coal	(d) Fossil fuel

Assertion and Reason Type Questions

Direction: In each of the following questions, a statement of Assertion is given and a corresponding statement of Reason is given just below it. Of the statements, given below, mark the correct answer as:

(A) Both assertion and reason are true and reason is the correct explanation of assertion.
(B) Both assertion and reason are true but reason is not the correct explanation of assertion.

(C) Assertion is true but reason is false.
(D) Both Assertion and Reason are false.

1. **Assertion:** Lichens are indicators of pollution.
Reason: Lichens grow mainly in polluted areas.

2. **Assertion:** Venus has atmosphere.
Reason: The atmosphere on Venus mainly comprises of carbon dioxide.

3. **Assertion:** Carbon monoxide is less dangerous than carbon dioxide.
Reason: Carbon monoxide is a non-poisonous gas.

4. **Assertion:** Roots of leguminous plants have nodules.
Reason: Rhizobium bacteria lives in the roots of legumes.

5. **Assertion:** If all plants become extinct then human will not be able to survive on the Earth.
Reason: Plants are the only source of oxygen in the atmosphere.

6. **Assertion:** Substances are transported from one part of the body to the other in a dissolved form.
Reason: Water is a good solvent.

7. **Assertion:** We get oxygen from plants.
Reason: Photosynthesis is the food making process of plants where they release oxygen molecule into atmosphere.

8. **Assertion:** Cutting of trees leads soil erosion.
Reason: Plant roots tightly hold water hence soil erosion gets prevented.

9. **Assertion**-Pesticides makes soil infertile.
Reason- Pesticides destroy the soil structure by killing the soil microorganisms that recycle nutrients in the soil.

10. **Assertion**-Manure makes soil fertile.
Reason- Manure releases N, P, K into the soil.

Comprehension Type Questions

Passage 1: In the upper reaches of the atmosphere, a molecule containing three atoms of oxygen is found. This would mean a formula of O3 and this is called ozone. ozone is poisonous and we are lucky that it is not stable nearer to the Earth's surface. But it performs an essential function where it is found. It absorbs harmful radiations from the Sun. Recently it was discovered that this ozone layer was getting depleted. Various man-made compounds like CFCs were found to persist in the atmosphere. Once they reached the ozone layer, they would react with the ozone molecules. This resulted in a reduction of the ozone layer and recently they have discovered a hole in the ozone layer above the Antarctica. It is difficult to imagine the consequences for life on Earth if the ozone layer dwindles further, but many people think that it would be better not to take chances. These people advocate working towards stopping all further damage to the ozone layer.

1. Identify the correct statement.
Statement 1 – Ozone is poisonous.
Statement 2 – Absorbs harmful radiations from the Sun.
Statement 3 – Ozone prevents those harmful radiations from reaching the surface of the Earth.
Statement 4 – Molecule containing three atoms of oxygen is termed as ozone.
(A) Both 1 and 4 (B) Both 2 and 4
(C) Only 3 (D) All of the above

2. The molecule containing three atoms of oxygen is termed as:
(A) Oxygen (B) Ozone
(C) Diatomic oxygen (D) None of above

3. What is the molecular formula of ozone?
(A) O (B) O_2
(C) O_3 (D) O_4

4. Why ozone layer is important?

Passage 2: Oxygen is a very abundant element on our Earth. It is found in the elemental form in the atmosphere to the extent of 21%. It also occurs extensively in the combined form in the Earth's crust as well as also in the air in the form of carbon dioxide. In the crust, it is found as the oxides of most metals and silicon, and also as carbonate, sulphate, nitrate and other minerals. It is also an essential component of most biological molecules like carbohydrates, proteins, nucleic acids and fats (or lipids).

5. How much oxygen is present in our atmosphere?
(A) 20 % (B) 21 %
(C) 22 % (D) 23 %

6. Identify the correct statement.
Statement 1 – Oxygen is also an essential component of most biological molecules.
Statement 2 – Oxygen is returned to the atmosphere through process called photosynthesis
Statement 3 – Oxygen cycle maintains the levels of oxygen in the atmosphere.
Statement 4 – Our atmosphere have 21 % oxygen.
(A) Only 1 (B) Both 2 and 3
(C) Both 1 and 4 (D) All of the above

7. Oxygen from the atmosphere is used up in three main processes:
(A) Combustion
(B) Respiration
(C) Formation of oxides of nitrogen
(D) All of the above

ASSESSMENT CORNER

8. By which process oxygen is returned to the atmosphere?
   (A) Respiration (B) Photosynthesis
   (C) Photolysis (D) None of the above

9. Write the molecular formula of oxygen.
   (A) O (B) O_2
   (C) O_3 (D) None of these

Passage 3: The fossil fuels like coal and petroleum contain small amounts of nitrogen and sulphur. When these fuels are burnt, nitrogen and sulphur too are burnt and this produces different oxides of nitrogen and sulphur. Not only is the inhalation of these gases dangerous, they also dissolve in rain to give rise to acid rain. The combustion of fossil fuels also increases the amount of suspended particles in air. These suspended particles could be unburnt carbon particles or substances called hydrocarbons. Presence of high levels of all these pollutants cause visibility to be lowered, especially in cold weather when water also condenses out of air. This is known as smog and is a visible indication of air pollution. Studies have shown that regularly breathing air that contains any of these substances increases the incidence of allergies, cancer and heart diseases. An increase in the content of these harmful substances in air is called air pollution.

10. Identify the correct statement.
    Statement 1 – The unburnt carbon particles which suspended in air called hydrocarbons.
    Statement 2 – Fossil fuels like coal and petroleum contain small amounts of nitrogen and sulphur.
    Statement 3 – In cold weather when water condenses out of air. This is known as smog.
    Statement 4 – Smog is the indication of air pollution
    (A) Both 1 and 4
    (B) Both 2 and 4
    (C) Only 3
    (D) All of the above

11. The unburnt carbon particles or substances which suspended in air are termed as ____
    (A) Smog.
    (B) Fog
    (C) Hydrocarbons
    (D) Ozone

12. An increase in the content of harmful substances in air is called as _______.
    (A) Pollution
    (B) Air pollution
    (C) Smog
    (D) All of the above

13. What are hydrocarbons?

Free Response Type

Very Short Answer Type Questions

1. Mention two causes of over exploitation of natural resources.
2. Write the name of any two air pollutants?
3. What is SMOG?
4. Name three process for which oxygen is used.
5. What are aerosol?
6. Defined water pollution?
7. Mention the two forms of precipitation in nature when the temperature of air is very low.
8. Name the bacteria which help in nitrogen fixation?
9. Write the full form of CFC.
10. Define greenhouse effect.

Short Answer Type Questions

1. What is soil? How is it formed?
2. What is greenhouse effect?
3. What determines the rainfall patterns?
4. How is cloud formed?
5. How ozone layer is useful to us?
6. Enlist the main causes of soil erosion.
7. Name the major pollutants from industries.
8. What will be the consequences of global warming?
9. Ozone is poisonous but important. Explain.
10. Dust is a pollutant. Justify.

Long Answer Type Questions

1. Carbon dioxide is necessary for plants. Justify this statement. Why do we consider it as a pollutant?
2. Why is the atmosphere essential for life?
3. Define water pollution with its causes and control.
4. What is meant by air pollution? Explain any two human activities that causes air pollution. Mention any three harmful effects of air pollution?
5. Draw nitrogen and carbon cycle.

Case Based Questions

Case 1: The ozone layer is the region of Earth's atmosphere responsible for absorbing sun UV rays. It is about 15 to 35 kilometres above the Earth's surface. It acts as a barrier between the earth and the harmful ultraviolet rays. If the ozone layer were absent in the stratosphere, we would be more prone to skin cancer, cataracts, and weak immune systems.

1. The ozone layer is found in the
   (A) Stratosphere
   (B) Mesosphere
   (C) Troposphere
   (D) None of the above
2. Which of the following artificial materials is responsible for ozone layer depletion?
   (A) Chlorofluorocarbon (CFC)
   (B) Formalin
   (C) Polyvinylchloride (PVC)
   (D) Biopolymers
3. What is the primary risk associated with extreme UV rays through the atmosphere because of ozone layer depletion?
   (A) Skin Cancer
   (B) Brain Haemorrhage
   (C) Liver Damage
   (D) None of the above
4. When was the first ozone hole discovered?
   (A) 1950 (B) 1960
   (C) 1970 (D) 1980

Case 2: Mumbai was in news for smog due to increased air pollution. Smog resulted in reduced visibility, traffic jams and also caused harmful effects to biotic components in the capital.

1. What is smog? Is it a primary or secondary pollutant?
2. Justify by giving two reasons why is it harmful to man?

Case-3: It is observed that rhinoceros' population has been increased in some pockets in Northeast region of India. These animals consumed foliage in large amount and then moved to water bodies where they defaecate. Recently, these water bodies are witnessing algal growth and are getting ultimately choked of affecting even activities of rhinos.

1. What is the possible reason of algal growth in these water bodies? Name the process involved.
2. What will be the consequence of excessive choking of water bodies with algal bloom?
3. List at least one step that government must take to save such water bodies.

Level 2

Multiple Choice Questions

1. The use of disposable paper-cups is more beneficial over disposable plastic-cups, because
   (A) it is cheaper
   (B) it is easily available
   (C) it can be reused
   (D) its recycling process has no harmful impact on environment
2. Population size is controlled by
   (A) death rate
   (B) birth rate
   (C) demographic transition
   (D) carrying capacity of environment
3. A renewable source of energy is –
   (A) petroleum
   (B) coal
   (C) nuclear fuel
   (D) trees
4. The function of Nitrosomonas bacteria in nitrogen cycle is to :
   (A) oxidizes ammonium salts into nitrites
   (B) oxidize nitrites into nitrates
   (C) oxidize nitrities into ammonium salts
   (D) oxidize nitrates into nitrites
5. Which of the following constitute a food chain?
   (A) Grass, Wheat, Mango
   (B) Grass, Cow, Human
   (C) Cow, Goat, Elephant
   (D) Grass, Fish, Goat
6. Which of the following is not a biodegradable material?
   (A) Aluminium foil (B) Animal bone
   (C) Wood (D) Cotton
7. Which one of the following is a renewable resource?
   (A) Coal (B) Oil
   (C) Forest (D) Petrol

8. According to origin, identify the secondary air pollutant.
(A) SO_3
(B) Ash
(C) Smoke
(D) Radioactive compound

9. In residential area at nights, the standard limit of sound intensity is ______ Decibel.
(A) 55 (B) 70
(C) 45 (D) 40

10. Maximum air in which we breath is present at
(A) troposphere (B) stratosphere
(C) ionosphere (D) mesosphere

11. Which of the following is the example of the waste bio-decomposition of living beings?
(A) Vegetable (B) Glass
(C) Plastic (D) Metal

12. The three R's, which can, help us to conserve natural resources for future generation are
(A) Reduce, Regenerate, Redistribute
(B) Reduce, Recycle, Regenerate
(C) Reduce, Reuse, Recycle
(D) Redistribute, Regenerate, Recycle

13. Select the group which contains only non-biodegradable items?
(A) Wood, paper, leather
(B) Polythene, glass, PVC
(C) Plastic, glass, grass
(D) Plastic, nylon, cardboard

14. Corrosion of statues and monuments occurs due to:
(A) photochemical smog
(B) stratosphere
(C) acid rain
(D) methane

15. The part of biosphere dominated by human beings is known as
(A) Troposphere (B) Hemisphere
(C) Stratosphere (D) Noosphere

16. Gases referred to as 'greenhouse gases' are
(A) CO_2, O_2, NO_2, NH_3
(B) Chlorofluorocarbon, CO_2, NH_3, N_2
(C) CH_4, N_2, CO_2, NH_3
(D) Chlorofluorocarbon, CO_2, CH_4, NO_2

17. Acid rain is secondary effect of
(A) sound pollution
(B) soil pollution
(C) air pollution
(D) water pollution

18. Which is not non-biodegradable pollutants?
(A) market garbage (B) polythene bags
(C) animal wastes (D) soft drink cans

19. The life supporting zone of the earth is
(A) Lithosphere (B) Hydrosphere
(C) Atmosphere (D) Biosphere

20. Which of the following is/are not gaseous cycle?
(A) Oxygen cycle
(B) Nitrogen cycle
(C) Hydrogen cycle
(D) Phosphorus cycle

Higher Order Thinking Skills (HOTS)

1. (a) Fill in the blanks : A, B and C.

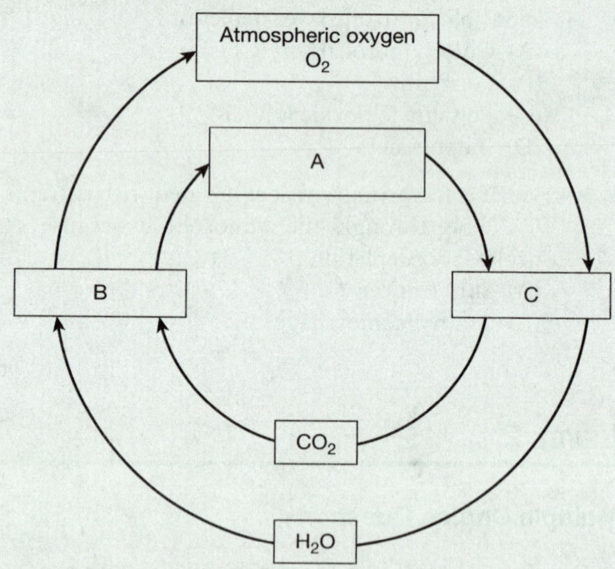

(b) Identify the biogeochemical cycle.

2. (a) Fill in the blanks: A to F.

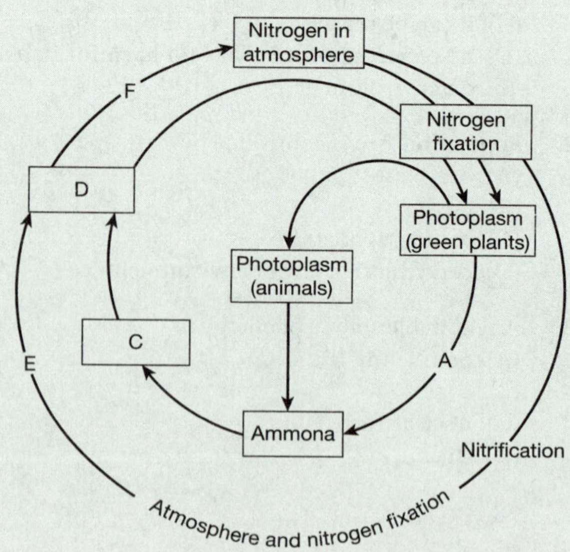

(b) What will happen if the step A does not take place?

(c) What will happen if the step F does not take place?

3. How does the temperature of Earth's atmosphere remain fairly uniform during the day?

4. Why do not lichens occur in Delhi whereas they commonly grown Manali or Darjeeling?

5. Why does Mathura refinery pose problems to the Taj Mahal?

6. A motor car, with its glass totally closed, is parked directly under the Sun. The inside temperature of the car rises very high. Explain why?

7. What would happen if the sun heated the earth's surface equally everywhere?

8. The flow of energy is unidirectional whereas the biogeochemical transfer is cyclic. Why is it so?

ARCHIVE CORNER

1. Read the given paragraph. Soil L is well aerated but cannot hold much water, soil M is well aerated and has a very good water holding capacity. Soil N has excellent water holding capacity but is poorly aerated. Select the correct statement regarding soils L, M and N.
   (A) Soil M is commonly found in those regions where xerophytes are abundant.
   (B) Soil N is best suited for growing garden plants.
   (C) Soil L is best suited for making pots, statues and toys.
   (D) Soil L and N are not suitable for plant growth whereas soil M is best suited for plant growth.

2. Refer to the given statements.
   (i) Soil X contains very small quantity of silt and clay and cannot hold much water.
   (ii) Soil Y is poorly aerated but can hold much water.
   (iii) Soil Z is porous and has very good water holding capacity.
   Identify soil types X, Y and Z and select correct statement regarding them.
   (A) Soil X represents loamy soil and it is not fit for plant growth.
   (B) Soil Y represents clayey soil and is suited for growth of crops like paddy.
   (C) Soil Y represents sandy soil and is well suited to grow all types of plants.
   (D) Soil X, Y and Z represent clayey, sandy and loamy respectively.

3. Select the incorrect match.
   (A) Particulate matter – Air pollutant
   (B) Detergent – Chemical water pollutant
   (C) Glass object – Biodegradable soil pollutant
   (D) Mercury – Neurotoxic water pollutant

4. Read the given statements and select the correct option.
   Statement 1 : Concentration of DDT goes on increasing from one trophic level to another as it enters a food chain.
   Statement 2 : DDT is a non-biodegradable compound which does not get metabolised hence gets stored in the body tissue.
   (A) Both statements 1 and 2 are true and statement 2 is the correct explanation of statement 1.
   (B) Both statements 1 and 2 are true but statement 2 is not the correct explanation of statement 1.
   (C) Statement 1 is true but statement 2 is false.
   (D) Both statements 1 and 2 are false.

5. Which of the following is/are incorrectly matched?

(i)	To reduce harmful gases emitted by vehicles	Use catalytic converter
(ii)	Greenhouse gas	Oxygen
(iii)	To prevent pollution of the sea	Educate the public not to throw litter or dump refuse into the sea
(iv)	Acid rain	Chlorofluorocarbon

   (A) (ii) only
   (B) (iii) only
   (C) (ii) and (iv) only
   (D) (i), (ii), (iii) and (iv)

6. Which of the following statements is correct?
   (A) Good ozone occurs naturally in the troposphere.
   (B) Nitrogen oxide is an example of suspended particulate matter or SPM.
   (C) SO_2 combines with haemoglobin and affects the oxygen carrying capacity of the blood.
   (D) Chlorofluorocarbons are the major ozone depleting substances which produce active chlorine in the presence of UV radiations.

7. Read the given paragraph.
   Soil L is well aerated but cannot hold much water, soil M is well aerated and has a very good water holding capacity. Soil N has excellent water holding capacity but is poorly aerated.
   Select the incorrect statement regarding soils L, M and N.
   (A) Soil M is commonly found in those regions where xerophytes are abundant.
   (B) Soil N is best suited for growing garden plants.
   (C) Soil L is best suited for making pots, statues and toys.
   (D) All of these

8. Read the given passage where some italicised words are put incorrectly.
   Rainfall is a major source of ground water. When the rain falls, some water is lost as run off. The remaining water percolates into the ground

through pore spaces of soil particles under the influence of gravity. Some water forms an extremely thin, tightly held film around soil particles and is termed capillary water. The down-moving water called hygroscopic water finally reaches the underground water table. Most of the water drawn by plants from the soil is the gravitational water.

Identify the incorrect italicised words and select the incorrect statement regarding them.

(A) Rainfall and runoff should not be replaced as they are correctly mentioned.
(B) Capillary should not be replaced as it is correctly mentioned.
(C) Hygroscopic should be replaced by gravitational.
(D) Gravitational should be replaced by capillary

9. Identify X in the given statement and select the correct option regarding it. "When soil is completely saturated with water and excess water accumulates around plant roots in the field, the condition is referred to as X". X could damage crops because.

(A) It reduces air spaces between soil particles
(B) It cuts off oxygen supply to roots hence, they are not able to breathe
(C) It increases amount of salt in the soil and reduces its fertility
(D) All of these.

10. Some water falling on ground, forms an extremely thin, tightly held film around the soil particles called _________ while some water moves down upto the water table and is called _________.

Select the option that correctly fills the blanks in the above statement.

(A) Gravitational water, capillary water
(B) Hygroscopic water, surface runoff
(C) Hygroscopic water, gravitational water
(D) Capillary water, surface runoff

11. Read the given paragraph.

Soil X has very poor water holding capacity, soil Y is well drained and contains one part clay and two parts each of sand and silt. Soil Z has excellent water holding capacity but is poorly aerated.

Select the correct statement regarding soils X, Y and Z.

(A) Soil X is commonly found in those regions where xerophytes are abundant.
(B) Soil Z is best suited for growth of plants like Casuarina, Eucalyptus and watermelon.
(C) Soil Y is best suited for making pots.
(D) All of these

12. Refer to the given outline of nitrogen cycle. Identify X and Y and select the correct statement regarding them.

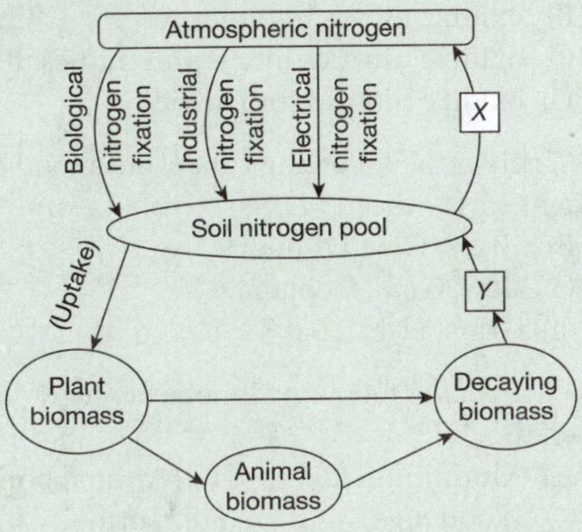

(A) In the process X, protein i s converted into ammonia by the action of bacteria while in the process Y, nitrates present in the decaying remains get converted into free nitrogen gas.
(B) In the process X, nitrates present in the soil get converted into free nitrogen gas while in the process Y, proteins are converted into ammonia by the action of bacteria.
(C) Process X represents the conversion of ammonia into nitrates while process Y represents the conversion of nitrates into the free nitrogen gas.
(D) Process X represents the conversion of ammonia into nitrites while process Y represents the conversion of complex organic compounds like proteins into ammonia.

13. The use of disposable paper-cups is more beneficial over disposable plastic-cups, because

(A) it is cheaper
(B) it is easily available
(C) it can be reused
(D) its recycling process has no harmful impact on environment

14. Population size is controlled by

(A) death rate
(B) birth rate
(C) demographic transition
(D) carrying capacity of environment

15. Depletion of ozone layer is mainly due to

(A) Methane
(B) Carbon monoxide
(C) Chloroflorocarbon
(D) Nitrogen

16. The function of Nitrosomonas bacteria in nitrogen cycle is to:
(A) oxidizes ammonium salts into nitrites
(B) oxidize nitries into nitrates
(C) oxidize nitrities into ammonium salts
(D) oxidize nitrates into nitries

17. Which of the following constitute a food chain?
(A) Grass, wheat, Mango
(B) Grass, Cow, Human
(C) Cow, Goat, Elephant
(D) Grass, Fish, Goat

18. Which of the following is not a biodegradable material?
(A) Aluminium foil (B) Animal bone
(C) Wood (D) Cotton

19. Which one of the following is a renewable resource?
(A) Coal (B) Oil
(C) Forest (D) Petrol

20. According to origin, identify the secondary air pollutant.
(A) SO_3
(B) Ash
(C) Smoke
(D) Radioactive compound

21. In residential area at nights, the standard limit of sound intensity is _____ Decibel.
(A) 55 (B) 70
(C) 45 (D) 40

22. Which of the following gases mainly increases global warming?
(A) Carbon monoxide (B) Nitrous oxide
(C) Carbon dioxide (D) Sulphur dioxide

23. Which of the following is the example of the waste bio-decomposition of living beings?
(A) Vegetable (B) Glass
(C) Plastic (D) Metal

24. The three R's, which can, help us to conserve natural resources for future generation are
(A) Reduce, Regenerate, Redistribute
(B) Reduce, Recycle, Regenerate
(C) Reduce, Reuse, Recycle
(D) Redistribute, Regenerate, Recycle

25. Select the group which contains only non-biodegradable items.
(A) Wood, paper, leather
(B) Polythene, glass, PVC
(C) Plastic, glass, grass
(D) Plastic, nylon, cardboard

26. Which of the following gases related with acid rain?
(A) $NO_2$and CO_2 (B) $CH_4$and SO_2
(C) $CO_2$and SO_2 (D) $SO_2$and NO_2

27. The part of biosphere dominated by human beings is known as
(A) Troposphere (B) Flemisphere
(C) Stratosphere (D) Noosphere

ANSWER KEYS

LEVEL 1

Fixed Response Type

Multiple Choice Questions

1. D 2. A 3. C 4. A 5. B 6. A 7. A 8. B 9. D
10. C 11. B 12. D 13. B 14. D 15. D 16. B 17. B 18. D
19. A 20. D 21. A 22. A 23. C 24. D 25. C 26. B 27. B
28. D 29. C 30. B

Fill in the Blanks

1. 21% 2. air, water and the soil 3. Prevents
4. Global warming 5. CO_2 6. Air
7. Humus 8. Transpiration 9. Nitrogen
10. 75%

True/False

1. True 2. True 3. True 4. False 5. True 6. False 7. False 8. True 9. False
10. True

Match Type Questions

1. (i)-(d), (ii)-(a), (iii)-(b), (iv)-(c)
2. (i)-(b, d), (ii)-(a, c), (ii)-(c), (iv)-(b, d)

Assertion and Reason Type Questions

1. C 2. A 3. D 4. B 5. A 6. B 7. A 8. A 9. A
10. A

Comprehension Type Questions

Passage 1
1. D 2. B 3. C

Passage 2
5. B 6. D 7. D 8. B 9. B

Passage 3
10. D 11. A 12. B

LEVEL 2

Multiple Choice Questions

1. D 2. D 3. D 4. A 5. B 6. A 7. C 8. A 9. C
10. A 11. A 12. C 13. B 14. C 15. D 16. D 17. C 18. C
19. D 20. D

Archive Corner

1. D	**2.** B	**3.** C	**4.** A	**5.** C	**6.** D	**7.** D	**8.** B	**9.** D
10. C	**11.** A	**12.** B	**13.** D	**14.** D	**15.** C	**16.** A	**17.** B	**18.** A
19. C	**20.** A	**21.** C	**22.** C	**23.** A	**24.** C	**25.** B	**26.** D	**27.** D

CHAPTER 6

Improvement in Food Resources

Learning Outcomes

At the end of this chapter, you would be able to:

- discuss green revolution.
- classify the type of crops.
- discuss crop production, management and protection.
- describe improvement in crop yield.
- explain bio-fertilizer, organic farming and crop rotation.
- describe storage of grains.
- discuss animal husbandry.

Geekspeak

- Agriculture
- Horticulture
- Cereals
- Selection
- Manure
- Fertilizer
- Pesticide
- Intercropping
- Fumigation
- Operation flood
- Revolution
- Roughage
- Concentrate
- Ration
- Weedicide

Introduction

All living organisms required food for their growth and survival. The food supplies carbohydrates, proteins, fats, vitamins and minerals. The two major source of food are the plants and animals which are obtained from agriculture and animal husbandry. In present time, due to the tremendous increases of human population, demand of food and shelter are also increased. This demand can be fulfilled by farming on more land and increase our production efficiency for both crops and livestock. green revolution contributed to increases in grain production in our county and white revolution for better efficient milk supply. however, this revolution used natural resources more intensively and Causes damage to them. hence, sustainable practices in agriculture and animal husbandry are needed.to obtain high yield from farms scientific management practices should be undertaken.

Sustainable agriculture: the practice of farming and production of maximum agriculture yield through management of natural resource without disturbing the environment.

Green Revolution: The great increase in the yield of wheat crop during the 1970s is called green revolution. Dr. N. E. Borlaug was the scientist behind the green revolution. He developed high yielding triple dwarf maxi can wheat varieties.

Importance:

- It increased the buffer stocks of food grains.
- It improved the economic conditions of farmers.
- It provided employment opportunities to large number of people.

Following are the important revolutions of India:

- **Green Revolution** – Cereals
- **White Revolution** – Milk
- **Blue Revolution** – Fish
- **Grey Revolution** – Fertilizers
- **Red Revolution** – Meat/Tomatoes
- **Golden Revolution** – Horticulture
- **Pink Revolution** – Prawn
- **Silver Revolution** – Eggs and Chicken
- **Round Revolution** – Potato
- **Yellow Revolution** – Oil Seeds

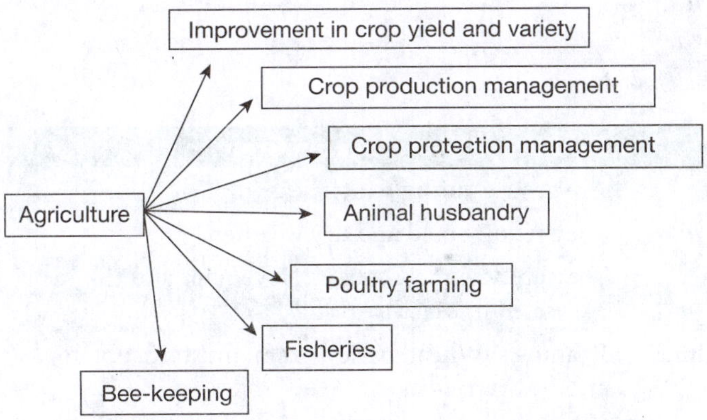

Figure 6.1 Branches of Agriculture

> **Keystone**
>
> **Agriculture:** Ager means field; culture means cultivation. It is the applied biological science which deals with the production of plants and raising of animals useful to man, involving soil cultivation, breeding and management of crops and livestock.
>
> **Horticulture:** Hortus-garden; culture-cultivation. It is the branch of agriculture and the science of growing vegetables, fruits and ornamental plants.
>
> **Silviculture:** Sylvan – wood and trees. Cultivation of wood and trees, e.g., pine, teakwood, sesame, etc.

Sources of Food

Agriculture is a vast industry, which helps to provide us food, its branches divert into numerous sub-fields such as, fisheries, poultry, bee-keeping etc. (as shown in Fig. 6.1)

Food is mainly provided by plants and animals. Plants provide us food like cereals, oil seeds, fruits and vegetables. On this basis plants are classified as follows:

Crop: Plant of same kind are grown and cultivated at one place on a large scale are known as crops. Types of crops are discussed in Table 6.1.

Table 6.1 Different Types of Crops

Types of Crop Plant	Examples	Importance
Cereals	Wheat, rice, maize, minor millets, sorgum	Rich in carbohydrates for enrgy requirements.
Pulses	gram (chana), pea (matar) black gram (urad), pigeon pea (arhar), lentil (masoor), etc.	Rich in proteins that are body Builders.
Oli speed crops	Soyabean, groundnut sunflower, niger, sesame, castor, mustard, linseed.	Rich in oil and fatty acid.
Root crops	Turnip, carrot, turmeric, sweet potato and ginger.	It is utilized as the vegetables and medicines.
Sugar crops	Sugarcane and beet.	Important for sugar and alchohal industry.
Fibre crops	Jute and cotton	Important for jute and cotton industry.
Plantation crops	Tea, coffee, coconut and rubber.	Increases cash and also called as cash crops.
Fodder crops	Berseem, maize, sorgum and elephant grass.	Provide fodder for animals
Horticulture crops (Fruits and vegetables)	Apple, banana, guava, pomegranate, pears, chillies, coriander, jeera, carrot, radis, cabbage, cauliflower, spinach, cucurbit.	Provide vitamins, minerals along with small qunatities of carbohydrates, proteins and oils.

Different crops required different **climatic conditions, temperature** and **photoperiod** for their growth and completion of their life cycle.

> **Keystone**
>
> **Photoperiods:** It is a duration of sunlight require by plants for their growth and flowering to complete their life cycle.

- **Kharif Season Crops:** These crops are grown during the rainy season from the month of **June to October**. e.g., Paddy (rice), soyabean.
- **Rabi Season Crops:** These crops are grown during the winter season from the month of **November to April**. e.g., wheat, gram, peas.
- **Zaid Crop**: In Indian sub-continent, the crops grown on irrigated land which do not have to wait for monsoon, in short duration between Rabi and Kharif crops, mainly from **March to June** are called as Zayed crops. It requires warms day weather for growth and longer day length for flowering. e.g., watermelon, bitter gourds, cucumber and musk melon.

❖ INTEXT QUESTIONS

1. Differentiate between kharif and rabi crops.

S. No.	Kharif Crop/Rainy Season Crop	Rabi Crop/ Winter Season Crop
1.	Are grown during monsoon/rainy season.	Are grown during winter season.
2.	They require warm and wet weather.	They require cold and dry weather.
3.	They are sown in June/July and harvested in September/October.	They are sown in October/November and harvested in March/April.
4.	Examples: Rich, jowar, bajra, cotton, groundnut, urad, moong, etc.	Examples: Wheat, barley, gram, mustard, potato, etc.

2. What are photoperiods related to?

Ans: Duration of sunlight

3. What is the duration of Rabi season?

Ans: From the month of November to April.

4. What was blue revolution meant for?

Ans: Fish production.

Check Point 1

1. Define sustainable agriculture.
2. Who is the father of white revolution?
3. Name any 2 rabi crops.
4. What are Zaid crops?

Improvement in Crop Yield

This step depends on a crop variety that can give a good yield. In India, there has been four times increase in the production of food grains from 1960 to 2004 with only 25% increase in the cultivable land area. The major groups for improving crop yields cab be classified as:

- Crop variety improvement (the choice seed for planting)
- Crop production improvement (the nurturing of the crop plant)
- Crop protection management (the protection of the growing harvested crops loss)

> **Keystone**
>
> Introduction or deletion of genes that would provide the desired characteristics to crops and yield. **Genetically modified crops** (GMCs), called genetic engineering.

Crop Variety Improvement

The desirable superior character in variety can be incorporated through various methods of genetic improvement of crops like as plant breeding and genetic engineering. The science of improving crop varieties is called **plant breeding**. These involve introduction, selection of plant and then **hybridization.**

- **Introduction:** The seed of a plant species having some special features are brought from some other place and grown in a new place where it was not grown before. This is called introduction.
- **Selection:** It is the process in which economic plants having best desired characters are picked up from the given population and seeds of such plants are used for future cultivation. Each of which has at least one desirable quality, such of high yield or resistance of disease.

Hybridization

Hybridization means the process of cross breeding of two genetically dissimilar varieties of crop plants (each having a specific and better characteristics) to obtain a new crop plant having both the desired characteristics is called as hybridization (as shown in Fig. 6.2).

Crop plants produced in this way are called as hybrid varieties or high yielding varieties.

Parent 1 (with a desired character, like high-yield) × **Parent 2** (with a desired character, like disease resistance)

↓

Hybird variety (High-yielding and disease-resistant)

Figure 6.2 Hybridization

Hybridization may be of three types:

- **Intervarietal** (between two different varieties of same species)
- **Interspecific** (between two different species of the same genera)
- **Intergeneric** (between two different genera)

Object of Plant Breeding

- **Higher Yield:** To increase crop productivity per acre.
- **Improved Quality:** It varies among different crops. For eg. In wheat baking quality is considered. Similarly, protein quality in pulses, oil quality in oil seeds and preserving quality in fruits and vegetables, etc., are important.
- **Biotic and Abiotic Resistance:** Crop production can decrease due to various biotic (diseases, insects and nematodes) and abiotic (drought, salinity, water lodging, heat, cold and frost) stresses. Thus, crop varieties produce must be resistant to the stresses so that, crop production can be improved.
- **Change in Maturity Duration:** Shorter the maturity duration of crop, more will be its economical output. Such short duration allows farmers to grow multiple rounds of crops in a year and also reduces the cost of crop production. Besides that, uniform maturity makes harvesting process easy and reduces losses during harvesting.
- **Wider Adaptability:** It help in stabilizing the crop production under different environmental conditions. Thus, one variety can be grown under different climatic conditions in different areas.
- **Desirable Agronomic Characteristics:** It depends on types of crops. For example, for fodder crops, desirable agronomic characteristics are tallness and profuse branching and for cereals like dwarfness to reduce chances of lodging and less consumption of nutrients by these crops are important factors. Thus, crop productivity increases.

Keystone

The scientist, which develop new varieties of seed, are known as plant breeders.

The science and art of improving the heredity of plants in relation to their economic use is known as Plant breeding.

Competition Corner

Green Revolution was a process by which India's production of wheat, rice maize and several other food grains was tremendously increased in the late 1960s and early 1970s.

- India, which was earlier said to carry a 'begging bowl' to the West for food grain, claimed self-sufficiency.
- This revolution was due to the new agricultural technologies whereby high-yielding hybrid varieties of wheat and rice were grown in India.
- Fertilizer and pesticides were used. Irrigation facilities were improved. **Dr. M.S. Swaminathan** played a key role in bringing about the 'green revolution'.
- Padam Vibhushan Professor, Dr. M.S. Swaminathan, FRS (Fellow of Royal Society), in the **Father of green revolution in India.** He stressed the need for the work led to the era of dwarf varieties in India. In 1967, he developed a high-yield dwarf variety of wheat, Sharbti Sonara. Being a plant geneticist, he has developed a high-yield dwarf variety of wheat.
- **Sharbti Sonara:** Being a plant geneticist, he has contributed to the development of agriculture in India.

Crop Production Management

Successful crop production depends upon:

- Understanding how crops develop and grow.
- How various factors affect the growth and development of crops.
- How each factor can be modified and managed.

Approaches for crop production includes:

- Nutrient management
- Irrigation
- Cropping Patterns (mixed cropping, crop rotation, inter cropping, etc.)

Nutrient Management

The plants require inorganic elements, which they chiefly obtain from the soil, where these elements occur in the form of **minerals.** These nutrients are the source of ATP in the metabolism of plant and by getting these the plant grows and produces high yield of crops.

Nutrients are of two types:

- **Macronutrient:** Nutrients which are required by the plant in large amount are termed as macronutrients. **e.g.,** nitrogen, phosphorus, potassium, calcium, magnesium, sulphur.
- **Micronutrient:** Nutrients which are required by the plant in trace or very low amount are termed as micronutrients. **e.g.,** iron, manganese, boron, zinc, copper, molybdenum, chlorine.

Characteristics of an essential plant nutrient:

- In the absence of such element, the plant is not able to complete its life cycle.
- Such element must have a direct influence on the plant nutrition and metabolism.
- The requirement of such element must be specific and cannot be replaced by another element.
- Deficiency of such element can be corrected or prevented only by supplying that nutrient.

Deficiency of the nutrients affects physiological process in plants as well as their reproduction, growth and susceptibility to diseases. To overcome the deficiency of nutrients, the soil can be enriched by adding manures and fertilizers. Besides these, **carbon, oxygen and hydrogen** are called **framework elements.**

Classification of plant nutrient:

There are 16 essentials for growth and development to plant.

Table 6.2 Essential Nutrient for Growth and Development

Sources	Nutrient	Types
Air	Carbon, Oxygen ←	Macro nutrients
Water	Framework ← Hydrogen element	Macro nutrients
Soil	(i) Nitrogen, Phosphorus, Potassium, Sulphur, Calcium Magnesium (ii) Iron, Manganese, Boron, Zinc, Copper, Molybdenum, Chlorine.	Macro nutrients. Micro nutrients

Manures: Manure are organic substances are obtained from the decomposition of plant and animal waste, which added to soil in order to increase soil fertility, aeration and water holding capacity.

Types of manures (as shown in Fig 6.3):

- Farmyard Manure (FYM)
- Compost
- Green Manuring

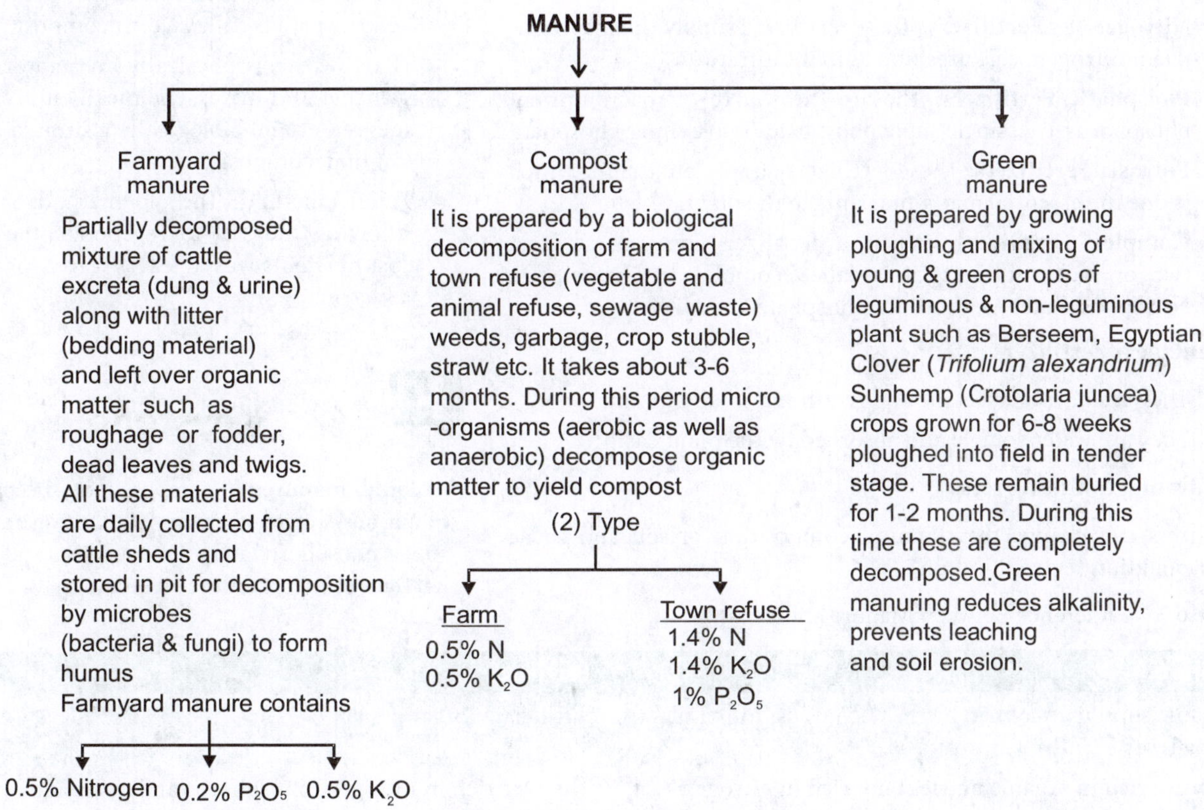

Figure 6.3 Types of Manure

Advantages of manure:

- Increase organic matter in soil and have low cost.
- Reduced soil erosion.
- Increase soil fertility, water holding capacity and aeration.
- Improve the texture of soil
- Increase the number of friendly microbes.

Disadvantages of manure:

- They have low amount of nutrient.
- Manure is bulky and not easy to be absorbed.

Competition Corner

Green manure used before sowing of the crop seeds. For this purpose, legume plants (Generally sun hemp and guar) are used, their roots contain symbiotic rhizobium bacteria, helps in nitrogen fixation. Plants are grown and then mulched by ploughing them into the soil. By action of decomposers, these green plants are converted into green manure, which helps in Enriching the soil in nitrogen and phosphorus.

Fertilizers: There are commercially manufactured inorganic salt containing one or more essential plant nutrients like N, P, K which are used to increase soil fertility.

Types of fertilizer:

- **Nitrogenous Fertilizers:** These fertilizers supply the macronutrient nitrogen. e.g., urea and amount nitrate.
- **Phosphatic Fertilizers:** The are the source of macronutrient phosphorus. e.g., single super phosphate, Triple super phosphate
- **Potassic Fertilizers:** These fertilizers supply potassium which is one the essential macronutrients to the plant.
- **Complex Fertilizers:** When a fertilizer contains at least two or more nutrients it is called complex fertilizers. e.g., Nitrophosphate, Ammonium phosphate and NPK.

Advantage of fertilizers:

- They are nutrient specific and require in small amount
- They are water soluble and absorbed by the plant easily.

Disadvantage of fertilizers:

Fertilizers can change the chemical composition of soil and cause water pollution (eutrophication)

Keystone

- The degradation of organic waste through the consumption by the earthworm is called Vermicompost.
- Earthworm is physically an aerator, crusher and mixer; chemically it is a degreaser and biologically a stimulator of decomposition.
- Fallow method: The old method of allowing the soil to regenerate the lost nutrients was to leaves it free for a season.

Keystone

Liquid manure: It composed of sheep dung and water. It contains 0.8 % nitrogen, 0.5 % phosphorus and 0.4% potassium and all trace elements for use on seeding.

Table 6.3 Difference Between Manure and Fertilizer

Manure	Fertilizer
Organic substances obtain by the decomposition of plant animal waste.	Artificial inorganic salts.
They are rich in organic nutrient not rich in nitrogen, phosphorus and potassium (NPK).	They are rich in nitrogen, phosphorus and potassium (NPK).
They are not nutrient specific.	They are nutrient specific.
They are not soluble in water so slowly absorbed plants.	They are soluble in water and quickly absorbed.
They are not harmful to the environment.	They are harmful to the environment.
They have nutrients in small quantity so needed in large quantity.	They have higher amount of nutrients so required in very small quantity.
They are bulky substance so difficult to store and transport.	They are in concentrate form and enasy to transport and storing.
They are prepared in field.	They are prepared in factories.

Competition Corner

Water Pollution and Eutrophication

Excessive use of fertilizers, in particular nitrogenous ones, causes buildup of nitrates in the soil. From the foil, the nitrates as well as phosphates are washed by rain and carried to lakes ponds and rivers. Here, they stimulate excessive growth of microscopic plants like algae resulting in the formation of blooms.

The algae grow quickly then die and decomposed. During decomposition, the algae deplete aquatic animals.

This excessive growth of algae and the subsequent depletion of oxygen content of water is called eutrophication. Fertilizers, Therefor, must be used carefully and judiciously in limited quantity.

Organic Farming: Cultivation of land without conserving soil fertility and soil structure would lead ultimately to the development of deserts. Excessive and indiscriminate use of pesticides, fungicides and herbicides as is done in Present day agriculture could lead to:

- Changes in biological balance; population of soil organisms will be affected.
- Increase in the occurrence of cancer and other diseases.
- Contamination of water (water pollution) and eutrophication (enrichment of water bodies with nutrients leading to excessive growth of phytoplankton.)

These are some of the problems due to the adoption of improved agricultural practices in order to increases food production for the ever-increasing human population. Scientists are greatly concerned about these problems and attempts have been made to develop alternatives to chemical agriculture. The alternatives consist of adoption **"green or ecofriendly technologies"** or "ecological farming." or **organic farming**.

Organic farming is a farming system in which chemical fertilizers, herbicides or pesticides are minimally used or not used at all, instead of, manures recycled farm wastes and biofertilizers are used in place of chemical fertilizers.

Advantages of Organic Farming:

- Natural ecosystem is not disturbed, as organic farming is in harmony with the natural ecosystem.
- Soil fertility is preserved.
- Harmful effects of chemicals on the living organisms are avoided.
- Pollution of air, water and soil does not take place.

The basic objective or cropping is to achieve insurance against total crop failure under poor rainfall conditions and thereby minimizing risk and monetary loses. In this system, bio-agents like blue-green algae, some bacteria are used as biofertilizers, and neem leaves or turmeric are used in grain storage as bio-pesticides with healthy cropping system like mixed cropping, inter-cropping and crop-rotation. Beneficial in insect, pest and weeds control beside providing nutrients. No chemical agents are used so that doesn't cause pollution etc. Like side effects.

Rhizobium and Azotobacter are some examples of symbiotic bacteria. These bacteria provide nutrition to plants and are therefore called biofertilizers.

Biofertilizers: Biofertilizers are micro-organisms (like bacteria, algae and fungi used singly or in combination) or biologically active products which are used to enrich soil fertility. Some of the biofertilizers are given below:

- Legume – Rhizobium symbiosis
- Azolla – Anabaena symbiosis
- Free-living bacteria (Azotobacter) living in soil symbiotically
- Cyanobacteria (Anabaena, Nostoc)
- Mycorrhiza (symbiotic association of fungi with roots of higher plants)

❖ INTEXT QUESTIONS

5. **Name two plants which are used as biopesticide in organic farming.**

   Ans: Turmeric and leaves of Neem plant are used as biopesticide in organic farming.

6. **Name any two fodder crops.**

   Ans: Berseem and sudan grass.

7. **What is the name given to crops obtained by introducing a gene that provides the desired characteristic?**

   Ans: Genetically modified crops.

8. **What is green manure?**

   Ans: Some plants like sun hemp or guar are grown in the field prior to the sowing of the crop seeds. These are then mulched by ploughing them into the soil. These green plants gradually decompose and turn into green manure which helps in enriching the soil in nitrogen and phosphorus

Check Point 2

5. Define the biofertilizers.
6. Write differences between manure and fertilizer.
7. What is the advantage of manure?
8. Write the name of framework elements.

Irrigation

In India, most of agriculture is dependent on rain. So, poor monsoons cause crop failure. Due to scarcity or irregular distribution of rains drought occurs. It causes great problem in those areas where farmers don't use irrigation methods. Process of supplying water to crop plants growing in the fields by means of canals, reservoir, wells, tube-wells, etc., is known as irrigation (as shown in Fig. 6.4).

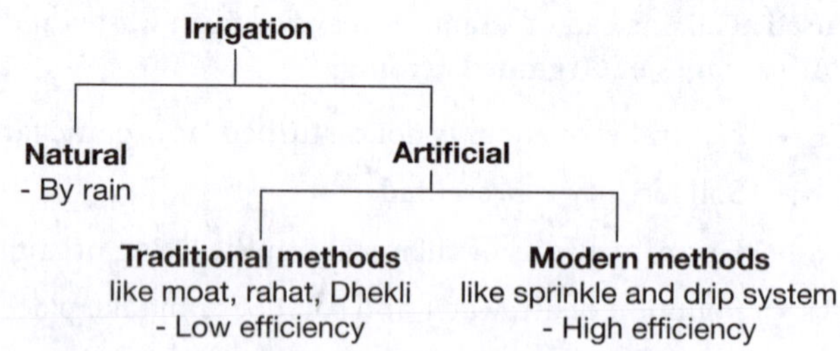

Figure 6.4 Types of Irrigation

Water requirements or irrigation of crop plants depends on two factors:

- **Crop-based Irrigation:** Water requirement of different crop plants varies at different stages of their growth and maturation e.g., paddy crop is transplanted in standing water and also requires continuous water supply whereas this is not so for wheat, gram, cotton, maize crops, etc.
- **Soil-based Irrigation:** Irrigation also depends on the nature of soil in which crop is grown e.g., if two wheat crops are grown together one in sandy and another in clay soil, then in sandy more frequent irrigation is needed than clay soil. Light and sandy soil have less water retention capacity. So, in these areas' crops get adversely affected by drought conditions.

India has a wide variety of climatic conditions and water resources. So, different irrigation systems are used to supply water to agriculture lands in different area.

Keystone

- **Perennial Canals:** These canals are fed by water stored behind a large dam or barrage and can thus be supplied water, all the year round.
- **Indundation Canals:** These canals lead water from a river at the time of flood. These are simple and do not supply water all the year round.

Sources of Irrigation: Well, tube well, ponds, lakes, river, canal and dams.

- **Canal System:** Canals usually receive water from rivers and usually are an elaborate, extensive network of irrigation system.

  Canal • Branch canal • Field channels • Then irrigate individual fields or a group of fields.
- **Tanks:** Tanks are usually small water storage reservoir, constructed at higher elevations in hilly areas.

  They intercept and store the runoff water of small catchment areas.
- **Wells:** Wells are dug and constructed wherever ground water is exploitable.
  - **Wells are of two types:**
    - **Dug Wells:** In which water is collected from water bearing strata, i.e., bottom below the ground water table. In these wells, water from lower strata slowly accumulates.
    - Water from these wells is usually lifted for irrigation purpose by mechanical means such as bullock operated devices.
    - **Tube Wells:** They are dug in the deeper strata much below the ground water table.

Deep bore tube-well can supply water continuously.

Water from tube-well is pumped up directly from fields through narrow lanes by using diesel or electrical pumps.

- **River Lift System:** It is used in the area where either canal flow is insufficient or irregular due to insufficient reservoir water release. In this system, water is directly drawn from the rivers (using pumps) in order to supplement irrigation in the areas adjoining rivers.
- **River Valley System:** Due to heavy rain fall, many rivers valley are found in Western Ghats and Karnataka. This results in higher run off and discharge flow in the rivers. To prevent this coffee, rubber, coconut, arecanut are cultivated on the slopes of these valley and growing single rice crop on bottom.

Modern Methods of Irrigation

- **Sprinkler Irrigation System:**
  - It is water efficient system and is being introduced in the canal irrigated areas of Haryana, Rajasthan and Madhya Pradesh.
  - This system spreads water uniformly over crop plants and fields, required quantity of water is supplied (as shown in Fig. 6.5).
  - Useful for sandy soil and uneven land.
  - Spread water uniformly over crop plant and field.
  - In this system the perpendicular pipes having rotating nozzles no top, are joined to main line at regular. Intervals.
- **Drip-Irrigation System:**
  - Modern system being encouraged in Maharashtra, Karnataka, Andhra Pradesh, Orissa and Tamil Nadu for fruit crops.
  - Fertigation is an innovative method for applying fertilizers through drip irrigation to maximize farm productivity with available water (as shown in Fig. 6.6).
  - Boon in poor water region.
  - Provide water to plants drop by drop at the root.
  - Water is not wasted at all.
  - Best irrigation technique for fruit crop, garden and trees.

Figure 6.5 Sprinkler Irrigation System

Figure 6.6 Drip Irrigation System

Advantage of irrigation:

- Supply of essential elements → Irrigation water supplies two essential elements to cropls i.e hydrogen and oxygen.
- Gemination of seeds → Moisture available in soil to germination of seeds.
- Growth → Growth of root s occur inside the soil by availability of water in soil.
- Absorption of nutrients → Water made available for filed by the process of irrigation help in absorption of nutrient by plants from the soil.

Keystone

Rice plants are transplanted into standing water and need continuous irrigation.

Clay soil retains a lot of water and hence need less irrigation, while sandy soil needs more water for irrigation.

Competition Corner

- **Water logging:** Standing water in field to excess irrigation is water logging which result in inhibition of seed germination and the roots of plants fail of to breathe.
- **Water lodging:** Falling of mature crops due to excess irrigation or strong current is water lodging which damages the quality and quantity of grains.
- **Trickle irrigation:** Slow application of water drop by drop to the root zone of a crop. It is also called as drop irrigation.
- **Fertigation:** Method for applying fertilizers through drip irrigation.

❖ INTEXT QUESTIONS

9. In which country, drip irrigation method is invented?

Ans: Israel

10. Name any three methods of irrigation and briefly describe them.

Ans: Drip irrigation: In this kind of irrigation, water is supplied drop by drop near the roots of the crops or plants. It is generally used in the areas where there is a scarcity of water. However, it is very expensive.

Sprinkler system: In this system, the water escapes from the revolving nozzles and is sprinkled like rain on the crops. This system is used for sandy soils and uneven land.

Surface irrigation: Method to supply water to agricultural lands from well, river, dam, etc.

11. Describe about the river lift system.

Ans: In this system, water is directly drawn from the rivers (using pumps) in order to supplement irrigation in the areas adjoining rivers.

Check Point 3

9. What is fertigation?

10. What is irrigation?

11. Define the trickle irrigation.

Cropping Patterns

Involves different ways of growing crops to obtain maximum benefit. The main patterns are discussed below:

(I) Mixed Cropping: It is the practice of growing two or more types of crops simultaneously on the same piece of land. Different crops to be grown are selected in such a way that products and wastes from one crop can stimulate the growth of other crop.

Crop combinations used in mixed cropping:

- Growing wheat crop + gram
- Growing cotton crop + groundnut
- Growing groundnut + sunflower
- Growing ragi + gram
- Growing turmeric + groundnut

Advantages of mixed cropping:

- Saving of time and labour.
- Optimum utilization.
- Avoids depletion in soil nutrients.
- No risk of crop failure.
- Varity of product
- Increase in yield
- Minimizing pest damage.
- It is impossible to use any labour saving implement or machinery on the field.

(II) Intercropping:

- Growing of two or more crops simultaneously on the same field in a definite pattern, i.e., few rows of one crop alternate with a few rows of second crop (as shown in Fig. 6.7). For e.g., soyabean +Maize or finger millet (bajra) + cowpea (lobia) etc.
- For this pattern, those crops are selected which have different nutrient requirements. So, maximum utilization of the nutrients can be ensured without competition.
- Pests and disease couldn't be spread to all the plants belonging to one crop in a field.
- Thus, both crops can give better returns.
- Improved version of traditional mixed cropping in which two or more crops are grown simultaneously in the same field but in a definite row pattern is called intercropping.

Figure 6.7 Intercropping

Criteria to accomplish intercropping:

- Spatial arrangement
- Plant density
- Maturity dates of crops
- Plant architecture

Types of intercropping:

- **Row intercropping:** In this intercropping all crop combinations of mixed cropping are used in definite row pattern 1: 1, 1: 2 or 1: 3.
- **Strip intercropping:** Growing two or more crops simultaneously in strips, wide enough to permit separate crop production using machines.

Advantages:

- Productivity is increased.
- It economizes spaces and time of cultivating two or more crops.
- It helps to maintain soil fertility.

Table 6.4 Comparison Between Mixed Cropping and Inter Cropping

Mixed Cropping	Inter Cropping
Aim is to minimize risk of crop failure.	Aim is to increase productivity per unit area
Seeds of component crops are mixed before sowing.	Seeds of component crops are not mixed.
Sowing is not done in rows.	Sowing is done in rows.

- **Crop Rotation:** The process in which different types of crops are grown alternately in the same field is called crop rotation (as shown in Fig. 6.8). In this pattern, one crop must be of legume family to maintain fertility of soil. Two or three crops can be grown in a year with good harvest if method is done properly.

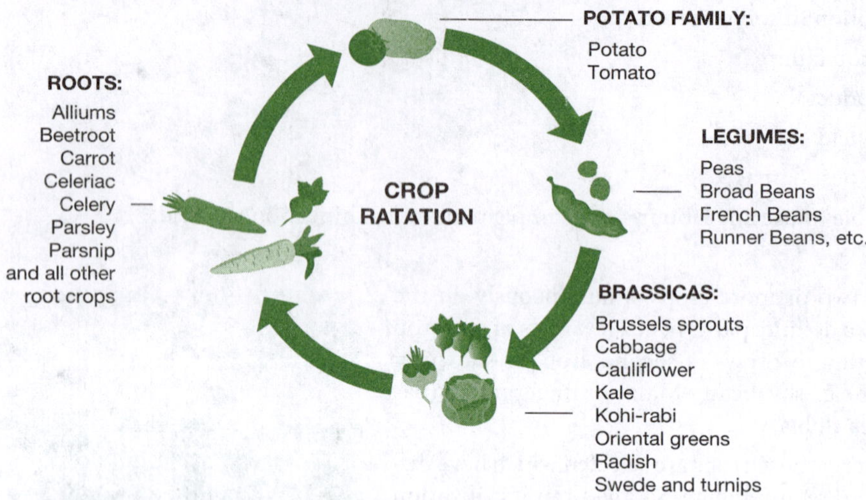

Figure 6.8 Crop Rotation

Choice of crop after one harvest depends on:

- Duration of growth
- Availability of moisture
- Irrigation facilities

Depending upon the duration, crop rotation may be of following three types:

- **One year rotation**
  - Maize - Mustard
  - Rice - Wheat
- **Two years rotation**
  - Maize - Mustard-Sugarcane - Fenugreek
  - Maize - Potato- Sugarcane - Peas
- **Three years rotation**
  - Rice - Wheat - Mung - Mustard
  - Sugarcane - Berseem
  - Cotton - Oat - Sugarcane - Peas - Maize -Wheat

Crop rotation confers following benefits:

- All crops do not require the plant nutrients in the same proportion.
- By growing crops in rotation, the fertility of the soil is utilized more evenly. The soil is not depleted in a particular nutrient.
- When different crops are grown, the operations concerned with the preparation of soil, manuring, sowing, harvesting and other operations are spread throughout the year, thereby reducing the work pressure at any particular time.
- When different crops are grown on the field one after another, the yields of product obtained are greater than when the same crops are grown year after year.
- The incidence of weeds, pests and diseases is reduced.
- In this pattern, one crop must be of legume family to maintain fertility of soil.
- Two or three crops can be grown in a year with good harvest if method is done properly

Crop Protection Management

In fields, crops have to be protected from weeds, insects – pests and disease- causing organisms like fungi. All these cause damage to crop plants so much that most of the crop is lost. It includes eradication of pathogens, weeds and other organisms that causes harm to the crop plants and are collectively called as pests.

Pest

Any destructive organism that causes that causes economic damage or destroying crop plants are called pests. Examples: weeds, insects, mites, nematodes.

Pesticide/Biocide: It refers to a chemical that is used to kill a pest organism which includes insecticides (for killing the insects), weedicides (for killing the weeds,) fungicides (for killing the fungi) nematicides (for killing nematodes) and rodenticides (for killing rodents), they are discussed in Table 6.5.

Table 6.5 Pesticide and there Affected Organism

Pesticide	Affected Organism	Example
Weedicide	Weeds	2, 4- D, 2,45-T, Triazine, Nitrofen, Atrazine
Insecticide	Insect	DDT. Aldrin, Malathion
Fungicide	Fungal pathogen	Brodeaux mixture, Burgndy mixture, HgCl32
Algicide	Algal pathogen	CuSO4
Rodenticide	Rodents (rat, moles)	zinc phosphide, ZnSO4
Nematicide	Nematode	Chloropicrin, Methy bromide

Disadvantages of using pesticide:

- Spray can affect wildlife in a particular area.
- They can enter the food chain.
- Water pollution.

Preventive measures avoiding use of pesticides:

- Crop rotation and multiple cropping.
- Use of pest and disease resistant hybrid varieties of crop plant.
- Sowing healthy and summer ploughing
- Selection of optimum time of cropping.

Weed

They are the small – sized unwanted plants which grow along with a cultivated crop a filed. Weeds are economically vary important as they can severely reduce crop yields by competing for light, water and nutrients.

Some common weeds are Tribulus terrestris (Gokhroo), Parthenium (Gajar grass), Cyperus rotundus (Motha), Amaranthus (Chaulai), Chenopodium (bathua).

Methods of weed control:

- **Mechanical Method:** Uprooting, hand hoeing, ploughing, burning and flooding.
- **Biological Method:** Use of insects or some organisms which consume and destroy the weed plants, e.g., Prickly – pear cactus (Opuntia) is controlled by cochineal insect and aquatic weeds (Hydrilla) are controlled by Carps fish
- **Chemical Control:** Spraying of chemical like herbicides or weedicides, e.g., Isoproturon, 2. 4-D, MCPA, Atrazine.

Crop Disease

When the pathogens such as bacteria, fungi and verses get favorable condition for growth and propagation. They spread and infect the crop plants crop diseases, Depending upon their mode of occurrence.

Crop disease are of three types:

1. **Seed borne:** Spread through the seed.

   Example: Ergot of bajra and leaf spot of paddy.
2. **Soil borne:** Spread through the soil.

   Example: Smut of bajra and Tikka of ground nut.
3. **Air borne:** Spread through the air.

   Example: Rust of wheat.

- **Effective methods to control pests:** Chemicals (poisons) used to kill pests of plants such as insects, fungi, weeds, mites, rats, etc., are known as pesticides. They are of following types:
  - **Fungicide** : To kill fungi
  - **Weedicide** : To kill weeds
  - **Rodenticide** : To kill rodents like rats, moles
  - **Nematicide** : To kill nematodes
- **Preventive measures should be adopted instead of using pesticides as:**
  - Use of pest and disease resistant hybrid varieties of crop plants.
  - Selection of optimum time of cropping
  - Crop rotation and multiple cropping
  - Clean cultivation
  - Summer ploughing
  - Sowing of healthy seeds
- **Insect - Pest Control:** Insect pests attack the plants in three ways.
  - They cut root, stem and leaf
  - They suck the cell sap from various parts of plants.
  - They bore into stem and fruits.
- **Weed:** These are unwanted plants which are grown along with main crop and compete the crop for light, space, minerals and nutrients. e.g., Xanthium (gokhroo), Parthenium (gajar ghas), Cyperinus rotundus (motha).

> **Keystone**
>
> Bacillus thuringiensis is an insect pathogen, used as a bio-pesticide. It kills a wide range of insect larvae.

It can be control by following ways:

- **Mechanical methods:** By removing weeds from crop fields by harrow, interculture ploughing, burning and flooding (weeding).
- **Chemical methods:** Using chemicals called herbicides or weedicides.

  e.g., 2, 4-D, Nitrofen, Atrazine
- **Biological methods:** Employ living organisms to destroy weeds.
  - Cassia plant prevents the growth of parthenium weed.
  - Herbivorous fish feed on aquatic weeds.

> **Keystone**
>
> Contact insecticides are the toxic chemicals that penetrate the exoskeleton of insect pests and kill them.
>
> Systemic insecticides are those chemicals which are absorbed first by tissue of the food plant and then into the insect-pest and kill the pests.

❖ INTEXT QUESTIONS

12. Mention any two abiotic factors that affect crop production.

Ans: Drought, salinity, waterlogging, heat, cold and frost are the abiotic factors that affect crop production.

13. What is mixed cropping? How does it help a farmer?

Ans: Mixed cropping is the practice of growing two or more crops simultaneously on the same piece of land. For example, wheat and gram, or wheat and mustard, or groundnut and sunflower. It helps the farmer as it reduces the risk and gives some insurance against the failure of one of the crops.

Check Point 4

12. Differentiate between strip cropping and row cropping.
13. Name any 2 weedicides.
14. State any two advantages of mixed cropping.
15. Why are legumes desirable in crop rotation?

Storage of Grains

Food materials can be broadly classified in to two types:

1. **Perishable food materials:** They get spoiled easily on keeping for some time at room temperature.
   Example: Fruits, Vegetables, meat, milk, etc.
2. **Non-perishable food materials:** They do not get spoiled for long time at room temperature.
   Example: Wheat, Maize, Pulses, Rice.

- Non-perishable food materials are stored on a commercial scale in gunny bag or in grain silos. Pesticides are applied on the stored food grains either by spraying or by fumigants.
- Various biotic factors like insects, rodents, fungi, mites and bacteria and abiotic factors like in appropriate moisture.
- Temperature of storage house, etc., are responsible for grain losses.
- these factors cause loss in weight, degradation in quality, poor germinability, discolouration of seeds, etc., which decreases marketability.
- grains losses can be controlled by proper treatment and by systematic management of warehouses.
- Moisture control is an important factor in storage of grains. Generally, grains are stored in jute bags or metallic bins. However, large scale storage of grains is done in silos and granaries to protect them from pests like rats and insects. dried neem leaves are used for storing food grains at home.
- Preventive and control measures should be used before storage of grains like:
  (a) strict cleaning.
  (b) proper drying in sun light first, followed by in shade.
  (c) fumigation by using chemicals that can kill pests.

Keystone

Fumigants: Volatile pesticide are called fumigants, for example, ethylene dibromide (EDB), aluminum phosphide, CH_3Br, zinc phosphide.

Spraying: Malathion and pyrethrum are commonly used by spraying.

- Rice plants are transplanted into standing water and need continuous irrigation.
- Clay soil retains a lot of water and hence need less irrigation, while sandy soil needs more water for irrigation.

Animal Husbandry

Science which deals with the scientific management of farm animals including their feeding, breeding, weeding and heeding (disease control) is called as animal husbandry. There are four main practices involved in keeping of animals or animal husbandry.

- **Breeding:** It is done to obtain animals with desired characters. Through breeding, we can develop high milk-yielding and high meat-yielding cattle.
- **Feeding:** It deals with the study of proper food (called feed), mode and time or feeding of different animals.
- **Weeding:** This concerns with the elimination of uneconomical animals.
- **Heeding:** It means the proper care and management of animals.

Various types of animal farming are:

- **Cattle farming** (Milk producing or milch animals)
- **Poultry farming** (Egg yielding animals)
- **Fish farming** (Meat providing fishes)
- **Bee keeping** (Honey providing bees)

Keystone

- India ranks fifth in the worlds in its population of cattle and buffaloes.
- The average annual milk yield per cow is 220 kg in India as against 4250 kg. is USA

Cattle Farming

Farming of cattle for milk and labour is called cattle farming. Milk providing animals are cows, buffaloes, goats, camels.

Breeds of Cow: Cows are a good source of milk for food of human beings and bullocks help in farming and transport purposes. Based upon the milk production and other utility, various breeds of cow are categorized in three types (as shown in Fig. 6.9).

Milch or Dairy Breeds

Milch or dairy breed cows are of three types in India. These are:

- Indigenous breeds
- Exotic breeds and
- Cross breeds.

Indigenous Breeds

These are the Indian breeds of milch or dairy cows. These are:

- Red sindhi
- Sahiwal
- Gir

Exotic Breeds

These are foreign breeds of cows which have been introduced in our country. The selected breeds of cows that have been successfully used for cross breeding in our country are:

- **Jersey**: England
- **Holstein Friesian**: Holland
- **Brown Swiss**: A dual purpose breed of cow from Switzerland

Figure 6.9 Indian and Foreign Cow Breeds

Cross Breeds/Improved Breeds of Cows

Cross or improved breeds of dairy cows have been developed in India at **National Dairy Research Institute (NDRI) Karnal (haryana).** The successful

Cross breeds of cow in our country are:

- **Karan Swiss:** This is the cross breed of **Brown Swiss and Sahiwal.**
- **Karan Fries:** This is the cross breed of **Holstein-Friesian from Holland and Tharparkar of India.** The yield of milk from new cross breed cows has increased two to three times more than our indigenous cows.

Milk produced by different cow breeds is discussed in Table 6.6.

Table 6.6 Average Milk Production by Cow Breed

Dairy breeds of cows	Average milk production (litres)	Lactation periods (days)
Sahiwal	2800	300
Holstein Friesian	16000	365
Frieswal	5000	326

Draught Breeds

Cattle of this breed are strong and sturdy. They are the **'beasts of burden'**. They are used for drawing bullocks carts, ploughing land of crop fields and transporting materials from one place to another. The cows of these breeds produce less milk. Some of the common examples of these breeds are **Malvi, Nagauri, Hallikar, Kangayam, etc.**

Dual purpose or general utility breeds: In these breeds, the cows are good milk yielders and bullocks are good for draught work. Some of the breeds of this category are **Haryana, Tharparkar, Ongole, Kankrej, etc.**

Table 6.7 Types of Breeds of Cattle

Draught Breeds	Strong and sturdy chiefly for labour
Dairy of milk breeds	Specialized in milk production
Dual purpose	Both for milk production and labour

Competition Corner

Milk as drawn from the cattle is known as full cream milk. When the cream is separated and the remaining milk is called toned milk. This milk contains no fat and is known as skimmed milk.

The various milk products are:

- **Cream:** It is prepared by churning milk. The fat comes on the top which is separated by draining out the liquid. It is known as cream with 10-70%fat contents.
- **Curd:** Milk is converted to curd due to bacterial activities.
- **Buttermilk:** It is the left-over liquid after removal of butter.
- **Ghee:** After heating butter, the water evaporates and fat contents are almost 100%, forms ghee.

- **Breeds of Cow:** Cows are a good source of milk for food of human beings and bullocks help in farming and transport purposes. Based upon the milk production and other utility, various breeds of cow are categorized in three types.
- **Breeds of Buffalo:** Buffaloes are the major source of milk in our country. These are domesticated in great number. The important breeds of buffaloes with high yield of milk are as follows.
  - **Murrah :** This is original breed of Haryana and Punjab. Its average yield of milk is 1800 to 2500 litres with fat contents up to seven per cent.
  - **Mehsana :** This is a breed of Gujarat especially from Vadodara and Mehsana districts. It is cross between Murrah and Surti. Their milk production is about 1200 to 2500 litres.
  - **Surti :** This breed of buffalo is native of Kaira and vadodara districts in Gujarat. Their average milk yield is from 1600 to 1800 litres.

Competition Corner

- Cows are members of the sub-family 'Bovinae' of the family 'Bovidae'. This family also includes gazelles, buffalo, bison, antelopes, sheep and goats.
- There is an estimated 1.3 billion herd of cattle and 920 breeds of cow in the world today. Cows are referred to as the 'fosters mothers to the human race' because they produce most of the milk that people drink.
- A cow spends up to 6 hours a day eating. Cows spend over 8 hours a day chewing their cud which is regurgitated, partially digested food. Cow's each drink is equivalent to a bath tub full of water in a day.

WHITE REVOLUTION Just like the green revolution in case of crop plants, the increase in milk production has been possible due to the launching of countrywid programme called' operation flood' which resulted in the white revolution in India. This operation involved use of new imporved high milk – yielding crossbreeds of milch animals and following the practices of animal husbandry providing the with proper feed and health care. Dr. V. Kurien in credited with the designing and implementation of the largest dary development programme – the operation flood, and sharing in of the white revolution in India. He is know as the father of white revolution and is the founder chairman of the National Dairy Development Board (NDDB).

Feeding of cattle:

Cattle food is of two types:

- **Roughage:** Rich in fibre content. It includes green fodder, silage, hay.
- **Concentrate:** Rich in all types of nutrients, lacks fibre. It includes maize, oat, barley, jowar, etc.

Characterstics of healthy cattle: A healthy animal is recognized by :

- Its regular feeding
- Normal posture
- A definite body temperature
- Normal pulse and respiration rates

Symtoms of sick animal:

- The animal stops eating and becomes lethargic, looks tired and remains isolated.
- The animal shivers with high body temperature.
- The animal shows excessive formation of saliva which sometimes hangs from the mouth.
- Blisters appear on skin surface, eyes turn red, and the animal may have a running nose.
- The animal passes loose dung and coloured urine.
- The lips and ears of the animal droop.
- Milk-yield, egg-laying capacity or working capacity of the animal is reduced.

Diseases: Diseases caused are broadly of three types (discussed in Table 6.8):

- **Parasitic**
- **Infectious**
- **Non-infectious**

Table 6.8 Disease of Dairy Animals and their Causal Organism

Causal	Disease
Virus	Foot and mouth disease, Pox
Bacteria	Anthrax
Fingi	Ringworm, Dermatitis

Prevention and control:

- Providing proper shelter.
- Ensuring animal hygiene (frequent bathing and grooming) and proper disposal of dead animals and animal wastes.
- Periodic screening of animals for diseases and immediate isolation of diseased animals.
- Providing proper diet and suitable medicines under the advice of a veterinary doctor.
- Hygienic handling of all animal products and by products.
- Compulsory vaccinations.

Poultry Farming

Poultry is the collective term for domestic birds such as chicken, ducks, pheasants, geese, etc., raised for their egg and meat. Rearing, breeding and caring of fowls and related birds for eggs and meat is called Poultry farming. An egg laying poultry bird is called hen and the poultry birds reared for obtaining meat are called chicken (broilers).

- **Broiler:** They are chickens which feed on protein rich diet so that they can utilize for food purpose.
- **Layer:** Egg laying poultry is termed as layers.

Breeds of Poultry

- **Indigenous (desi) breeds of hen**

  Aseel (Indian gaming breed) Ghagus ,kadaknath
  Basara (Burrsa) Chittagong (Chattisgarh)
  Brahma Cochin

- **Exotic breeds used in India**

  White Leghorn Rhode Island Red
  Black Minorcha Plymouth
  Light Sussex

  Silver Revolution: Increase in egg production on large scale.

Competition Corner

Eggs are laid by females of many different species, including birds, reptiles, amphibians and fish they have probably been eaten by mankind. Bird's and reptile's egg consist of a protective eggshell, albumin (eggwhite), and vitellus (egg yolk), contained within various thin membranes. Egg has a calcareous shell made up of calcium carbonate. If you crack the shell and break the egg in a plate, you will find a yellow coloured solid material, called yolk. Egg yolk stores significant amount of proteins in it. Yolk is surrounded by a transparent mucilaginous material, known as albumin. Both these parts get solidified when you boil the egg and peel off its shell.

Improvement of poultry breeds: It involves the following:

- Developing of new varieties. They have following advantages.
- Number and quality of chicks are increased.
- Summer adaptation capacity.
- Low maintenance requirements.
- Dwarf broilers present for commercial chick production.

Poultry diseases: These birds suffer from many diseases caused by bacteria, fungi, viruses and parasites along with nutritional deficiencies, discussed in Table 6.9.

Table 6.9 Diseases of Poultry Birds

Name of disease	Cuasative organism	Symptoms
Dermatitis	Virus	Irritation, blisters and erruption on the skin suface.
Fowl pox	Virus	Wart like pox lesions on comb, wattles, lesions in mouth, diffulty in breathing, yellow chees like discharges from eyes and nose.
Rinderpest	Virus	Constipation followed by severe diarrhoea, discharge from eyes and nostrils, losse of appetite.
Fowl Chloera	Bacteria	Loose motions and dehydration.
Aspergilliosis	Fungus	Patches on the skin due to growth of moulds.

These can be prevented by proper cleaning sanitation and spraying of disinfectants.

Poultry farming offers other advantages like:

- Investment involved is small
- Area required is small
- Maintenance is easy
- Returns are quick

❖ INTEXT QUESTIONS

14. Name two breeds of buffaloes.

Ans: Murrah and Mehsana.

15. What are 'Sahiwal' and 'Jersey' breeds?

Ans: Sahiwal is an indigenous breed of cow whereas Jersey is the exotic breed of cow.

16. Mention two advantages of animal husbandry.

Ans: Animal husbandry is advantageous to get higher milk production from cattle and higher egg production from poultry. It helps in Utilization of animal wastes in a beneficial way.

Check Point 5

16. Name 2 Cross breeds of cow in our country.

17. Name any 2 poultry diseases caused by virus.

18. Differentiate between broiler and chicken.

19. Write any 4 characterstics of healthy cattle.

Pisciculture

Fish Farming: Fishes have been used as protein rich diet for human beings since pre-historic period. Fishes are aquatic animals and their production is called fish farming or water agriculture. Fishes are a valuable and easily accessible source of food, rich in protein, highly nutritious and easily Digestible. the production of useful aquatic plants and animals such as fishes, prawns, shrimps, lobsters, crabs, molluscs by the proper utilization of small and large water bodies called **aqua-culture.** The production and breeding of fishes by man in ponds called **pisciculture**. Fishes are freshwater and marine.

Various ways to obtain fishes:

- **Capture fishing:** From natural resources.
- **Culture fishing**: Fish farming in land water fishes, ponds, lakes, marine fishes.
- **True fishes**: finned
- **Shellfish**: prawns and molluscs

Marine Fisheries

From coastline (7500 km) and deep sea. Ex. Pomphret, mackerel, tuna, sardines, and Bombay duck are common marine fishes. Fishing is done by nets and fishes are located by satellites and echo sounders. Marine fish of high economic value are finned fishes like mullets, bhetki and pearl spots, shellfish such as prawns, mussels and oyster (for pearl).

- Prawns are crustacean (arthropoda) animal. Its common species are:
  - ***Macrobrachium rosenbergii*** (freshwater)
  - ***Peneaus monodon*** (marine)
- Oysters are bivalved molluscan animals. These are marine as well as freshwater animals.
- Common oysters used for pearl culture are:
  - ***Pinctada vulgaris*** and other species of pinctada (marine)
  - Mytilus, ***Placuna maxima*** (freshwater)

Mariculture: Marine fish culture is called **mariculture.** India's marine fishery resources include 7500 km of coastline and the deep seas beyond it.

- Indian major carps such as **Catla, Rohu, Mrigal (*Cirrhina*) (as shown in Fig. 6.10).**
- Exotic varieties such as **silver carp and grass carp.**
- **Catla** is the fastest growing carp of great economic significance.
- Popular marine fish varieties are **pomphret, mackerel, tuna, sardines and Bombay duck.**
- Yield are increased by locating large schools of fish in the open sea using satellites and echo-sounders.
- Some marine fish of high economic value are also farmed in seawater.
- This includes **finned fishes like mullets, bhetki, and pearl spots, shellfish such as prawns mussels and oysters as well as seaweed.**

Inland Fisheries

- Aquaculture is done inland fisheries:
- Yield is less.
- Fresh water resources include canals, ponds, reservoirs and rivers.
- Some fishes can be cultured alongwith rice crop called paddy culture.
- Composite fish culture system is more intensive fish farming in which both local and imported fish species are used (non-competing).

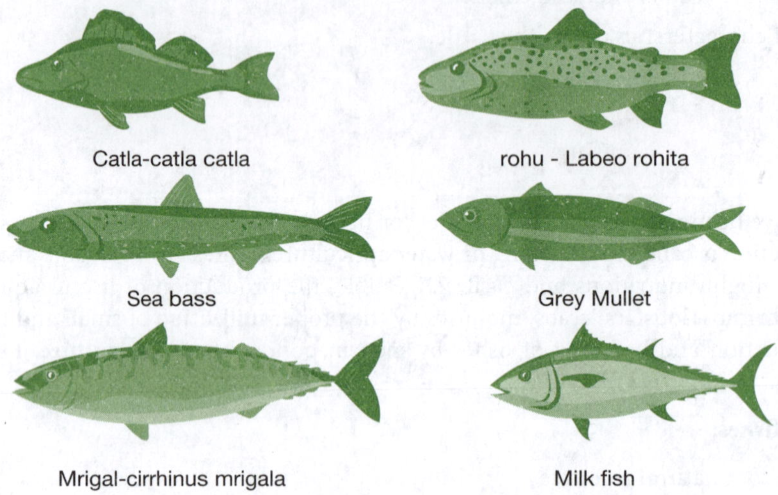

Figure 6.10 Fresh Water Fishes

- In this system, 5 or 6 fish species is used in a single fish pond. These species are selected so that they do not compete for food as they have different food habits. Thus, food available in all the parts of the pond is used. For example:
    - Catla: Surface feeders
    - Rohu: Middle zone feeders
    - Mrigals and common carps: Bottom feeder
    - Grass carp: Feed on the weeds

Benefits:

- Increases the fish yield from the pond.
- Utilization of complete food present in pond.
- Limitation of composite fish culture system.
- Breed only during monsoon.
- Lack of good quality fish seed

Steps to overcome limitations:

- Hormonal stimulation for breedingin pond called induced breeding.
- This ensure supply of pure fish seed in desired quantities.

Competition Corner

Terms fisheries is used to include all animal resouces from water (both marine and fresh water) which include fishes, crustaceans (prawns, carbs and lobsters) and molluscs.

Production of useful aquatic plants and animals, like fishes, prawns, crabs, losbters, mollusec, etc., by the use of various type of water sources is called aquaculture.

Rearing, breeding and management of fishes on large scale under controlled condition is called pisciculture.

Apiculture

Apiculture is the process of rearing of honeybees in the artificial hives, called apiaries, for the production of honey at commercial level.

Species of Honeybees: Honeybees belong to phylum Arthropoda and class Insecta. There are several species of honeybees some of which are indigenous while some of them are exotic which have been introduced to increase the yield of honey.

Indigenous Species

- **Apis dorsata:** It is commonly called rock bee or giant bee (being largest sized). Though it produces maximum amount of honey but is ferocious and migratory bee so it is difficult to domesticate this variety.
- **Apis indica:** It is commonly called Indian bee. It can be domesticated easily as it is very gentle in nature but is less producing species.
- **Apis florae:** It is commonly called little bee (being smallest sized). It is also very docile but yield is less.

Exotic Species

- **Apis mellifera:** It is commonly called Italian bee. It is preferred over the indigenous species for the commercial production of honey because of its docile nature, high yield of honey, prolific egg production, less swarming and with good defence mechanism.
- **Honeybee Colony and Social Organization:** Honeybees are social and polymorphic insects. These live in large colonies, called hives or combs, of about 40,000 to 100,000 individuals (as shown in Fig. 6.11). In a colony, there are three castes of bees which are structurally and functionally different from one another so polymorphism is associated with division of labour.

Three castes of bees are:

- **Queen:** Every healthy colony has only one fertile female called queen (as shown in Fig. 6.12). It is the mother of the colony and has well developed ovaries. It has long tapering abdomen, short legs and wings. Its sole function is to lay the eggs at the rate of 1500 to 2000 in a day, while during its life span of about 3 years, a queen lays about 1.5 to 2.0 million eggs. A queen lays two types of eggs: fertilized and unfertilized eggs. Queen and workers develop from fertilized eggs while drones develop from unfertilized eggs.

Figure 6.11 Honeybee Colony

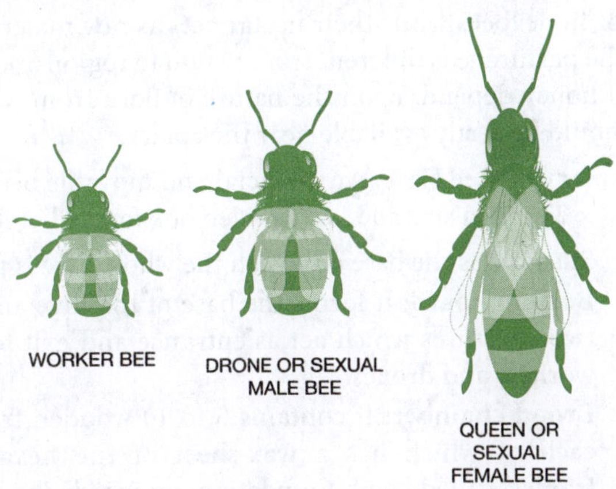

Figure 6.12 Different Castes of Honeybees

- **Workers:** These are largest in number (about 50,000 to 60,000) but smallest sized members. These are most active and perform variety of jobs like : attend the queen and nursery, clean the hives, form a new hive and produce wax, repair the comb, keep the comb cool, defend the members etc. So the workers have strong wings, long mouth parts, wax glands on abdomen, pollen collecting apparatus on the legs and a sting at the end of abdomen.
- **Drones:** These are male members of the colony and are of intermediate size. These have reduced mouth parts and are sluggish. Their sole function is to copulate with the queen.

Importance of Apiculture: Products of honeybees include honey, bees wax, bee venom and royal jelly.

- **Honey:** It is produced by the workers from the collected nectar and cane sugar. It is formed of levulose, dextrose (23%), maltose (40%), enzymes and pigment (25%), minerals, vitamins and water.

- **Bees wax:** It is used in cosmetics, paints, ointments, polishes etc.
- **Bee venom:** It is used to cure certain diseases like gout and arthritis.
- **Royal jelly:** It is used as tonic to heart patients and growing children.

Competition Corner

HONEY

Honey is viscous sweet syrup,which is formed fromthe nectar of flowers.Worker bees colect nectar

Form flowers, modify and concentrate them to form honey. Honey contains 20–40% water, 60–80% sugar, 0.2–0.5% vitamins, propolis, enzymes and pollen grains.

Importance of Honey

- It is usefull in the treatment of disorders of humans related to digestion, vomitingand stomach, liver ailments.
- It acts as blood purifier, a cure against cough and cold, sore throat, ulcer of stomach and intestine.
- It helps in growth of human body as it is a source of iron and calcium.
- It acts as a source of sugar in confectionary items.
- It helps in building up haemoglobin.
- It acts as an immediate source of energy.

Management: Involves all those steps which are required to be undertaken to obtain good quality and higher yield of honey from the honeybees. It involves following considerations:

Keystone

Honeybees are chief cross-pollinating agents. Apiculture provides additional income generating activity to the farmers.

- **Bee Forage or Pasturage:** It includes all those flowering plants which provide pollens and nectar to the honeybees, e.g., mango, coconut, almond, tamarind, ber, berseem, litchi, cotton, shisham, apple, mahua, coriander, cashew, coffee, rubber plant, guava, sunflower, etc. Their pollens form the proteinrich food for honeybees while their nectar acts as raw material of honey.
  The pasturage is different from region to region and depends upon the geographical location. The quality and taste of honey depend, upon the nature of flora from which the nectar is collected. For increased yield, the pasturage should be easily available near the apiary.
- **Apiary or Bee Hive:** An artificial and movable bee hive, commonly called apiary (as shown in Fig. 6.13), is about 46 × 23 cm in size and is a wooden box formed of following parts:
  - **Stand:** It is the base on which the whole hive is placed.
  - **Bottom board:** It forms the base of the hive and has two apertures which act as entrance and exit for the workers and drones.
  - **Brood chamber:** It contains 5 to 10 wooden frames, each of which has a wax-sheet of the hexagonal frames, called comb foundation, on which the honey form the combs.
  - **Super:** It provides extra space for the expansion of the hive.
  - **Inner cover:** It is a hole-bearing wooden cover.
  - **Top cover:** It is a plain zinc sheet for the protection of hive.
  - **Location of Apiary:** To get maximum yield of honey, a number of bee hives should be placed in that area where abundance of bee-flora is available within 1 or 2 km radius for honey collection.

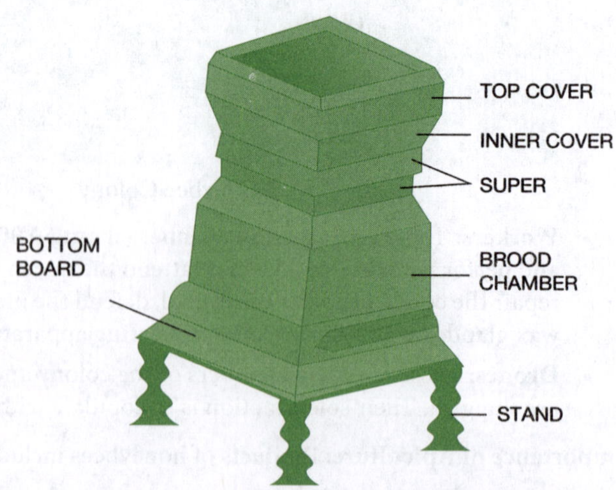

Figure 6.13 An Artificial Bee Hive (Apiary)

- **Honey Flow Season:** The yield of honey upon the total period for which large number of nectar and pollen-yielding plants are available in the vicinity of the apiary is called honey flow period. So, honey yield will be more if the bee hives are established in an area having abundance of bee flora for longer period. While the period when no nectar and pollen is available, it is called dearth period.
- **Swarming:** It is the process of leaving off the colony by the old queen with some workers and drones to establish a new colony at a new place and to provide the existing hive for the progeny. It normally occurs by the end of spring or early summer. But the frequent swarming decreases the yield of honey and increases the maintenance cost of the bee hives. So to get higher yield of honey, less swarming variety of honeybees (e.g., Apis mellifera) should be reared.

❖ INTEXT QUESTIONS

17. How is culture of Pomphret and Mackeral different from that of Catla and Rohu?

Ans: Pomphret and Mackeral are marine fishes cultured in sea water called mariculture. Whereas Catla and Rohu are freshwater fishes grown in inland fisheries like ponds, canals, reservoirs and rivers called composite fish culture.

18. What is meant by beekeeping?

Ans: Beekeeping is the practice of rearing the honeybees for obtaining honey and bee wax.

19. State the meaning of capture fishing and culture fishing.

Ans: Capture fishing: It is done from natural resources.

Culture fishing: It is done by fish farming.

20. Which species of the honeybee is commonly used for commercial honey production throughout the country?

Ans: Apis mellifera, the Italian variety of bee is commonly used for commercial honey production throughout the country

Check Point 6

20. What is apiculture?
21. Name the products obtained from apiculture.
22. What is pisciculture?
23. Give difference between apiculture and aquaculture.

STRUCTURAL OUTLINE

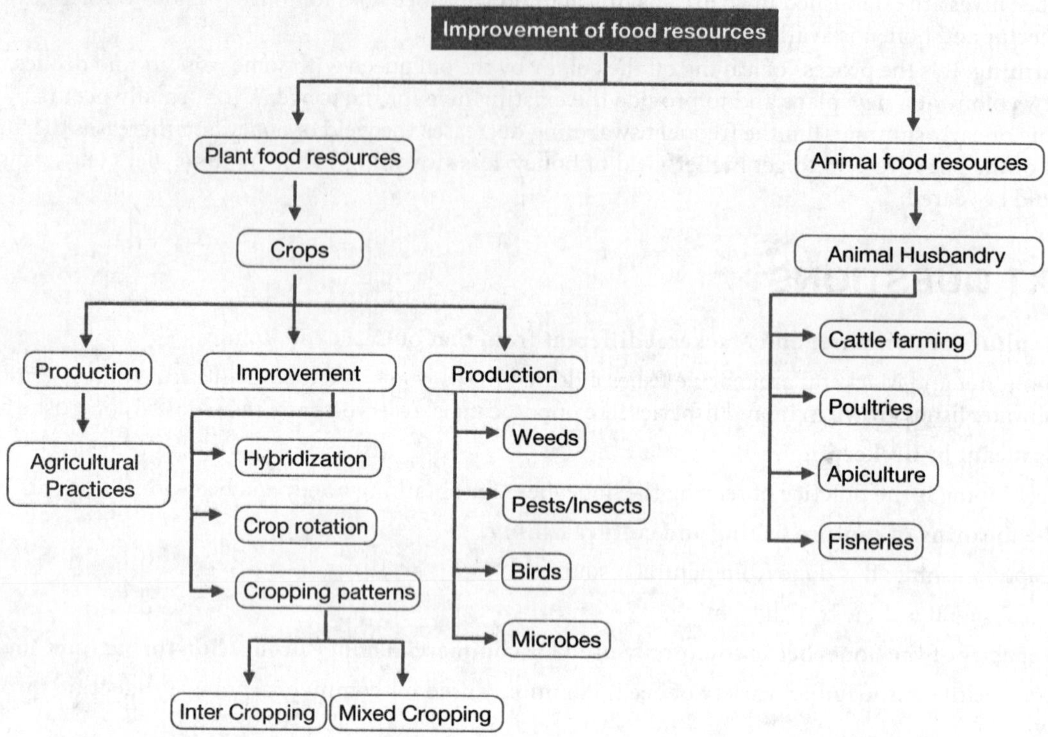

EXEMPLIFICATION

Q1. What do you mean by mariculture?

Ans: Mariculture is a practice in which marine fishes like mullets, bhetki, and pearl spots are cultured in coastal waters on a commercial scale.

Q2. How does Catla differ from Mrigal?

Ans: Catla are surface feeders while Mrigals are bottom feeders.

Q3. Name two kharif crops.

Ans: Paddy and maize.

Q4. How many nutrients are essential for plants?

Ans: Sixteen.

Q5. Name two foreign cattle breeds that are selected for long lactation periods.

Ans: Jersey and Brown Swiss.

Q6. Describe any two irrigation systems adopted in India to supply water to agricultural lands.

Ans The 2 irrigation systems are:

- **Wells:** There are two types of wells: dug wells and tube wells. In a dug well, water is collected from water-bearing strata. Tube wells can tap water from the deeper strata. From these wells, water is lifted by pumps for irrigation.
- **Canals:** In this system canals receive water from one or more reservoirs or from rivers. The main canal is divided into branch canals having further distributaries to irrigate fields.
- **River lift systems:** In this system, water is directly drawn from the rivers for supplementing irrigation in areas close to rivers.

Q7. Name two kharif and two rabi crops.

Ans.

Kharif crops: Paddy and soyabean.

Rabi crops: Wheat and gram.

Q8. Differentiate between compost and vermicompost.

Ans: Compost formation is the process in which decomposition of the organic wastes takes place to produce manures.

Vermicompost is the degradation of organic matter present in waste to produce manures with the help of earthworms.

Q9. Name the nutrients that plant obtains from air and water.

Ans:

Air - Carbon and oxygen

Water - Hydrogen and oxygen

Q10. How is the use of manure beneficial for our environment?

Ans: Manure is beneficial because they help in protecting the damage of environment from chemicals such as pesticides and fertilizers and it also help in recycling the biological wastes, i.e., animal excreta and plant wastes, thus preventing the accumulation of these things.

NCERT COMPENDIUM

1. Explain any one method of crop production which ensures high yield.

Ans:

One method used for crop production which ensures high yield is plant breeding. It is the science involved in improving the varieties of crops by breeding plants. The plants from different areas/places are picked up with desired traits and then hybridization or cross-breeding of these varieties is done to obtain a plant/crop of desired characteristic.

The high-yielding crop variety shows characteristics like high yield, early maturation, less water for irrigation, better quality seeds are produced, less fertilizers required, adapts itself to the environmental conditions.

2. Why are manure and fertilizers used in fields?

Ans:

They are used to ensure good vegetative growth (leaves, branches and flowers), giving rise to healthy plants, that results in high crop production.

3. What are the advantages of inter-cropping?

Ans:

Advantages of using inter-cropping are:

- It helps to maintain soil fertility.
- It increases productivity per unit area.
- Save labour and time.
- Both crops can be easily harvested and processed separately.

4. What is genetic manipulation? How is it useful in agricultural practices?

Ans:

Genetic manipulation is a process of incorporating desirable (genes) characters into crop varieties by hybridization. Hybridization involves crossing between genetically dissimilar plants. This is done for production of varieties with desirable characteristics like profuse branching in fodder crops, high yielding varieties in maize, wheat, etc. Genetic manipulation is useful in developing varieties which shows:

- Increased yield
- Better quality
- Shorter and early maturity period
- Better adaptability to adverse environmental conditions
- Desirable characteristics

5. How do storage grain losses occur?

Ans:

The factors responsible for loss of grains during storage are:

Abiotic factors like moisture (present in food-grains), humidity (of air) and temperature.

Biotic factors like insects, rodents, birds, mites and bacteria.

6. How do good animal husbandry practices benefit farmers?

Ans:

Good animal husbandry practices are beneficial to the farmers in the following ways:

- Improvement of breeds of the domesticated animals.
- Increasing the yield of foodstuffs such as milk, eggs and meat.
- Proper management of domestic animals in terms of shelter, feeding, care and protection against diseases, which ultimately helps the farmers to improve their economic condition.

7. What are the benefits of cattle farming?

Ans:

Cattle farming is beneficial in the following ways:

- Milk production is increased by high yielding animals.
- Good quality of meat, fibre and skin can be obtained.
- Good breed of draught animals can be obtained.

8. For increasing production, what is common in poultry, fisheries and bee-keeping?

Ans:

Through cross breeding, the production of poultry, fisheries and bee-keeping can be increased.

9. How do you differentiate between capture fishing, mariculture, and aquaculture?

Ans:

Capture fishing: It is the fishing in which fishes are captured from natural resources like pond, sea water and estuaries.

Mariculture: It is the culture of fish in marine water. Varieties like prawns, oysters, bhetki and mullets are cultured for fishing.

Aquaculture: It is done both in fresh water and in marine water.

ASSESSMENT CORNER

LEVEL 1

Fixed Response Type

Multiple Choice Questions

1. Which of the following is an oil seed crop?
(A) Rice (B) Cotton
(C) Carrot (D) Sunflower

2. For which crop transplantation is done?
(A) Paddy (B) Maize
(C) Cotton (D) Wheat

3. Beet root is used for
(A) Manure (B) oil
(C) Sugar (D) None

4. The principal cereal crop of India is
(A) wheat (B) rice
(C) maize (D) orghum

5. Which is the most important source of food and fodder?
(A) Algae (B) Fungi
(C) Lichen (D) Cereal

6. Which one of the following includes only macronutrients?
(A) C, N, Ca (B) H, Fe, P
(C) O, K, Cl (D) K, S, Zn

7. Which one is an oil yielding plant among the following?
(A) Lentil
(B) Sunflower
(C) Cauliflower
(D) Hibiscus

8. Hybridization can be done in between
(A) intervarietal
(B) interspecific
(C) intergeneric
(D) all of these

9. Green revolution refers to
(A) maintain soil fertility
(B) development of new crop variety fulfill our need
(C) use of green plants for covering the earth
(D) growing green plants to establish balance of nature

10. Plants can be made drought resistant by
(A) breeding (B) hormones
(C) colchicine (D) heat

11. Plants can be made disease resistant by
(A) heat treatment
(B) hormone treatment
(C) breeding with their wild relatives
(D) colchicine treatment

12. The element which is required in largest quantity by plants is
(A) sulphur (B) calcium
(C) phosphorus (D) nitrogen

13. Nodules with nitrogen-fixing bacteria are present in
(A) mustard (B) wheat
(C) gram (D) cotton

14. Application of nitrogenous manure to a plant cause
(A) vigorous vegetative growth
(B) early flowering
(C) early fruiting
(D) growth retardation due to toxicity of NH_3

15. Rotation of crops is essential for
(A) getting different kinds of crops
(B) increasing quality of minerals
(C) increasing quality of proteins
(D) increasing fertility of soil

16. The unwanted plants are known as
(A) grasses (B) shrubs
(C) weeds (D) fodder crops

17. Damp grains in storage gets heated due to
(A) infestation by insects
(B) decrease in humidity
(C) decrease in atmospheric pressure
(D) high moisture content and growth of moulds

18. Green manuring refers to
(A) add green leaves to the soil
(B) add nitrogen ferilizers to the soil
(C) add decomposed organic matter to soil
(D) grow young and green crops of leguminous plants along with non leguminous

19. Vermicomposting involves
(A) leech (B) cockroach
(C) earthworm (D) roundworm

20. Which one is not a source of carbohydrate?
(A) Rice (B) Millets
(C) Sorghum (D) Gram

ASSESSMENT CORNER

21. Cattle food rich in one or more nutrients but lacks fibres is called as
(A) roughage (B) concentrate
(C) sap (D) none of these

22. Find out the wrong statement from the following
(A) White revolution is meant for increase in milk production
(B) Blue revolution is meant for increase in fish production
(C) Increasing food production without compromising with environmental quality is called as sustainable agriculture
(D) None of the above

23. The specific term for poultry used for meat purpose is
(A) layers (B) broilers
(C) growers (D) none of these

24. Which species produces maximum amount of honey?
(A) Apis plorae (B) Apis indica
(C) Apis dorsata (D) None of these

25. Nitrogen, phosphorus and potassium are examples of
(A) Micro-nutrients (B) Macro-nutrients
(C) Fertilizers (D) Both I and II

26. Murrah, Surti and Mehsana are the indigenous breeds of
(A) cows (B) buffaloes
(C) poultry (D) pigs

27. Inland fisheries are referred to
(A) culturing fish in fresh water
(B) deep sea fisheries
(C) extraction of oil from fishes
(D) capturing fishes from seas

28. Green revolution in India was possible due to
(A) Better irrigation, fertilizers and pesticide facilities
(B) Exploitation of high yielding varieties
(C) Intensive cultivation
(D) All of the above

29. Leghorn is related to
(A) Apiculture
(B) Dairy farming
(C) Pisciculture
(D) Poultry

30. Compost manure is produced from
(A) Farmyard manure and green manure
(B) Farm refuse and household refuse
(C) Organic remains of biogas plants
(D) Rotted vegetables and animal refuse

Fill in the Blanks

1. Water acts as a _______ for absorption of water.
2. Pigeon pea is a good source of _______.
3. The chemical used to destroy weeds are known as _______.
4. Rust is a disease of wheat crop caused by _______.
5. 2, 4 – D and MCPA both are example of _______ .
6. Growing two or more crops in definite row patterns is known as _______
7. _______ is an organic matter obtained from decomposition of animal and plant waste.
8. Manure and fertilizers are the main sources of _______ supplied to crops.
9. Berseem is an important _______ crop.
10. The growing of different crops on a piece of land in pre-planned succession is called _______.

True/False

1. Fish may be obtained from marine and inland resources.
2. Animal feeds include vitamins and protein mainly.
3. The cross between genetically dissimilar plants is called hybridization.
4. Capture fishing is the process of obtaining fish from natural resources.
5. Chemicals that kill weeds are known as herbicide.
6. Cattle feed induces roughage and concentrate.
7. Malathion is a rodenticide.
8. Manures cannot restore soil structure.
9. Manures and fertilizers are used in fields to enrich the soil with organic matter and nutrients.
10. Sahiwal is an Indian cattle breed.

Match Type Questions

1. Match the following I and II.

Column I		Column II	
(i)	Kharif	(a)	Rice
(ii)	Rabi	(b)	Wheat
(iii)	Tilling	(c)	Urea
(iv)	Fertilizer	(d)	Ploughing

2. Match the following I and II.

Column I		Column II	
(i)	Micronutries	(a)	Soyabean
(ii)	Kharif crop	(b)	Bee
(iii)	Rabi crop	(c)	Wheat
(iv)	Apis mellifera	(d)	Molybdenum

3. Match the following I and II.

Column I		Column II	
(i)	Rearing honeybee	(a)	Pisciculture
(ii)	Manure	(b)	Add humus
(iii)	Culturing fish	(c)	Unwanted plant
(iv)	Weeds	(d)	Apiculture

Assertion and Reason Type Questions

***Direction:** In each of the following questions, a statement of Assertion is given and a corresponding statement of Reason is given just below it. Of the statements, given below, mark the correct answer as:*

(A) Both assertion and reason are true and reason is the correct explanation of assertion.
(B) Both assertion and reason are true but reason is not the correct explanation of assertion.
(C) Assertion is true but reason is false.
(D) Both Assertion and Reason are false.

1. **Assertion:** It is not good idea to rely on rainfall as source of irrigation.
Reason: Timing of monsoon season is highly fluctuating.

2. **Assertion:** All living organisms requires food.
Reason: Plant can synthesize their own food.

3. **Assertion:** Manure is advantageous for our environment.
Reason: Manure contains chemicals like nitrogen, phosphorus and potassium.

4. **Assertion:** Proper cleaning for cows and buffaloes is required.
Reason: Proper cleaning maintains the health of animals and also helps in clean milk production.

5. **Assertion:** Fungicides act against fungal pathogens.
Reason: Fungicides are not harmful to human beings.

6. **Assertion:** Earthworms are friends of farmers.
Reason: They fulfil the nutritional requirements of soil.

7. **Assertion:** Inter cropping prevents pests.
Reason: Pests can be controlled biologically by their natural parasites and pathogens.

8. **Assertion:** Vaccinations are given to farm animals.
Reason: Vaccinations protect the farm animals from a number of diseases caused due to virus and bacteria.

9. **Assertion:** Nutrients are applied in the form of fertilizers.
Reason: Chemical fertilizer contains the necessary plant nutrients.

10. **Assertion:** 2,4-D is a weedicide chemical.
Reason: It is produced synthetically in factories.

Comprehension Type Questions

Passage 1: Apiculture is done for producing honey, wax and medicine. The varieties used for apiculture includes A. dorsata, A. florae, etc., because they sting less and live longer in given beehive.

1. Rearing of bee is done for
(A) Honey (B) Wax
(C) Furfural (D) Both (A) and (B)

2. Honeybee are kept in
(A) Cage (B) Cave
(C) Beehive (D) All

3. Useful honeybee is/are
(A) A. Florae (B) A. dorsata
(C) Both (D) None of these

Passage 2: Poultry farming means to raise poultry birds for egg and meat. Improved poultry breeds are developed and farmed to produce layers for eggs and broilers for meat. The cross-breeding programmes between Indian (indigenous, for example, Aseel) and foreign (exotic, for example, Leghorn) breeds for variety improvement Broiler chickens are fed with vitamin-rich supplementary feed for good growth rate and better feed efficiency and sent to market for meat purposes. The housing, nutritional and environmental requirements of broilers are somewhat different from those of egg layers. The daily food requirement for broilers is protein rich with adequate fat. The level of vitamins A and K is kept high in the poultry feeds.

4. Aseel is an _________ poultry breed.
(A) Indian
(B) Exotic
(C) Cross
(D) None of these

ASSESSMENT CORNER

5. Poultry breeds which are produce for eggs are termed as __________.
   (A) Layers (B) Broilers
   (C) Indigenous (D) Exotic

6. Poultry breeds which are produce for meat are termed as __________.
   (A) Layers (B) Broilers
   (C) Indigenous (D) Exotic

Passage 3: Plants manufacture their food in sunlight by the process of photosynthesis. There are some crops, which are grown in rainy season, called the kharif season from the month of June to October. Examples: Paddy, soyabean, pigeon pea, maize, cotton, green gram and black gram, etc. Some of the crops are grown in the winter season, called the rabi season from November to April. Examples: Wheat, gram, peas, mustard, linseed.

7. What is kharif season period?
   (A) June to July
   (B) June to October
   (C) June to November
   (D) June to December

8. What is rabi season period?
   (A) November to April
   (B) November to March
   (C) November to February
   (D) November to January

9. Plants manufacture their food in sunlight by the process called ___________.
   (A) Photosynthesis (B) Photoperiod
   (C) Photolysis (D) None of the above

Free Response Type

Very Short Answer Type Questions

1. Define silviculture.
2. What is meant by agriculture?
3. Name the two growing seasons for crops in our country also give examples.
4. Defined Eutrophication?
5. What are the two main components of cattle feed?
6. Why legumes are desirable in crop rotation?
7. Why is manure important for crop production?
8. Name any two poultry diseases.
9. Define a fertilizer.
10. What is compost?

Short Answer Type Questions

1. What are fertilizers? Mention three important features of fertilizers.
2. What is the different between pisciculture and aquaculture?
3. Define organic farming. Why is organic farming important to us?
4. Name two diseases of each of the following:
   (i) Cattle (ii) Poultry
   (iii) Fish
5. Write short note on honey.
6. Write short note on cattle feeding.
7. What factors may be responsible for losses of grains during storage?
8. What method is commonly used of improving cattle breeds and why?
9. Name two types of animal feed and write their functions.
10. Differentiate between compost and vermicompost?

Long Answer Type Questions

1. What are the various irrigation systems adopted in India?
2. Compare the use of manures and fertilizers in maintaing soil fertility.
3. What is the advantage of intercropping and crop rotation?
4. Discuss the role of hybridization in crop improvement.
5. Discuss various methods for weed control.

Case Based Questions

Case 1: Honeybee rearing is now becoming an extra source of income for farmers. apiculture is practiced for producing honey, wax and medicine. The varieties used for apiculture includes A. dorsata, A. florae, etc., because they sting less and live longer in given beehive.

1. Rearing of bee is done for
   (A) Honey
   (B) Wax
   (C) Furfural
   (D) Both (A) and (B)

2. Honeybee are kept in
(A) Cage (B) Cave
(C) Beehive (D) All of the above

3. Useful honeybee is/are
(A) A. Florae (B) A. dorsata
(C) Both (A) and (D) (D) None of these

Case 2: Abhishek is rearing poultry birds in the backyard of his house. He started Rearing, breeding and caring of fowls and related birds for eggs and meat. chickens were fed on protein rich diet so that they can utilize for food purpose. he also reared some exotic breeds to get more egg production.

1. Name of egg laying fowl.
(A) Layer (B) Broiler
(C) Breeder (D) None

2. Name the fowl used for meat purpose.
(A) Layer (B) Broiler
(C) Breeder (D) None

3. Which is best exotic breed for egg production?
(A) Aseel
(B) Dhadhas
(C) Kadaknath
(D) Leghorn

Case 3: Meera went to vegetable market with his father, a biology teacher. There, she saw many varieties of different vegetables such as different kind of chilies and several varieties of potato and tomatoes, etc. He asked his father some questions:

1. What is the need of producing so many varieties of different crop plants?
2. What is the name of branch of science which deals with crop improvement?
3. What are the methods used by plant breeders?
4. What is hybridization?

Level 2

Multiple Choice Questions

1. Three crops that contribute maximum to global food grain production are
(A) Wheat, Rice and Maize
(B) Wheat, Rice and Barley
(C) Wheat, Maize and Sorghum
(D) Rice, Maize and Sorghum

2. Which of the following plant disease can be controlled by chemical control?
(A) Viral disease
(B) Diseases caused by nematodes
(C) Fungal disease
(D) All of these

3. Which of the following is not an intention of producing plants using a portion of a plant tissue or cells in a suitable nutrient medium based on the principle 'plant cells have the capacity to produce plants of their own kind'?
(A) To obtain disease resistant and high yielding variety of plants
(B) To reduce the period of life span of plants
(C) To develop large number of plants in a limited space and time
(D) To obtain plants which produce more fertile seeds

4. Which one of the following is not a cereal crop?
(A) Wheat (B) Rice
(C) Sorghum (D) Mustard

5. 'Sonalika' is a variety of
(A) Rice (B) Wheat
(C) Maize (D) Bajra

6. Using fertilizers in farming is an example of
(A) No cost production
(B) Low cost production
(C) High cost production
(D) None of these

7. Nodules with nitrogen-fixing bacteria are present in
(A) gram (B) wheat
(C) mustard (D) cotton

8. Which of the following plant store food in their root?
(A) Radish (B) Potato
(C) Tomato (D) Maize

9. Potato tuber is an underground stem because it bears
(A) Buds and nodes
(B) Adventitious Root
(C) Abundant food reserve
(D) Chlorophyll is not found

10. Parthenium is a type of
(A) Disease
(B) Pesticide
(C) Weed
(D) Pathogen

11. Reena has a burning sensation in her stomach due to acidity she needs to eat
(A) Tomato (B) Apple
(C) Tamarind (D) Baking soda

12. Which of the following organism is a saprophyte?
(A) Penicillium (B) Malaria parasite
(C) Leech (D) Ant.

13. Milk, soyabean, eggs are related to which of the following group?
(A) Energy giving foods
(C) Protective foods
(B) Body building foods
(D) Weight gaining foods.

14. Organic farming is the technique of raising crops through the use of
(A) Manure
(B) Biofertilizers
(C) Resistant varieties
(D) All of these

15. Which of the following phytohormone helps in fruit ripening?
(A) Auxin (B) Gibberellin
(C) Cytokinin (D) Ethylene

16. The wings of house fly and the wings of a sparrow are an example of
(A) Analogous organs
(B) Vestigial organs
(C) Respiratory organs
(D) Homologous organs

17. Jaya and Ratna are varieties of
(A) Maize (B) Rice
(C) Wheat (D) Bajra

18. Which of the following is not a weed?
(A) Pea (B) *Parthenium*
(C) Motha (D) *Xanthium*

19. High-yielding varieties of wheat were initially developed by an Indian scientist by cross breeding the traditional varieties with
(A) Mexican Varieties
(B) European Varieties
(C) American Varieties
(D) African Varieties

20. Pulses are rich in protein because of:
(A) Insectivorous habit
(B) Requiring high dose of nitrogen fertilizers
(C) Rhizobium
(D) Green manuring

Higher Order Thinking Skills (HOTS)

1. Irrigation systems are in practice in India for the supply of water in agricultural fields. Why?

2. Arrange these statements in correct sequence of preparation of green manure.
(a) Green plants are decomposed in soil.
(b) Green plants are cultivated for preparing manure or crop plant parts are used.
(c) Plants are ploughed and mixed into the soil.
(d) After decomposition it becomes green manure.

3. Write the modes by which insects affect the crop yield.

4. Nitrogenous fertilizers are usually not required by the leguminous crops. Why?

5. Figure shows the two crop fields [plots A and B] have been treated by manures and chemical fertilisers respectively, keeping other environmental factors same.
Observe the graph and answer the following questions.
(i) Why does plot B show sudden increase and then gradual decrease in yield?
(ii) Why is the highest peak in plot A graph slightly delayed?
(iii) What is the reason for the different pattern of the two graphs?

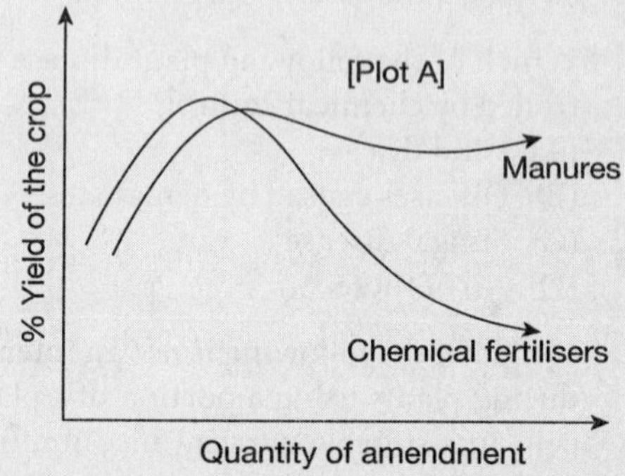

6. Why are crops like guar grown by some farmers before sowing the seeds of a crop?

7. Group the following and tabulate them as energy yielding, protein yielding, oil yielding and fodder crop.
Wheat, rice, berseem, maize, gram, oat, pigeon gram, sudan grass, lentil, soyabean, groundnut, castor and mustard.

ARCHIVE CORNER

1. Read the given statements and select the option that correctly identifies them as true (T) and false (F) ones.
   (i) Aphids and leafhoppers are sucking insects whereas locusts and grasshoppers are chewing insects.
   (ii) Exotic breed which is very popular for egg laying but is not ideal for meat production is Leghorn.
   (iii) Mycorrhiza is a symbiotic association of certain algae with roots of higher plants.
   (iv) Fertilisers are nutrient specific.
   (v) Red Sindhi is indigenous draught breed of cow whereas Holstein-Friesian is exotic milch breed of cow.

	(i)	(ii)	(iii)	(iv)	(v)
(A)	F	T	F	T	F
(B)	T	T	F	T	F
(C)	T	T	T	T	F
(D)	F	F	F	T	T

2. Refer to the given paragraph where few words have been italicised and select the incorrect option.
   Animals used in agriculture and for transport are called draught animals whereas animals used for milk production are called milch animals. Production of good quality milk depends much on the type of breed, e.g., exotic breeds of cattle like Red Sindhi and Jersey produce on an average 60L milk in a day. On the other hand, local breeds such as Sahiwal and Brown Swiss produce on an average only 6 - 8L of milk per day. Cattle suffer from several diseases which may reduce the milk production, e.g., anthrax is a fatal viral disease, whereas foot and mouth disease is a bacterial disease which broadly affect the health of cattle thereby, reducing milk production.
   (A) Milch and draught should not be replaced as they are correctly mentioned.
   (B) The positions of Red Sindhi and Brown Swiss should be interchanged.
   (C) The positions of viral and bacterial should be interchanged.
   (D) The positions of Jersey and Sahiwal should be interchanged.

3. Refer to the given table and select the option that correctly fills the blanks in it.

Animal	Indigenous breed	Exotic breed
Cow	X	Holstein-Friesian
Poultry	Aseel	Y
Honeybee	Z	A. adamsoni

	X	Y	Z
(A)	Red	Sindhi Busra	A. mellifera
(B)	Jersey	Rhode Island red	A. florea
(C)	Sahiwal	Australorp	A. dorsata
(D)	Brown Swiss	Kadaknath	A. indica

4. Identify crops X and Y from the given table and select the correct option regarding them.

S. No.	X	Y
(i)	These crops are grown in hot and wet conditions.	These crops are grown in cold and nearly dry conditions.
(ii)	These crops are sown in beginning of rainy season in June-July.	These crops are sown in October-November when monsoon is retreated.
(iii)	These crops are harvested during September-October.	These crops are harvested in March-April.

   (A) Crop X could be wheat whereas crop Y could be cotton.
   (B) Crop X could be green gram whereas crop Y could be linseed.
   (C) Crop X could be groundnut whereas crop Y could be jute.
   (D) Crop X could be rice whereas crop Y could be soybean

5. Two different fields X and Y were treated with two different substances to increase crop yield. Amount of humus in their respective fields was observed for a period of time as shown in the given graph.

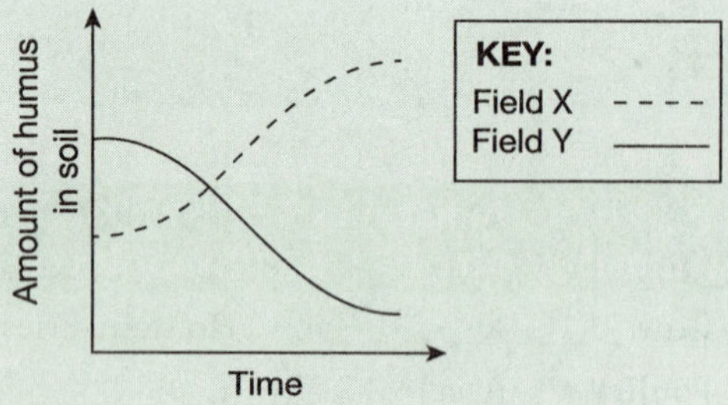

Select the incorrect statement regarding substances applied in both fields X and Y.

(A) Substance applied in field X removes general deficiency of soil whereas the one applied in field Y provides only specific essential nutrients to the soil.

(B) Substance applied in field X is readily absorbed by the crop plants whereas that applied in field Y is absorbed slowly.

(C) Substance applied in field X is cheap and can be prepared in rural homes whereas that applied in field Y is prepared in factories.

(D) Substance applied in field X does not cause pollution but that applied in field Y causes pollution.

6. Read the given statements.

(i) Bee wax obtained from beehive is deposition of excretory products of honeybee.

(ii) Fish culture is sometimes done in combination with rice crop so that fish are grown in the water accumulated in the paddy field.

(iii) Fish feed in different zones of pond to make most efficient use of available food.

(iv) Sahiwal and Murrah are exotic breeds used extensively in cattle farming.

(v) Intercropping is growing two or more crops simultaneously on the same field in a definite pattern.

Which of the given statements are incorrect?

(A) (i), (ii) and (iii) only

(B) (ii) and (iv) only

(C) (i) and (iv) only

(D) (i), (iv) and (v) only

7. Select the group that contains only the micronutrients.

(A) Sulphur, Molybdenum, Nitrogen

(B) Zinc, Copper, Manganese

(C) Oxygen, Iron, Potassium

(D) Carbon, Chlorine, Nickel

8. Refer to the given table and select the option that correctly fills the blanks in it.

Animal	Indigenous breed	Exotic breed
Cow	Sahiwal	P
Poultry	Q	Plymouth rock
Honeybee	A. indica	R

	P	Q	R
(A)	Jersey	Aseel	A.mellifera
(B)	Wyandotte	Malvi	A.dorsata
(C)	Alpine	Bakharwal	A.dorsata
(D)	Australorp	Ghagus	A.adamsoni

9. Three crops that contribute maximum to global food grain production are

(A) Wheat, Rice and Maize

(B) Wheat, Rice and Barley

(C) Wheat, Maize and Sorghum

(D) Rice, Maize and Sorghum

10. Which of the following plant disease can be controlled by chemical control?

(A) Viral disease

(B) Diseases caused by nematodes

(C) Fungal disease

(D) All of these

11. Which of the following is not an intention of producing plants using a portion of a plant tissue or cells in a suitables nutrient medium based on the principle 'plant cells have the capacity to produce plants of their own kind'?

(A) To obtain disease resistant and high yielding variety of plants

(B) To reduce the period of life span of plants

(C) To develop large number of plants in a limited space and time

(D) To obtain plants which produce more fertile seeds

12. Which one of the following is not a cereal crop?

(A) Wheat (B) Rice

(C) Sorghum (D) Mustard

13. 'Sonalika' is a variety of

(A) Rice (B) Wheat

(C) Maize (D) Bajra

14. Which species of Italian honeybee is useful for honey production?

(A) Epis serena indica (B) Epis corseta

(C) Epis flora (D) Epis meliphera

ARCHIVE CORNER

15. Honeybee culture is known as
(A) Silviculture (B) Apiculture
(C) Sericulture (D) Pisciculture

16. Which of the following plant store food in their root?
(A) Radish (B) Potato
(C) Tomato (D) Maize

17. Potato Tuber is an underground stem because it bears
(A) Buds and nodes
(C) Adventitious Root
(B) Abundant food reserve
(D) Chlorophyll is not found

18. Which is not a method to maintain the fertility of the soil?
(A) Crop rotation
(C) Weding
(B) Mixed cropping
(D) Leaving the land uncultibated for sometime

19. Reena has a buring sensation in her stomach due to acidity she needs to eat.
(A) Tomato (B) Apple
(C) Tamarind (D) Baking soda

20. Which of the following organism is a saprophyte?
(A) Penicillium (B) Malaria parasite
(C) Leech (D) Ant.

21. Milk, soyabeen, eggs are related to which of the following group?
(A) Energy giving foods
(C) Protective foods
(B) Body building foods
(D) Weight gaining foods

22. Organic farming is the technique of raising crops through the use of
(A) Manure
(B) Biofertilizers
(C) Resistant varieties
(D) All of these

23. Which of the following phytohormone helps in fruit ripening?
(A) Auxin
(B) Gibberallin
(C) Cytokinin
(D) Ethylene

24. The wings of house fly and the wings of a sparrow are an example of
(A) Analogous organs
(B) Vestigial organs
(C) Respiratory organs
(D) Homologous organs

25. Jaya and Ra1na are varieties of
(A) Maize (B) Rice
(C) Wheat (D) Bajra

26. Which of the following in NOT an ancient water harvesting structure?
(A) Kattas (B) Sargam
(C) Kulhs (D) Surangam

27. High yielding varieties of wheat were initially developed by an Indian scientist by cross breeding the traditional varieties with
(A) Mexican Varieties
(B) Europian Varieties
(C) American Varieties
(D) African Varieties

ANSWER KEYS

Level 1

Fixed Response Type

Multiple Choice Questions

1. D 2. A 3. C 4. A 5. D 6. A 7. B 8. B 9. A
10. C 11. D 12. C 13. B 14. D 15. C 16. D 17. D 18. C
19. D 20. D 21. B 22. D 23. B 24. C 25. B 26. B 27. A
28. D 29. B 30. B

Fill in the Blanks

1. Solvent 2. Proteins 3. Weedicides
4. Fungus (Puccinia) 5. Weedicides/Herbicide 6. Inter-cropping
7. Manure/compost 8. Nutrients 9. Fodder
10. Crop rotation

True/False

1. True 2. False 3. True 4. True 5. True 6. True 7. False 8. False 9. True
10. True

Match Type Questions

1. (i)-(a), (ii)-(b), (iii)-(d), (iv)-(c) 2. (i)-(d), (ii)-(a), (iii)-(c), (iv)-(b)
3. (i)-(d), (ii)-(b), (iii)-(a), (iv)-(c)

Assertion and Reason Type Questions

1. A 2. B 3. C 4. A 5. C 6. A 7. B 8. A 9. A
10. B

Comprehension Type Questions

Passage 1
1. D 2. C 3. C

Passage 2
4. A 5. A 6. B

Passage 3
7. B 8. A 9. A

Level 2

Multiple Choice Questions

1. A 2. D 3. B 4. D 5. B 6. C 7. A 8. A 9. A
10. C 11. D 12. A 13. B 14. D 15. D 16. A 17. B 18. A
19. A 20. C

ANSWER KEYS

Archive Corner

1. B	2. D	3. C	4. B	5. B	6. C	7. B	8. A	9. A
10. D	11. B	12. D	13. B	14. D	15. B	16. A	17. A	18. C
19. D	20. A	21. B	22. D	23. D	24. A	25. B	26. B	27. A

HINTS AND EXPLANATIONS

CHAPTER 1: THE FUNDAMENTAL UNIT OF LIFE

Check Point 1

1. The smallest unit that can live on its own and that makes up all living organisms and the tissues of the body is called cell.
2. The three criteria of defining the cell are:
   - All living organisms are composed of one or more cells.
   - The cell is the basic unit of structure and organization in organisms.
   - Cells arise from pre-existing cells.
3. **Unicellular organisms:** Bacteria, amoeba, paramecium

   Multicellular organisms: Humans, animals, plants

Check Point 2

4. Cellulose + Hemicellulose
5. Refer to the topic-Cell membrane.
6. Refer to the topic-Active and bulk transport.

Check Point 3

7. Refer to the topic-types of lysosomes.
8. Refer to the topic-differences between smooth and rough endoplasmic reticulum.
9. Mitochondria generate energy rich molecules ATP.
10. Refer to the topic-Cell division.

Level 1

Fixed Response Type

Multiple Choice Questions

1. **(D)** Lysosomes
2. **(C)** Robert Hooke
3. **(C)** Cytoplasm consists of the network of ER.
4. **(A)** Plant cells possess plastids called chloroplasts which are dedicated organelles to convert solar energy to chemical energy, i.e., photosynthesis. This makes plants autotrophic, i.e., they can make their own food.
5. **(A)** Chromosomes
6. **(C)** ATP
7. **(A)** Osmosis
8. **(A)** Plasma membrane is the outer lining of the cell, which separates the protoplasm from the external environment.
9. **(B)** Plant cells have a cell wall, as well as a cell membrane. In plants, the cell wall surrounds the cell membrane. This gives the plant cell its unique rectangular shape. Animal cells simply have a cell membrane, but no cell wall.
10. **(A)** Lysosomes act as the waste disposal system of the cell. They have hydrolyzing enzymes which can digest biological substances.
11. **(A)** WBC
12. **(B)** RBC lacks nucleus.
13. **(C)** ATP
14. **(A)** Robert Hooke
15. **(C)** J.E. Purkinje
16. **(C)** Protein synthesis is possible through ribosomes.
17. **(D)** Hydrolytic enzymes
18. **(A)** Tonoplast is the membrane surrounding the vacuole.

19. (C) Spindle formation is possible through centriole.
20. (C) Golgi apparatus is associated with cell secretion.
21. (D) Starch
22. (B) Nucleus would not be considered as the part of cytoplasm.
23. (D) Ribosomes
24. (C) Centrosome
25. (A) DNA is the common feature.
26. (B) Double and porous
27. (B) It disappears at late prophase.
28. (C) Eukaryotes
29. (C) Nucleolus is continuous with cytoplasm through nuclear pores.
30. (A) Fontana

Assertion and Reason Type Questions

1. (B) Both assertion and reason are correct but the reason is not the correct explanation of the assertion. All plants and animals are composed of cells; and plants and animals are made up of DNA.
2. (A) The cell membrane is called selectively permeable as it only allows specific molecules like water and gaseous molecules can pass through the cell membrane directly.
3. (A) If the cell is placed in a **hypotonic solution**, water will enter into the cell through osmosis and the cell will become swollen.
4. (A) In plants, a single, large, and permanent vacuole is present which is surrounded by a membrane called tonoplast and is filled with cell sap.
5. (A) Both assertion and reason are correct, and reason is the correct explanation for assertion. Mitochondria produce energy (in form of ATP) by oxidation of food.
6. (A) In all life forms, including bacteria, plants, animals, and humans, the cell was defined as the most basic structural and functional unit.
7. (D) Assertion is false but reason is true. Plant cells have cell wall to counteract **turgor pressure (T.P)** by exerting exactly equal and opposite wall pressure. Wall pressure stops entry of water into plant cells beyond a certain limit, thus prevents their bursting.
8. (C) Assertion is true but reason is false. As mitochondria and chloroplasts have their own DNA and ribosomes, they produce only a small proportion of their own proteins.
9. (A) Both assertion and reason are correct, and reason is the correct explanation for assertion. DNA or deoxyribonucleic acid, is the hereditary material in humans and almost all other organisms. Nearly, every cell in a person's body has the same DNA.
10. (B) Both assertion and reason are true but reason is not the correct explanation of assertion. Carbon dioxide and oxygen move across the cell membrane by diffusion process but plasma membrane only permit the entry and exit of selective materials in and out of the cell.

Comprehension Type Questions

1. **M.J. Schlieden** and **Theodore Schwann**
2. Rudolf Virchow
3. This statement was given by **Rudolf Virchow**.
4. All plants and animals are composed of cell. Cell is the structural and functional unit of life. All cells arise from pre-existing cells.
5. Plasma membrane is called **selectively permeable membrane** because it allows the entry and exit of selected materials in and out of the cell.
6. Movement of solutes from higher concentration to lower concentration is called **diffusion**.
7. Movement of solvent water from high concentration to lower concentration through **semi-permeable membrane**.
8. Movement of solvent water into cell is called **endosmosis** while movement of solvent water out of the cell is called exosmosis.
9. The entire matter found inner to the cell membrane is called **protoplasm**.
10. Cytoplasm and nucleus
11. Protoplasm
12. The substance present between cell membrane and nucleus is called cytoplasm.

Free Response Type

Very Short Answer Type Questions

1. Ribosome.
2. These are isolated cells, whose cell wall is withdrawn and are enveloped by plasmalemma. They can be the cells of fungi, plants, or bacteria. They are also known as naked cells.
3. Endocytosis is found only in animals because the cell wall is absent in animals.
4. Osmosis is the movement of water molecules from a solution with a high concentration of water molecules to a solution with a lower concentration of water molecules, through a cell's partially permeable membrane.
5. The cell membrane is called selectively permeable as it only allows specific molecules to pass.
6. The golgi apparatus is responsible for transporting, modifying, and packaging proteins and lipids into vesicles for delivery to targeted destinations.
7. PPLO (Pleuro Pneumonia Like Organisms)
8. Mitochondria are utilized to generate adenosine triphosphate (ATP) from the food. This ATP acts as the energy currency of the cell.
9. They remove cell debris, hence they are called scavengers of the cells.
10. Refer page number 1.24 Under the functions of lysosomes.

Short Answer Type Questions

1. Refer to the topic-plastids.
2. When ribosomes attach to the surface of an ER, it is called Rough ER. Smooth ER does not have ribosomes on its surface. The smooth endoplasmic reticulum helps make fats and lipids, and along with proteins aids in cell membrane assembly and membrane biosynthesis. As cell membrane consists of lipids and proteins.
3. Osmosis is a process in which water moves from a region of high water concentration to a region of low water concentration through a semipermeable membrane.
4. Refer to Figure No. 1.5
5.

Prokaryotic cell (primitive nucleus)	Eukaryotic cell (well-developed nucleus)
1. The cells having incipient of primitive nucleus (i.e., nucleus lacks nuclear envelope, nucleolus) and membrane bound cell organelles [mitochondria, plastids er. Golgi apparatus etc.] Are absent called prokaryotic cell.	1. The cells having will defined nucleus (i.e nucleus contain nuclear envelope & nucleolus) and membrane bound cell organelles (mitochondria, plastids er. Golgi apparatus etc.] Are called eukaryotic cells
2. Ribosome – 70s type	2. Ribosome – 80s type
3. Normal size – 1 to 10 μm	3. Normal size – 5 to 100 μm
4. DNA – circular and lack histone protein	4. DNA – linear and having histone protein
5. Respiration by plasma membrane E.g., bacteria, mycoplasma, blue green algae	5. Respiration by mitochondria E.g., protists, fungi, plantae, animalia

6. Refer to Intext question no. 2.
7. Refer to the topic-Chloroplast.

   Function: This is the site of dark reaction of photosynthesis.
8. Ribosome is the granular structure first observed under the electron microscope as dense particles by George Palade (1953). They are composed of ribonucleic acid (RNA) and proteins and are not surrounded by any membrane. Ribosomes are found in all kinds of cells prokaryotic as well as eukaryotic. In prokaryotic cells, they float freely in the cytoplasm.

70S Ribosome

80S Ribosome

Function: Site of protein synthesis, so these are also called as protein factories.

9. Cell division is the process by which a parent cell divides into two or more daughter cells. During cell division, the cell nucleus splits and the DNA is replicated. There are two types of cell divisions: mitosis and meiosis.

10. In animal cells, centrioles play important role in initiation of cell division by arranging spindle fibres between two poles of cell. The location of centrioles during cell division decides the plant of division. It forms the basal granule of cilia and flagella in microorganisms, zoospores, and motile gametes. It forms tail of sperm.

Long Answer Type Questions

1. **Mitochondria**

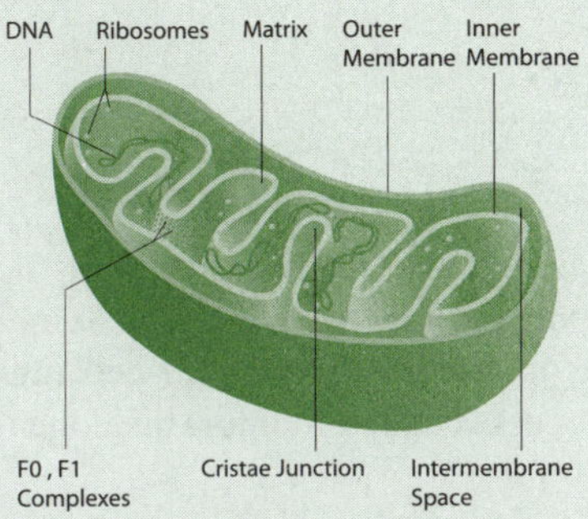

It is a rod-shaped structure found in the cytoplasm of all eukaryotic cells except mammalian erythrocytes. They also do not exist in prokaryotes. Most mitochondria are found in metabolically active cells and are also called as "**cell power station**" or "**battery storage**". It is a double-membrane structure in which the outer membrane has specific proteins and the inner membrane folds inward to form chambers called cristae. A 'crista' is a fold of the inner mitochondrial membrane that contains enzymes for respiratory cycles such as the Kreb cycle. ATP synthesis units are called oxisomes or F0-F1 particles. The space between the inner and outer membranes of mitochondria is called the peri-mitochondrial space. The liquid present in the mitochondria is called the matrix.

Functions:

Its main function is to generate and store energy in the form of ATP.

It is part of the Krebs respiratory cycle because it contains enzymes of the **Krebs cycle**.

2.

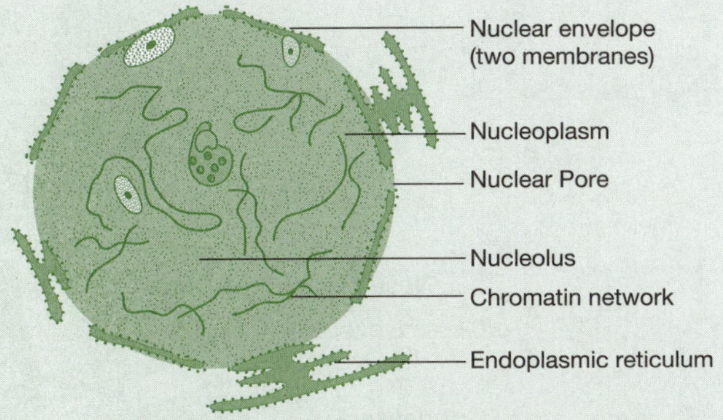

Difference between nucleus and nucleoid.

Nucleus	Nucleoid
Nucleus is the cell structure, which is spherical or oval, usually located in the eukaryotic cell.	Nucleoid is the part of a prokaryotic cell having undefined nuclear region.
DNA with histone protein	DNA without histone
Nucleolus present	Nucleolus absent

3. Refer to the topic-Endoplasmic Reticulum.

4. Refer page number 1.13.

5. Structure of compound/light Microscope:

The microscope used in schools is called compound microscope (Fig 1.3). A compound microscope has following parts :

(i) **Base:** It is the basal, metallic, horseshoe-shaped structure. It bears the whole weight of microscope.

(ii) **Handle:** It is the curved part to hold the microscope.It is also called as arm.

(iii) **Stage:** A rigid metal rectangular horizontal plate attached to a handle.

(iv) Stage Clamps: Two clamps are attached to the stage to hold the slide in place.

(v) **Condenser:** Below the stage is a condenser for concentrating the light beam.

(vi) **Body Tube:** A wide hollow tube attached to the top of the arm. The lens is attached to this tube.

(vii) **Adjustment Screws:**

- **Coarse Adjustment:** This is the larger screw used to move the body tube up and down.
- **Fine adjustment:** Small screw for fine focus adjustment.

(viii) **Reflector:** Reflects light rays so that they pass through the object being viewed.

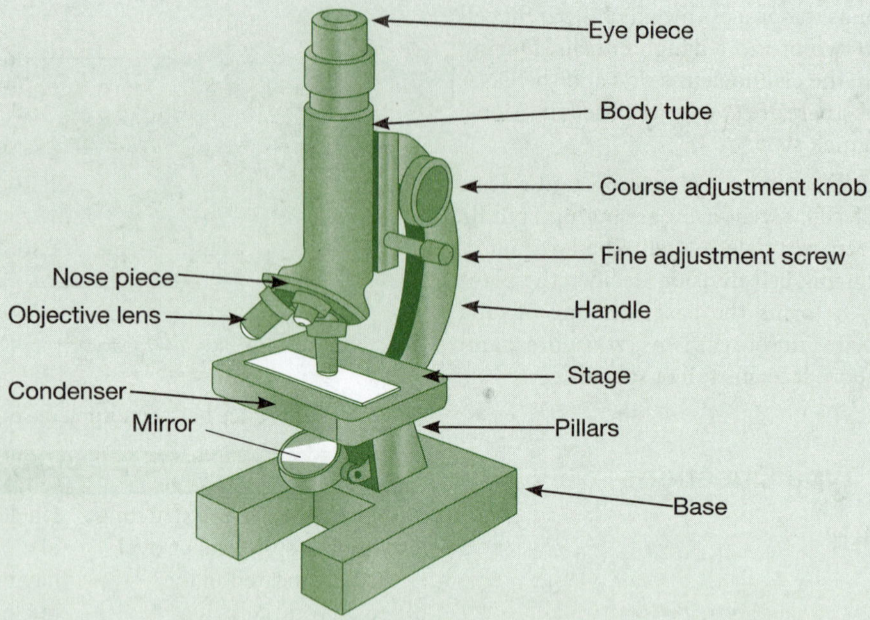

Compound Microscope

Working of Compound Microscope: The specimen or item to be examined is commonly mounted on a clear glass slide and placed between the condenser and objective lenses on the specimen stage. A condenser lens concentrates a beam of visible light from the base on the specimen. The objective lens collects the light emitted by the specimen and magnifies it inside the body tube to form a primary image. The ocular lens or eyepiece enlarges this image once more. When a higher magnification is necessary, the nose piece of the compound microscope is turned after low power focusing to align the higher magnification objective (usually 45X) with the lit section of the slide. It was sometimes necessary to use extremely high magnification (e.g. for observing bacterial cells). An oil immersion objective lens (often 100X) is used in this situation.

Case Based Questions

Case 1:

1. (A) **Porter and Thompson** discovered the Endoplasmic Reticulum.
2. (A) Cisternae, tubules, and vesicles are the components of Endoplasmic Reticulum.
3. (C) Endoplasmic reticulum membrane which is associated with ribosomes is called Rough Endoplasmic Reticulum.
4. Smooth endoplasmic reticulum and rough endoplasmic reticulum.
5. **SER** helps make fat molecules or lipids that are important for cell function. Some of these proteins and lipids help build cell membranes. This process is called membrane biogenesis.

Case 2:

1. (B) 1-Cell wall, 2- Nucleoid, 3- Plasma membrane
2. (A) Chromosome
3. (C) Nuclear region of bacterial cell is poorly defined and lack any covering while nuclear region of an animal cell is well-defined and membrane bound.
4. (B) A single cell can perform all the life processes independently.
5. (D) Amoeba

Case 3:

1. (D) All statements are true.
2. (B) Suitable term for the various components of cells is Cell organelles.
3. (D) The jelly-like fluid substance present in cells is called Cytoplasm.
4. Cell organelles are the specialized organelles present with in the cells these organelles are involved in carrying out essential functions.
5. Endoplasmic Reticulum, Golgi apparatus, Lysosomes, Ribosomes, Nucleus, Chloroplast, Mitochondria and Plastids.

Level 2

Multiple Choice Questions

1. (C) The nucleolus is composed of RNA and proteins, which form around specific chromosomal regions.
2. (B) Plastids
3. (B) Pinocytosis
4. (C) Peroxisomes contain the enzyme glycolic acid oxidase. It oxidizes glycolic acid to glyoxylic acid, a key step in photorespiration.
5. (A) The rough endoplasmic reticulum has on it ribosomes, which are small, round organelles whose function it is to make those proteins.
6. (B) r-RNA
7. (C) Ribosome
8. (D) Inner membrane
9. (A) 70s Ribosome
10. (A) Endoplasmic reticulum
11. (C) Both have DNA
12. (A) The vacuoles (Latin, vacuus = empty) are non-living inclusions of cytoplasm. Some of these are found in the form of minute droplets in the cytoplasm of meristematic cells.
13. (D) Vacuoles are essentially enclosed compartments which are filled with water containing inorganic and organic molecules including enzymes in solution.
14. (D) Protoplasm, cell wall and vacuole
15. (D) Centriole
16. (C) The centrosome is duplicated during the S-phase. The two centrosomes will give rise to the mitotic spindle, the apparatus that orchestrates the movement of chromosomes during mitosis.
17. (D) Start of cell division.
18. (B) Ribosomes are called organelles within the organelle.
19. (C) Leads to formation of parental type of daughter cells.
20. (B) Nerve cell

Higher Order Thinking Skills (HOTS)

1. (A) It is figure representing nucleus.
   (B) X- Nucleolus, Y- Chromatin.
   (C) Function of X - synthesis of ribosomes.
2. (A) A cells - Turgid cells; B cells - Plasmolyzed cells.
   (B) B cells kept in hypotonic solution will become plasmolyzed, if done immediately after plasmolysis.
   (C) A cells kept in hypertonic solution will become plasmolyzed.
3. W-Golgi apparatatus, X-Vacuole, Y-Ribosomes, Z-Lysosome.
   (A) Covering membrane of X-Tonoplast.
   (B) Lysosome contains hydrolytic enzymes.
   (C) Golgi apparatus takes part in storage, modification and packaging.
4. Mitochondria bring about stepwise oxidation of food which releases energy in form of ATP molecules. ATP is used for activities of the cell. On this account, mitochondria are called 'power houses' of the cell and ATP as the 'energy currency' of the cell.
5. (A) Bacterial cells have nuclear material not bounded by nuclear membrane, lack membrane-bound cell organelles such as mitochondria, ER, Golgi apparatus, lysosomes, vacuoles, etc.
   (B) Mitochondria have DNA, RNA, ribosomes and enzymes. These can synthesize some of their proteins. Hence, these are termed semi autonomous organelles.
6. Chloroplast is a semi autonomous cell organelle which on illumination can perform its function of photosynthesis and release oxygen even outside the cell provided it is kept in isotonic medium and receives raw material of carbon dioxide.
7. After 1 hour, the solution on both sides of the semipermeable membrane becomes isotonic due to the osmotic process.
8. Soap solution is a hypertonic solution. When our fingers are in contact for a long time, the process of penetration causes water to diffuse out of the epidermal cells of the finger, causing the skin to contract.

Archive Corner

1. (A) Vacuole is a space in the cytoplasm of a cell which is enclosed by a single membrane. A vacuole is filled with a liquid called cell sap which contains dissolved sugar and salts.

2. (B) Cell organelles that are present in both prokaryotic and eukaryotic cells without exception are, cytoplasm, plasma membrane and ribosome.

3. (B) The given figures P, Q, R and S are mitochondria, vacuole, chloroplast and ribosome respectively. Mitochondria involved in synthesis of ATP and ribosome involved in protein synthesis.

4. (C) P could be Chlamydomonas or Volvox, Q could be Aspergillus or Penicillium and R could be Lactobacillus or Nitrosomonas or Clostridium.

5. (A) (i) - Diffusion,
   (ii) - Phagocytosis,
   (iii) - Active Transport

6. (D) The given figure is of a plant cell. The labelling P, Q, R and S are cell wall, vacuole, plasma membrane and chloroplast respectively. Cell wall (P) is absent in animal cells. Vacuole is a single membrane bound organelle; the main function is to store various substances. Plasma membrane (R) is selectively permeable and maintain the exchange of only selected materials. Chloroplast (S) gives green colour to plant leaves.

7. (B) Light reaction occurs in granum of chloroplast whereas dark reaction occurs in stroma of chloroplast.

8. (C) According to the description given by Vivaan's teacher, the cell organelle is vacuole.

9. (A) In the given figure, W, X, Y and Z represents ribosome, chloroplast, mitochondria and Golgi body respectively. Only option A is correct that is W (ribosome) is engaged in protein synthesis.

10. (C) The given figure, labelled parts, X, Y and Z represent grana, inner membrane and stroma respectively. Stroma is the site of dark reaction during photosynthesis and grana is the site of light reaction during photosynthesis.

11. (A) Ribosomes are found freely in the cytoplasm or they may remain attached to the surface of endoplasmic reticulum. Thread-like structures called chromosomes are present in the nucleus.

12. (B) Labelled parts P, Q, R and S in the given figure are nucleolus, chromatin, endoplasmic reticulum and nucleoplasm, respectively. Chromatin condenses to form chromosomes. Chromosomes carry genes on them. Genes are the functional units of chromosomes that acts as unit of heredity and help in inheritance of characters.

13. (C) The process shown in the given figure is osmosis. Osmosis is the passive movement of water or any other solvent molecules from a region of higher solvent concentration to a region of lower solvent concentration through a semipermeable membrane. It is influenced by the number of solute particles dissolved in the solvent.

14. (C) According to the given Venn diagram, P, Q, R and S could be mitochondria, chloroplast, endoplasmic reticulum and centriole respectively. Golgi apparatus helps in the storage, modification and packing of secretory products in the vesicles. Mitochondria helps in oxidation of food stuff. Endoplasmic reticulum helps in synthesis and transport of proteins.

15. (A) (iv) (B); (v) (C); (i) (D); (ii) (E), (iii) (A)

16. (B) Endoplasmic reticulum contains flattened sacs called cisternae. Ribosomes occur freely in cytoplasm or may remain attached to the surface of endoplasmic reticulum.

17. (C) Pitch of a sound is decided by its frequency whereas loudness is decided by its amplitude.

    So, option C is correct.

18. (B) Mitochondria and chloroplast are capable of self duplication and synthesise some of their own proteins.

19. (B) Granum is the site of light reaction during photosynthesis, whereas stroma is the site of dark reaction during photosynthesis.

20. (A) In the given structure of a prokaryotic cell, P refers to capsule, Q refers to cell wall, R

refers to plasma membrane and S refers to pilus. Cell wall is single layered in Gram +ve bacteria and double layered is Gram –ve. Plasma membrane is a selectively permeable membrane that has structure similar to typical membrane. Pili helps in conjugation.

21. **(B)** **Ringer's solution** is isotonic to RBC. Therefore, RBC when placed with them appear normal as there would be no movement of water across their plasma membrane. RBC shrinks when placed in concentrated salt solution as concentrated salt solution is hypertonic to RBC. RBC when placed in water it swells as water is hypotonic to RBC.

22. **(B)** In the given paragraph X refers to active transport. Active transport is a rapid and uphill transport that takes place against the concentration gradient.

23. **(A)** In the given figure of cell, L refers to Golgi complex whereas M refers to vacuole. Golgi complex helps in the formation of lysosomes. Vacuoles are filled with cell sap and help to maintain osmotic pressure in a cell.

24. **(A)** 80S ribosome consists of a small 40S subunit and a large 60S subunit. Smooth endoplasmic reticulum mainly consists of tubules and vesicles whereas rough endoplasmic reticulum mainly consists of cisternae.

25. **(D)** Endoplasmic reticulum and Golgi apparatus are involved in the formation of lysosomes. Peroxisomes are involved in a variety of functions such as oxidation, signalling and lipid biosynthesis.

26. **(D)** Matrix of primary wall mainly consist of water, hemicellulose and glycoproteins. Suberin is a component of secondary wall in plants. In plants, secondary wall is laid inner to primary wall. Pits are usually absent in a primary wall whereas they are often occurring in the secondary wall.

27. **(A)** The labelled part P in the diagram is golgi apparatus and Q is endoplasmic reticulum. Polypeptides synthesised by ribosomes present on rough endoplasmic reticulum are transported to golgi apparatus for modification into functional proteins. Acrosome is synthesised by golgi apparatus with the help of its vesicles. Endoplasmic reticulum and golgi apparatus are present in pancreatic cells, salivary glands and liver cells.

28. **(A)** In the given experimental set-up, solution X must be 2 M sucrose solution whereas Y must be 0.1 M sucrose solution. Water molecules, from low concentration of sucrose, will enter visking tubing having high sucrose concentration. This occurs due to endosmosis of water making the tubing increase in volume.

29. **(B)** In the given experimental set up potato is used as a living plant tissue and just below, the section is filled with the distilled water. During the experiment, endosmosis will occur, i.e., solvent moved into the cell. So, the air bubble moves to the left.

30. **(C)** In the given Venn diagram, (W) could be chloroplast, (X) could be centriole, (Y) could be ribosomes. (V) could be cell wall the outer membrane which is composed of cellulose in plants and lipopolysaccharides in bacterial cell. (Z) could be mesosomes. W is double-membrane structure while X is not a membrane bound structure.

31. **(C)** A semipermeable membrane allows the solvent molecules to pass through it but not the solute particles.

CHAPTER 2: TISSUES

Check Point 1

1. Tips of shoots and roots in all vascular plants.
2. Intercalary meristem.
3. Apical meristem is responsible for increase in length of the plant.
4. Lateral meristems.

Check Point 2

5. Sclerenchyma.
6. Sclerenchyma tissue.
7. Lignin
8. **Sclerenchyma** and **Collenchyma**.

Check Point 3

9. The nervous tissue, contains densely packed cells called nerve cells or neurons, is present in the brain, spinal cord and nerves. The neurons are specialised for conduction of nerve impulse.

   Function – They control all the body activities, and co-ordinate between various body parts during any body function. Spinal cord and brain are made up of nervous tissue.

10. Well labelled diagram of cardiac muscles:

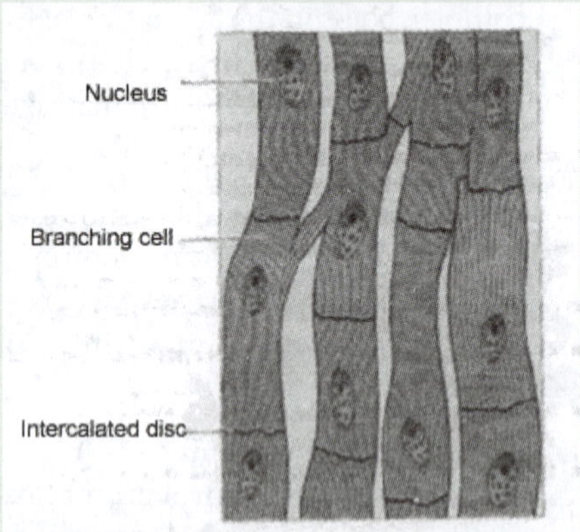

   Refer to the topic-difference between striated and non-striated muscle in chapter.

11. Areolar connective tissue provides nutrition to the cells and acts as a cushion to protect the organs from various external forces.

Level 1

Fixed Response Type

Multiple Choice Questions

1. (A) A group of cells having common origin and common function are called **tissue**.
2. (A) Tissue was termed by **Bichat**.
3. (A) Study of tissue is known as **histology**.
4. (B) Helps in excretion.
5. (A) Apical meristem helps in increasing the plant's length.
6. (A) Cell division is restricted up to meristematic cells.
7. (B) Intercalary meristem helps to increase the length of internodes in grasses.
8. (C) Dividing cells has special features, i.e., dense cytoplasm devoid of lacuna.
9. (B) Sclerenchyma
10. (D) All of the options are correct.

11. (B) Secondary tissue.

12. (C) Lateral meristem.

13. (A) Parenchymatous tissues have intercellular spaces.

14. (A) Parenchyma, in plants tissue typically composed of living cells that are thin-walled, unspecialized in structure, and therefore adaptable with differentiation to various functions.

15. (B) A permanent plant tissue made up of living cells having thickening at the corners is collenchyma.

16. (D) Sclerenchyma tissues are permanent tissues that are long, dead, and thick cells without any intercellular spaces. Their function is to provide mechanical support to the plant.

17. (B) Suberin

18. (B) Cuticle

19. (D) Cutin

20. (A) Retaining cytoplasm at maturity

21. (C) Sclerenchyma cells are permanent cells that are elongated, thin, and dead.

22. (A) Sclerenchyma is the plant tissue that lacks protoplasm at maturity.

23. (B) lateral meristem

24. (A) Tracheids

25. (B) Columnar epithelium is a type of epithelium composed of group of tall cells that arranged in the pillar-like structure. They are found in the inner lining of the small intestine.

26. (C) Blood is a fluid connective tissue containing plasma, red blood cells (RBC), white blood cells (WBC) and platelets.

27. (B) A tendon is a fibrous connective tissue that attaches muscle to bone.

28. (A) Ligament

29. (C) The areolar connective tissue is a type of connective tissue that is present throughout the human body. It provides support and helps to protect organs, muscles, and many other tissues.

30. (B) White blood cells are called soldiers of the body, because it provide immunity to our body.

Assertion and Reason Type Questions

1. (B) Both assertion and reason are correct but the reason is not the correct explanation of the assertion.

2. (B) Myelin sheath is discontinuous but this is not the reason of nodes of ranvier to occur in the myelinated nerve fiber.

3. (C) As the apical meristem is found at the tip of the stem and root, it is responsible for the growth of length of shoot and roots of the plant also known as primary growth. So, reason is false.

4. (B) Both assertion and reason are true but reason is not the correct explanation of assertion.

5. (B) Vessels are lignified but this is not the correct explanation of sieve tube and vessels to be meant for transportation purpose.

6. (A) The function of the cilia is to move particles, free cells or mucus in a specific direction. It is present in inner surfaces of some hollow organs such as fallopian tubes, bronchioles and small bronchi and help in movement of the particles present there.

7. (E) Both Assertion and Reason are correct but Reason is not the the correct explanation of Assertion.

8. (A) Collenchyma tissues have a polygonal shape of living cells with corners thickened with cellulose and pectin.

9. (C) Skeletal muscle fibers occur in muscles which are attached to the skeleton. They are striated in appearance and are under voluntary control.

10. (D) Parenchyma cells are typically alive in maturity and conduct most of the plant's metabolic functions, such as storage of energy (mainly in the form of starch and fats) and waste products (tannin, resins, gums, etc.).

Comprehension Type Questions

Passage 1:

1. (D) None of the answers are correct.
2. (C) Root that helps in anchorage, are specialized structures of embryo.
3. (B) Height of the plant above the soil increases due to meristematic tissue present in shoot tip.

Passage 2:

4. Squamous epithelial is found in the lining of mouth.
5. Its compact structure is like tiles on the floor, cells are also polygonal.
6. Stratum.
7. Mouth, oesophagous, nose, pericardium, etc.

Passage 3:

8. **(D)** None of these are voluntary actions.
9. **(A)** The muscles whose contraction is under our control are known as Voluntary muscles.
10. **(D)** All the options are correct.
11. Characteristic of striated muscles are:

    These muscles show alternate light and dark bands or striations, hence they are also called striated muscles.

    The cells of this tissue are long, cylindrical, unbranched and multinucleate.
12. Characteristic of unstriated muscles are:

    The cells of this tissue are long with pointed ends spindle-shaped and uninucleate.

    Striations are absent, hence they are also called unstriated muscles.

Free Response Type

Very Short Answer Type Questions

1. The plant tissue with dead cells is called the xylem.
2. The function of adipose tissue is to provide insulation, absorb shocks for the internal organs and store fats to be released in the shortage of glucose.
3. The meristematic tissues or meristems in a plant always remain in an active metabolic state. The reason for their constant activity is that the cells of these tissues never age and are constantly dividing.
4. Apical meristems give rise to the primary plant body and are responsible for the extension of the roots and shoots.
5. The function of lateral meristem is to increase the thickness of the plants.
6. Limbs, neck, facial muscles.
7. Refer on page 2.4 under competition corner.
8. Simple squamous epithelial cells form a membrane that allows selective diffusion of materials to pass through. Diffusion helps with filtration, absorption, and secretion functions.
9. Connective tissue can further be broken down into three categories: loose connective tissue, dense connective tissue, and specialized connective tissue.
10. Refer on page 2.14.

Short Answer Type Questions

1. Refer to the topic-Classification on the basis of origin.
2. • Parenchyma: photosynthesis, storage, and secretion.
   • Collenchyma: support and transportation of nutrients.
   • Sclerenchyma: support, protection, and transportation of water.
3. Refer on page 2.19.
4. **Leptome:** Main part of phloem involved in conduction of food, which is sieve tube. All elements except the hard tissue of the phloem live in the phloem.

   Hadrome: Tracheids and vessels are collectively called hadrome, as main conducting elements in xylem.
5. Refer to Intext question-3
6.

Striated Muscle	Non-striated muscle
Striated muscle cells are long, branched, and cylindrical	nonstriated muscle cells are spindle shaped
Striated muscles are voluntary muscles	nonstriated muscles are involuntary muscles

7. Blood has many different functions, including transportation of materials, defense, blood clotting, etc.
8. Refer on page 2.11.
9. They are made up of more than one type of cells. They are of two types xylem and phloem. Xylem, functions as a conducting tissue for water and

minerals from the roots to the stems and leaves. Phloem tissue carries food materials, from the place it is available to the places where it is needed.

10. Refer to the topic- Connective tissue proper.

Long Answer Type Questions

1. These tissues are primarily protective in function. They consist of:

(i) **Epidermis:** Epidermis forms one cell thick outermost layer of various body organs of plants such as leaves, flowers, stems. Epidermis is covered outside by cuticle.

- Cuticle is a waterproof layer of waxy substance called as cutin which is secreted by the epidermal cells.
- Cuticle is very thick in xerophytes.
- Cells of epidermis of leaves are not continuous at some places due to the presence of small pores called as stomata.
- Each stoma is guarded by a pair of bean shaped cells called as guard cells.
- These are the only epidermal cells which possess chloroplasts, the rest being colourless.

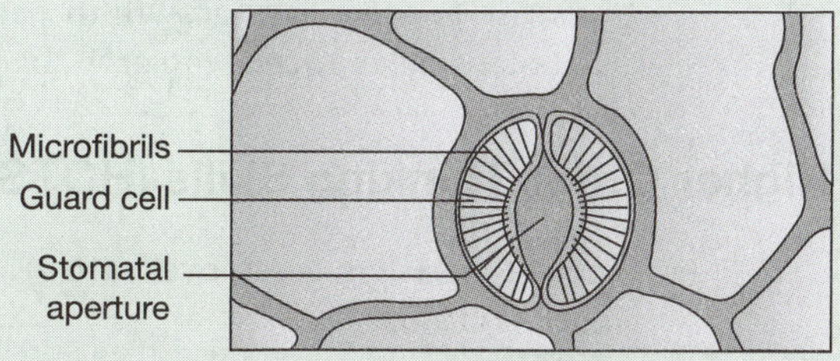

Stomatal opening and guard cell

Functions: The main function of the epidermis is to protect the plant from dehydration and infection. The cuticle of the epidermis suppresses transpiration and evaporation of water and prevents wilting. Stomata in the epidermis allow gas exchange during photosynthesis and respiration. Stomata also helps in transpiration.

(ii) **Cork or phellem:** In older roots and stems, tissues at the periphery become cork cells or phellem cells. Cork is made up of dead cells with thick walls and no intercellular spaces. The cell walls of cork are coated with a waxy substance called suberin. Deposition of suberin makes cork cells impermeable to water and gases. Cork cells have no protoplasm but are filled with resin or tannins.

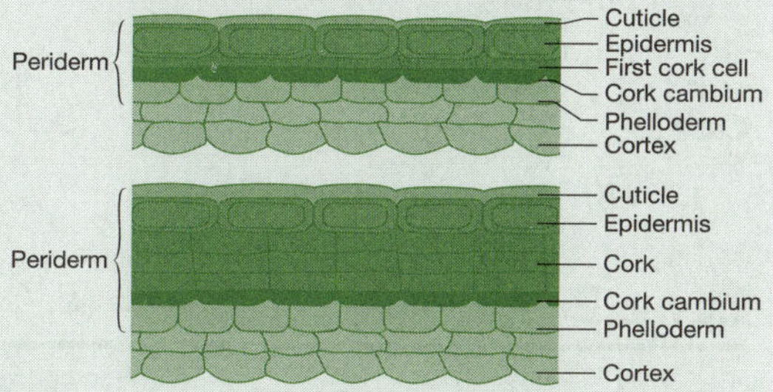

Epidermis, cork cambium and cork layer

Functions and Uses: Cork is protective in function. Cork cells prevent dehydration, infection and mechanical damage. Impermeability, lightness, toughness, compressibility, and elasticity make cork commercially valuable. Cork is used for insulation, as a shock absorber for linoleum. Cork is used to make a variety of sporting goods such as cricket balls, table tennis, shuttlecocks and wooden paddles.

2. Refer on page 2.7 under the topic protective tissue.

3. (A) **Parenchyma:** These are hexagonal, flattened, loosely packed cells that store food. If they contain chlorophyll, we call them chlorenchyma in aquatic plants contain large vacuoles that provide buoyancy. We call them aerenchyma.

(B) **Collenchyma:** These are elongated, irregularly thickened cells with little intercellular space. They provide support to the plant, e.g., tendril and stem of a climber.

(C) **Sclerenchyma:** These are elongated thickened cells with lignified walls and no intercellular spaces. They are dead cells that give plants strength and protection, e.g., coir of coconut.

4. Refer to the topic-Epithelial tissue.

5. Refer to the topic-Connective tissue.

Case Based Questions

Case 1:

Slide A is soft tissue and slide B is strong tissue. Sclerenchyma can be identified by long and narrow type cells due to thickened walls due to the presence of lignin.

Case 2:

(A) Xylem
(B) Phloem
(C) Vascular bundles

Case 3:

1. (B) Osteocytes
2. (D) Lamellae
3. (C) Bones
4. (D) Phosphates and carbonates of calcium and magnesium
5. (D) Ossein

Level 2

Multiple Choice Questions

1. **(A)** Fluid part of blood after removal of corpuscle is called plasma.
2. **(C)** Yellow muscle fibres are known as ligaments.
3. **(C)** Blood platelets are also called as thrombocytes.
4. **(C)** Contraction and relaxation are unique features of muscle tissue.
5. **(B)** The tissue which is under the control of an animal's will is striated muscles.
6. **(C)** Cardiac muscle
7. **(C)** Localised and dividing cells
8. **(D)** None of the above as it is composed of connective tissue with elastic fibers.
9. **(C)** Intercalated discs are present in the cardiac muscle.
10. **(B)** Voluntary muscles are found in the walls of the hollow organs such as the stomach.
11. **(C)** Tissue responsible for the movement in our body is muscular tissue. This is comprised of thin cylindrical muscular fibers. These fibers contract to move the part of the body and lengthen or comes to its original shape when the part is relaxed.
12. **(C)** The structural and functional unit of the nervous system is called a neuron or a nerve cell.
13. **(C)** Conduction of water
14. **(D)** Cartilage is formed from the mesoderm germ layer by the process known as chondrogenesis. Mesenchyme differentiates into chondroblasts which are the cells that secrete the major components of the extracellular matrix.
15. **(B)** The perichondrium is a dense layer of fibrous connective tissue that covers cartilage in various parts of the body.
16. **(B)** Phloem fibres
17. **(C)** Haversian canals are found in the bone matrix of the long bone of mammals (rabbit, rat, etc.).
18. **(A)** Tendon is a dense and regular connective tissue that binds the muscle to the bone. It is made up of modified white fibrous tissue.
19. **(A)** A Schwann cell forms a myelin sheath by wrapping its plasma membrane concentrically around the inner axon.
20. **(C)** Cambium is considered to be a lateral meristem because it is usually located laterally between the xylem and phloem tissues. It gives rise to secondary growth in perennial plants causing an increase in growth.

Higher Order Thinking Skills (HOTS)

1. (i) If apical meristem is removed, growth of the length will stop.

   (ii) Cork is not formed: If cork is not formed in older stems and roots, the outer tissues will rupture with the increase in girth and expose the interior to desiccation and infection.

   (iii) Epithelial tissue will not be effective as protective impermeable layer.

   (iv) Lymph is not returned to blood: blood volume will decrease while passage of materials from tissues to blood and vice versa would be dislocate.

2. (i) (A)-TS of Sclerenchyma fibres; (B)-TS of Parenchyma cells; C- TS of Collenchyma

   (ii) Mechanical strength and flexibility: collenchyma.

(iii) Hemp and jute: sclerenchyma fibres.

(iv) Aerenchyma: modification of parenchyma.

(v) Deposition of lignin: sclerenchyma.

3. (i) Identification: phloem tissue.

Function: conduction of organic food.

(ii) X - sieve tube cell.

Y - sieve plate

Z- companion cell.

(iii) From same mother cell: sieve tube cell and companion cell.

(iv) Living of sieve tube cells: it is controlled by nucleated companion cells with which they are connected by plasmodesmata.

4. Even after 3 years, the position of the nail does not change. This is because plants and trees grow from their top (trunk or root) rather than from the point where they meet the ground. The tree grows, but the nail stays in the same place on the tree trunk.

5. (A) Xylem

(B) Phloem

(C) Vascular bundles

6. A hand bone dislocation was caused by a break in the ligaments that connect two bones and hold them in place.

7. Removing the upper part of the cane does not remove the inter meristem of the plant. It is this meristematic tissue that increases plant length.

8. The plant dies within a few days after transplanting. This is due to the absence of meristematic tissue, which prevents roots from growing when root tips are removed. Additionally, poor root growth will result in poor mineral and water absorption.

Archive Corner

1. **(D)** Parenchyma consists of living cells with thin wall whereas cells of collenchyma are living and irregularly thickened at the corners. Sclerenchyma forms hard grit of pear fruit and hard walls of nuts.

2. **(C)** In the given diagram, X and Y are phloem tissue and adipose tissue respectively. Phloem is a plant tissue whereas adipose tissue is an animal tissue. Phloem is a major food conducting tissue and does not provide mechanical strength to the plant body. Phloem is composed of three types of living cells, i.e., sieve tube cells, companion cells and phloem parenchyma and one type of dead cells phloem fibres. Adipose tissue is composed of all living cells. Phloem conducts food in vascular plants in both upward and downward directions.

3. **(D)** In the given figure of nerve cell, X, Y and Z are cell body, dendrites and axon respectively. Axon transmits nerve impulse from one neuron to another whereas dendrites receive impulses.

4. **(D)** The tissues in the given figures are cuboidal, columnar, ciliated columnar and squamous epithelium respectively. Squamous epithelium lines the coelom and urinary tubules.

5. **(B)** According to given flow chart, P, Q, R and S could be meristematic tissue, sclerenchyma (Q), phloem and xylem respectively. Parenchyma is responsible for storage of food.

6. **(A)** The tissues given in diagrams X and Y are parenchyma and sclerenchyma respectively. Parenchyma (X) have thin cell walls while in sclerenchyma (Y) cell wall are thickened due to lignin. Intercellular spaces are present only in parenchyma (X).

7. **(D)** Sclerenchyma consists of thick-walled dead cells and their cell walls are thickened due to the deposition of a water-resistant material called lignin. Main function of sclerenchyma is to provide mechanical support to plant parts, and it also provides protective covering around seeds.

8. **(C)** The vascular cambium and cork cambium in dicots are examples of lateral meristem.

9. **(A)** Tissue X shown in the given figure is adipose tissue. It stores fat and insulates body against heat loss.

10. **(D)** P-(iii), (vii); Q-(i), (iv) R-(v), (vi); S-(ii), (viii)

11. **(D)** a – (iii) b – (i) c – (ii)

12. **(B)** Cartilage do not have blood supply (except in perichondrium) whereas bone have rich blood supply. Growth of cartilage is unidirectional whereas that of bone is bidirectional.

13. **(B)** In the given figures, X and Y are striated muscles and cardiac muscles respectively. Cells of striated muscles are multinucleated whereas that of cardiac muscles are uninucleated. Striated muscles are voluntary in nature and cardiac muscles are involuntary.

14. **(D)** In the given flow chart P, Q, R and S are apical meristem, parenchyma, phloem and xylem respectively. Xylem consists of four types of cells- tracheids, vessels, xylem parenchyma and xylem fibres. Tracheids, vessels and xylem fibres are dead only xylem parenchyma is living.

15. **(B)** In the given diagrammatic representation X is areolar connective tissue. Adipose connective tissue is a dense connective tissue that stores fat and insulates the body against heat loss. The loose connective tissue that connects skeletal muscles to bones are tendons. Adipose connective tissue is found beneath the skin and covering of heart.

16. **(C)** The given figures diagrammatic representation P and Q are phloem tissue and neuron respectively. Phloem tissue is associated with translocation of food in vascular plants. Phloem tissue is composed of mostly living cells and neuron is composed of all living cells.

17. **(B)** Lamellae, Osteocytes, Lacunae, Canaliculi

18. **(D)** In the given figure X, Y and Z are phloem parenchyma cell, sieve tube element and companion cell respectively. X is a living parenchyma cell that helps in storage of food.

19. **(B)** According to the given statements L, M, N and O could be squamous epithelium, cuboidal epithelium, columnar epithelium and ciliated epithelium respectively.

20. **(D)** It can be inferred from the given dichotomous key that P, Q, R, S, T and U could be squamous epithelium (it does not contain chondrin), adipose tissue, aerenchyma, collenchyma, xylem and phloem respectively. Sclerenchyma found in grit of guava, pear, etc.

21. **(D)** P - Squamous epithelium
Q - In subcutaneous tissue
R - Found in aquatic plants
S - Found in petiole, leaves
T - Stele or vascular cylinder of monocot root

22. **(B)** In the given picture of blood smear, (P) is RBC, (Q) is neutrophil, (R) is lymphocyte and (S) is platelets. Platelets help in blood clotting and a person who is unable to produce platelets bleeds continuously.

CHAPTER 3: DIVERSITY IN LIVING ORGANISMS

CHECK POINT 1

1. Walter Gilbert.
2. The branch of science is concerned with classification, especially of organisms and systematics.
3. **Taxon**–It refers to any rank or category in the hierarchical order of classification, e.g., kingdom, phylum etc. Taxonomy is the branch of science that deals with the study of principles and the procedures required for classification.
4. The lowest category is species.

CHECK POINT 2

5. Kingdom Protista consists of unicellular, eukaryotic organisms.
6. Thallophyta
7. Pteridophytes are the plants that do not exhibit seeds but phenerograms are the plants that bear seeds. Pteridophytes are primitive plants but the phenerograms are advance plants. Pteridophytes exhibit less developed reproductive organs whereas the phanerograms exhibit well developed reproductive organs.

CHECK POINT 3

8.

Platyhelminthes	Aschelminthes
Body is soft, thin, resembling the shape of a ribbon or leaf.	Obsolete phylum containing invertebrates such as roundworm.
Platyhelminthes do not contain a coelom (acoelomates).	Aschelminthes contain a pseudo-coelom.
Platyhelminthes have flame cells for excretion.	Aschelminthes does not have any special excretory system.

9.

Annelids	Arthropods
Annelids do not have appendages.	Arthropods have appendages that are joined together.
The true body cavity they have is called a coelom.	The presence of a blood-filled body cavity, known as a 'hemocoel.'
They are known as segmented worms.	Animals with jointed legs are what they are called.

10. Earthworms are **farmers' friends** because they improve the quality of the soil like water holding capacity, moisture, and nutrient content by burrowing into the soil. The soil becomes loose and porous. Also, the worm castings improve the distribution of organic matter in the soil.

CHECK POINT 4

11. Feathers, a four-chambered heart, beak with no teeth.
12. Refer to the Table 3.3.
13. Characteristics of Mammals: The presence of hair or fur, sweat glands, mammary glands, three middle ear bones.
14. Refer to the Table 3.5.

Level 1

Fixed Response Type

Multiple Choice Questions

1. (A) Phylogenetic classification
2. (A) Systematics
3. (B) Linnaeus
4. (C) Scales
5. (B) Species are the basic or lowest unit of classification.
6. (C) Taxonomy is the branch in which we study about the identification, nomenclature and classification of organisms.
7. (A) A species is a group of individual organisms that interbreed and produce fertile, viable offspring.
8. (A) **Carolus Linnaeus** proposed the two-kingdom categorization. He divided living organisms into two kingdoms: Plantae and Animalia.
9. (B) 3 kingdom classification was put forward by **Ernst Haeckel**.
10. (B) **Robert Whittaker's five-kingdom system** was a standard feature of biology textbooks during the last two decades of the twentieth century.
11. (B) **Mesoglea** is a characteristic of coelenterata: The mesoglea is primarily acellular, however it contains muscle bundles and nerve fibres in both cnidaria and ctenophora.
12. (C) Organs like cardiovascular lymphatic, digestive, Endocrine etc. are found in some animals with organ level organisation. Examples- annelids, arthropods, mollusca and chordate.
13. (B) Polymorphism is the phenomenon where individuals within the species exhibit various functional and structural differences. Physalia physalis is a coelenterata which shows polymorphism as there are individuals sighting of it possessing modified polyp like structures.
14. (D) Height of the plant
15. (D) None of the above
16. (C) The excretory organs in aschelminthes and platyhelminthes, respectively, are renette cells and flame cells.
17. (B) **Pharyngeal gill slits** are a chordate feature; these are openings between the pharynx to the outside. They have been modified hin the time of evolution. In primitive chordates, these slits are used to filter food particles from the water. In fishes and some amphibians, the slits bear gills and are used for gas exchange.
18. (D) Dorsal nerve cord
19. (D) None of the above are correct.
20. (B) Herdmania belongs to subphylum urochordata and amphioxus belongs to subphylum cephalochordata.
21. (C) **Balanoglossus or acorn** worm belongs to phylum hemichordata, which was earlier considered as a sub-phylum under phylum chordata but now it is placed as a separate phylum under non-chordata.
22. (A) Kingdom Monera
23. (B) Platyhelminthes animals are **acoelomate** animals. Both ascaris and ancylostoma belong to phylum aschelminthes which are pseudocoelomate animals.
24. (D) Round worm
25. (B) **Metamerism** is the characteristic of annelida. As metamerism is one type of body segmentation.
26. (A) **Nephridia** are the excretory organs in annelids.
27. (B) Pseudopodia- amoeba
28. (B) Darwin
29. (B) **Choanocytes** are cells that line the interior of asconoids, syconoid, and leuconoid bodies of sponges and are seen in members of porifera.
30. (B) **Cnidarians** have a true coelom or coelenteron, they are diploblastic and have tissue level of organization.

Assertion and Reason Type Questions

1. (A) Blue-green algae (cyanobacteria) are a group of prokaryotic, autotrophic microorganisms that contain the photosynthetic pigments (chlorophyll and phycocyanin). So, it makes its own food.
2. (B) Both assertion and reason are correct but reason is not the correct explanation of assertion.

3. **(A)** Animals in the phylum platyhelminthes are called flatworms because they are dorsoventrally flattened from head to tail.
4. **(B)** Prawns are the example of arthropods but this is not the correct explanation of the assertion.
5. **(B)** Aves are warm-blooded but this is not the reason of the sparrow coming under the class aves.
6. **(C)** Reason is false as bryophytes are called amphibians of the plant kingdom because these plants need both water and soil for their survival.
7. **(C)** Fishes have only two chambers of the heart-the atrium and ventricle. The oxygenation of blood happens through the gills.
8. **(A)** The members of platyhelminthes are commonly called flatworms. Reason: platyhelminthes have dorso-ventrally flattened body.
9. **(B)** Both assertion and reason are true but reason is not the correct explanation of assertion.
10. **(C)** Tube feet not only help the urchin move, they also are used to grasp food, and they are part of the respiratory or breathing system.

Comprehension Type Questions

Passage 1:

1. **(C)** Diversity is in terms of external appearance and internal structure both.
2. **(B)** The size of bacteria is few micron.
3. **(C)** Largest mammal is blue whale.

Passage 2:

4. **(C)** Linnaeus gave binomial nomenclature.
5. **(A)** Genus is the first word according to binomial nomenclature.
6. **(B)** Sapiens is the species name of human.

Passage 3:

7. **(B)** **Robert Whittaker** (1969) proposed five kingdoms.
8. **(D)** Monera, Protista, Animalia all are part of five kingdom system.
9. **(C)** Kingdom monera divided into **archaebacteria** and **eubacteria**

Free Response Type

Very Short Answer Type Questions

1. Notochord is solid unjointed of vacuolated cells, present on dorsal side between alimentary canal and nervous system in some animal. It is derived from mesoderm and act as primary axial skeleton.
2. (i) **Gymnosperms** (plants with "naked seeds"—such as conifers, cycads, and ginkgo), the ovules are not enclosed in an ovary.

   (ii) **Angiosperms.**
3. Species are the basic unit of classification.
4. Spiny ant eater, Duck—billed platypus.
5. Copeland
6. Arthropoda.
7. Gram, pea, pumpkin all have two cotyledons in the seed, so they are dicots. Rice, wheat, maize all have one cotyledon in their seed, so they are monocots.
8. Urochordata
9. Arthropoda.

Short Answer Type Questions

1. Seed-bearing plants are further classified into Angiosperms and monocots.
2. Nomenclature gives a single unique name and also a place in taxonomy based on the similarities and dissimilarities between different organisms, that helps in establishing a relationship between the organisms and classification.
3. Phanerogams or spermatophyta are the most advanced type of plants bearing seeds. They have roots, stems, leaves and flowers. They include gymnosperms and angiosperms.
4. Refer to the Table 3.4.
5. Refer to the topic-Characteristics of Mammals
6. Notochord is a long rod-like support structure that runs along the back of the animals, separating the nervous tissue from the gut. It acts as a supporting structure by providing a place for muscles to attach for the ease of movement.
7. Refer to the topic-protozoa.
8. Amphibians do not possess exoskeleton as their skin is thin, moist and act as a respiratory organ.

9. Characteristics of chordata- a notochord, a dorsal hollow (tubular) nerve cord, pharyngeal gill arches or slits, and a post-anal tail.

10. In binomial nomenclature, name of every organism is composed of two components—the first one is genus and the second one is species. the genus name starts with a capital letter whereas the species name starts with small letter. For example, the scientific name of man is "Homo sapiens". Here "Homo" is the genus and "sapiens" is the species name.

Long Answer Type Questions

1. Refer to the topic-Different system of classification.
2. Refer on page 3.7 under division thallophyte.
3. Characters: They are seedless vascular plants, primitive tracheophytes or vascular cryptogams. Plant body is differentiated into true stem, leaves & roots (Fig 3.6). they are the most evolved cryptogams. Vascular tissues are present. Fruits are absent. e.g., ferns (Dryopteris, Pteris), club moss (Lycopodium), horsetail (Equisetum), marsilea.
4. Refer on page 3.11.
5. (A) **Bilateral Symmetry:** The body has a head. Organs and limbs are paired. They are arranged laterally. Body is divisible into two equal halves by only one plane (mid-sagittal plane). Bilateral symmetry is found in platyhelminthes, nematoda, annelida, mollusca, arthropoda and chordate.

   (B) **Coelom:** It is mesoderm lined fluid filled space that occurs between alimentary canal and body wall which provides shock proof environment to various body organs. Depending upon the absence or presence of coelom animals are of three types-acoelomate, pseudocoelomate and eucoelomates.

   (C) **Triploblastic:** Animals having three germinal layers-outer ectoderm, middle mesoderm and inner endoderm, e.g., platyhelminthes to chordata.

Case Based Questions

Case 1:

1. Bryophyta.
2. (i) They are called amphibians of the plant kingdom.

   (ii) They do not have specialized vascular tissue.
3. True.
4. False. Bryophyta is called the **amphibian of plants.**

Case 2:

1. Whale belongs to class mammalia.
2. **No** Whale and fishes belong to two different classes. Whale belongs to class mammalia andfish belongs to class pisces.
3. (i) **Whale:** It is a mammal because it is warm blooded animal, it has four-chambered heart, and it breathes through lungs.

   (ii) **Fish:** They are cold-blooded animals with two chambered heart, and they breathe through gills.
4. They have a notochord at some point in their lives; they are warm-blooded and have his four-chamber heart.

Case 3:

1. These are generally called bryophytes.
2. These plants bind soil particles and thus prevent soil erosion. They also help in colonization of barren lands.
3. Lichens are also good indicators of atmospheric quality.

Level 2

Multiple Choice Questions

1. (A) Cryptogamae
2. (C) Pteridophyte is first terrestrial plant to have specialized conducting tissue-xylem and phloem. Xylem tissues are important for conduction of water and mineral in plants. Both xylem and phloem are present in the gymnosperms also.
3. (D) Gymnosperm, any vascular plant that reproduces by means of an exposed seed, or ovule—unlike angiosperms, or flowering plants, whose seeds are enclosed by mature ovaries, or fruits.

4. **(C)** Dogfish can be considered as a true fish among the following.
5. **(B)** **Echinodermata** can be considered exclusively marine.
6. **(A)** Arthropods and mollusca
7. **(A)** In arthropods, coelom cavity is completely filled with blood.
8. **(A)** **Bancroftian filariasis**, a mosquito-transmitted disease commonly known as elephantiasis, is caused by infection with the parasite *Wuchereria bancrofti*.
9. **(A)** It is most common feature of vertebrates to have notochord in them.
10. **(C)** Organisms belonging to class pisces and mammalia have scales on them.
11. **(C)** Most of the mammals are viviparous.
12. **(C)** Pteridophyta lacks flowers in them.
13. **(C)** Platyhelminthes
14. **(A)** Echinodermata
15. **(C)** Amphibians do not contain scales on their body
16. **(B)** Cyano bacteria and archae bacteria
17. **(D)** Height of the plant
18. **(B)** Saprotrophic or parasitic
19. **(A)** Tube feet are the locomotary organs which help echinodermata to move.
20. **(D)** Corals are the cnidarians that live in the colonies.

Higher Order Thinking Skills (HOTS)

1. (a) Dorsal fin

   (b) Caudal fin

   (c) Pelvic fin

   (d) Pectoral fin

   Function of caudal fins: Caudal fins help in streamlined movement in water.

2. (a) Thallophyte

   (b) Without specialized vascular tissue

   (c) Pteridophyte

   (d) Phanerogams

   (e) Bear naked seeds

   (f) Angiosperm

   (g) Have seeds thallophyte with two cotyledons

   (h) Monocots

3. (A) Plant 'P' has fibrous roots. Plant P is a monocot and it has fibrous roots.

4. (A) Identification.

   A-fern (male shield fern, dryopteris)

   B-moss (funaria).

   C—pinus.

   D—spirogyra.

   E—euglena.

   F-rhizopus.

   (b) Unicellular eukaryotic organism-euglena.

   (c) 1. Heterotrophic nutrition- rhizopus.

   2. Mixotrophic nutrition- euglena.

   (d) Non-vascular embryophyte- moss (funaria).

   (e) Xylem without vessels and phloem without companion cells- pinus.

   (f) Haploid endosperm- pinus.

5. (a) Identification-pila (apple snail). Phylum-mollusca.

   (b) 1. Locomotory organ-foot,

   2. Circulatory system-open (haemocoel).

   (c) Symmetry-asymmetry due to torsion (spirally coil)

6. (A) W-anus.

   X-gill slits.

   Y-notochord.

   Z-nerve cord.

   (B) Identification- basic characteristics of chordates.

   (C) Phylum with notochord- chordata.

   (D) Subphylum with notochord throughout life- cephalochordate.

7. (A) Identification

   a-Centipede.

   b-Hydra.

   c-Liverfluke (fasciola).

   d- Earthworm (*Pheretima posthuma*).

   (B) 1. Plathyhelminthes- liverfluke (fasciola)

2. Arthropoda-centipede (scolopendra).
3. Annelida-earthworm (*Pheretima posthuma*).

(C) 1. Tissue level organisation- hydra.
2. Primitive organ level organisation- liverfluke (fasciola)

(D) 1. Flame cells- liverfluke (fasciola)
2. Nephridia- earthworm (pheretima posthuma)

(E) Poison claw- centipede (scolopendra)

(F) 1. Diploblastic-hydra
2. Triploblastic- liverfluke (fasciola), centipede (scolopendra), earthworm (*Pheretima posthuma*).

Archive Corner

1. **(C)** Bryophyta: 2, 3, 4, 5, 6, 7; Pteridophyte: 4, 5; Thallophyta: 1, 2, 3, 5, 7, 8

2. **(D)** The given organisms (i), (ii), (iii), (iv) and (v) are:

Hyalonema, physalia, palaemon, octopus and antedon respectively. The presence of notochord is the characteristic feature of chordates. Octopus and antedon are non-chordates.

3. **(C)** According to the given dichotomous key, P could be an organism under phylum porifera. Q could be an organism under phylum chordata. R and S could be under phylum coelenterata. The body of organisms under phylum mollusca is differentiated into head, visceral mass and ventral foot.

4. **(D)** According to the given classification chart X, Y, P and Q are acoelomate, coelomate, radial body symmetry and bilateral body symmetry, respectively.

5. **(B)** According to the given flow chart, M could be coelenterate or ctenophore, N is platyhelminth, O is aschelminth and P could be annelid or arthropod or mollusc or hemichordate or chordate.

6. **(B)** The excretory organ in phylum arthropoda is malpighian tubule and they have open circulatory system.

Nephridia are present in phylum annelida and mollusca. The respiratory organ in mollusca is ctenidia.

7. **(D)**

Bryophytes	Pteridophytes
Main plant body is sporophytic (diploid).	Main plant body is gametophytic (haploid).
Plant is fixed to the substratum by roots.	Plant is fixed to the substratum by rhizoids.

8. **(B)** In the given figures X, Y and Z represent Taenia, Ancylostoma and Pheretima respectively. Taenia or tapeworm belongs to phylum platyhelminthes, ancylostoma or hookworm belongs to phylum aschelminthes whereas pheretima or earthworm belongs to phylum annelida.

9. (A) spongilla is the member of porifera.

10. **(C)** According to the given figures, plants X and Y are *Funaria* and *Selaginella* respectively. Funaria is a bryophyte whereas sellaginella is a pteridophyte. In both X and Y seed setting is absent and they reproduce through spores.

11. **(B)** Amoeba and paramecium both belong to kingdom protista same as candida and saccharomyces both belong to kingdom fungi.

12. **(B)** According to the given passage, P, Q, R, S and T refers to euplectella, obelia, dugesia, pheretima and palaemon, respectively.

13. **(D)** **Poriferans** possesses endoskeleton of calcareous spicules whereas coelenterates are always aquatic. Platyhelminthes could be parasite which attaches to the body of host through hooks and suckers whereas annelids possesses metanephridia for excretion. Arthropods sheds off their chitinous exoskeleton periodically during their growth which is referred to as moulting.

CHAPTER 4: WHY DO WE FALL ILL

Check Point 1

1. The state of being free from illness or injury is called "**Health**."

2. A disease can be defined as any disturbance in the structure or function of any organ or part of the body. It may be caused due to the attack of pathogens, lack of nutritious diet/balanced diet and lack of public health services.

3. Personal health refers to the mental, physical and social well-being of an individual, while community health is about enhancing and maintaining the health of the entire community (population).

4.

Acute Disease	Chronic Disease
These diseases occur suddenly.	They occur over a prolonged period.
They last for a shorter period.	They last longer, even for a lifetime.
E.g., Typhoid, bone fracture.	Eg., Diabetes, cancer.

Check Point 2

5. Infectious diseases commonly spread through the direct transfer of bacteria, viruses or other germs from one person to another. This can happen when an individual with the bacterium or virus touches, kisses, coughs or sneezes on someone who isn't infected.

6. Prophylaxis refers to the treatment given, or action taken to prevent disease.

7. The "incubation period" means the time between catching the virus and beginning to have symptoms of the disease. Most estimates of the incubation period for COVID-19 range from 1-14 days, most commonly around five days.

8. The major occupational diseases/morbidity of concern in India are silicosis, musculoskeletal injuries, coal workers' pneumoconiosis, chronic obstructive lung diseases, asbestosis, byssinosis, pesticide poisoning and noise induced hearing loss.

9. (a) **DPT:** Diphtheria-Pertussis-Tetanus vaccine.

   (b) **OPV:** Oral Polio Vaccine.

   (c) **BCG:** Bacille Calmette Guerin.

Level 1

Fixed Response Type

Multiple Choice Questions

1. **(D)** Cholera is spread by eating or drinking food or water contaminated by the feces (poop) of an infected person.

2. **(D)** **Carcinoma** cancer begins in the skin or in tissues that line or cover internal organs.

3. **(B)** Amoebiasis is caused by *Taenia solium*.

4. **(D)** Tuberculosis

5. **(C)** Saline helps to produce antibiotics.

6. **(C)** Anaemia is a disease caused by the lack of iron inside the body.

7. **(C)** Typhoid, dysentery, cholera.

8. **(B)** Female **Anopheles** is the mosquito that spreads malaria in man.

9. **(C)** **Kwashiorkor** manifests symptoms of protein deficiency. This can be prevented by giving children a protein-rich diet.

10. **(C)** Tuberculosis

11. **(B)** Before smallpox was eradicated, it was a serious infectious disease caused by the variola virus. It was contagious, meaning, it spread from one person to another.

12. (B) A lack of vitamin D or calcium is the most common cause of rickets. Vitamin D largely comes from exposing the skin to sunlight, but it's also found in some foods, such as oily fish and eggs. Vitamin D is essential for the formation of strong and healthy bones in children.

13. (C) Hydrophobia is a clinical sign characteristic of human rabies. This sign occurs following paroxysmal contractions of pharynx responsible for hydrophobic spasms.

14. (D) Rabies is a vaccine-preventable viral disease which occurs in more than 150 countries and territories. Dogs are the main source of human rabies deaths, contributing up to 99% of all rabies transmissions to humans.

15. (C) Both a and b.

16. (C) It is necessary to educate people to drink boiled water and not to eat exposed food to prevent them from having communicable diseases like Cholera.

17. (C) Protozoa

18. (C) A lymphocyte is a type of white blood cell that is part of the immune system. There are two main types of lymphocytes: **B cells and T cells.** The B cells produce antibodies that are used to attack invading bacteria, viruses, and toxins.

19. (A) Smallpox, typhoid, tuberculosis.

20. (D) All of the above.

21. (C) In the first month or so, after someone is infected, paragonimiasis worms spread through the abdomen, sometimes causing symptoms that can include, fever, ill-feeling (malaise) diarrhea.

22. (A) **HIV infection** causes alteration in several lines of host defenses in the lung and respiratory tract that contribute to an increased risk for lung complications.

23. (D) Typhoid.

24. (D) Elephantiasis.

25. (A) AIDS.

26. (B) **Pasteur** coined the word "Vaccine" for the first time.

27. (C) Malaria- *Salmonella*.

28. (C) The causative agent of "sleeping sickness" disease in humans is an intercellular parasite found in WBC.

29. (D) All of the above are correct.

30. (D) All of the above are correct.

Assertion and Reason Type Questions

1. (A) Viruses live and replicate inside the human cell and they cannot live outside this environment. Viruses insert their genetic material into a human cell's DNA in order to reproduce. Antibiotics cannot kill viruses because bacteria and viruses have different mechanisms and machinery to survive and replicate.

2. (B) Tuberculosis is mainly transmitted by droplet infections, but this is not the correct reason for it to be a bacterial disease.

3. (C) Cancer is NOT contagious. Close contact or things like sex, kissing, touching, sharing meals, or breathing the same air cannot spread cancer.

4. (D) As cold is a communicable disease, so it's not okay to sit near a person having cold as it may be transmitted to you and will make you unhealthy.

5. (B) Yes, the causal organism of AIDS is HIV, but this is not the correct explanation for the statement that a person having AIDS cannot fight even minor infections.

6. (D) Tuberculosis is not an acute disease as it lasts for a longer period of time and, thus, falls under the category of chronic diseases.

7. (A) Malaria and Kala-azar Malaria is caused due to *Plasmodium* and kala-azar is caused due to *Leishmania*. They both are protozoans.

8. (A) Elephantiasis occurs in the chronic stage of lymphatic filariasis due to the obstruction of lymphatic vessels by filariae. After invasion into lymph vessels, third stage larvae grow to maturity in the lymphatic system, mainly in and around the genitourinary system.

9. (E) There is no specific medicine to treat dengue infection. Antibiotics commonly block biochemical pathways important for bacteria. But virus do not use these pathways at all, and that is the reason why antibiotics do not work against viral infections.

10. (A) A child can catch hepatitis A by coming in contact with the blood or stool of a person who has the disease, eating food or drinking water that has been contaminated by blood or stools containing the HIV. Fruits, vegetables, shellfish, ice, and water are common sources of the disease.

Comprehension Type Questions

Passage 1:

1. (A) The most common method of spread of respiratory disease is through air.
2. (A) Chance of respiratory infection decreases when distance is more.

Passage 2:

3. (D) Both b & c
4. (A) Digestion of food is the function of digestive system.
5. (C) Diseases that last for only very short periods of time are termed as acute diseases.

Passage 3:

6. (D) All of the above.
7. Statement 1–Microbes are classified into: viruses, bacteria, fungus or protozoa is correct.
8. Malarial parasite is a protozoan disease.

Free Response Type

Very Short Answer Type Questions

1. Malaria is the most important single-celled parasite that infects humans.
2. Malaria and Kala-azar.
3. Communicable diseases are the diseases which transmits from one individual to another individual. A non-communicable disease is a disease that is not transmitted from person to person.
4. Most Deadly Bacterial Infections:
   (a) Tuberculosis.
   (b) Anthrax.
   (c) Tetanus.
   (d) Leptospirosis.
5. Most people who get HIV get it through anal or vaginal sex, or sharing needles, syringes, or other drug injection equipment (for example, cookers). But there are powerful tools that can help prevent HIV transmission.
6. Deficiency disease is a disease caused by the lack of an element in the diet.
7. Causal organisms/pathogens of disease are the real cause of the occurrence of the disease. These causative agents may be viruses, bacteria, fungi, or parasites.
8. Cholera vaccine is used for active immunization against cholera.
9. Signs and symptoms of malaria may include:
   (a) Fever.
   (b) Chills.
10. Refer on Page number 4.6.

Short Answer Type Questions

1. Personal health refers to the mental, physical and social well-being of an individual, while community health is about enhancing and maintaining the health of the entire community (population).
2. Communicable diseases are diseases that are transmitted from person to person in a variety of ways, including: inhaling airborne viruses; or by insect bites.

   Examples of communicable diseases include HIV, A, B, hepatitis C, measles, and salmonella.
3. When we suffer from a mild form of disease, our immune system forms antibodies against the invading antigens. At the second infection of that disease, the immune system responds faster to destroy the antigens as there are antibodies that already recognize them. As a result, we don't suffer from the severe form of the disease.
4. Any four factors necessary for a healthy person:
   (i) The surrounding environment should be clean.
   (ii) Personal hygiene prevents infectious diseases.
   (iii) Our body's good immune system requires proper and adequate diet and nutrition.
   (iv) Immunization against severe diseases.
5. **Vector:** Vectors are those infectious agents which carry infections from a sick person to a healthy person.

   Disease: Harmful deviation from the normal structural or functional state of an organism, generally associated with specific signs and symptoms, distinct from physical injury.

6. Symptoms are subjective and can be perceived only by the person affected, while signs are objective findings that can be seen or measured. Both signs and symptoms of an underlying health condition are important in making a diagnosis.

7. (a) AIDS: Non- infectious disease.
   (b) Tuberculosis: Non- infectious disease.
   (c) Cholera: Infectious disease.
   (d) High blood pressure: Non- infectious disease.
   (e) Heart disease: Non- infectious disease.
   (f) Pneumonia: Infectious disease.
   (g) Cancer: non- Infectious disease.

8. The immune system plays an important role. It protects the body from disease-causing pollutants, bacteria, and cellular changes. It is made up of various organs, cells and proteins. As long as your immune system is functioning smoothly, you won't be aware of its presence.

9. Refer on Page number 4.14.

10. (a) Acute disease: appendicitis, acute leukemia.
    (b) Chronic disease: cancer, heart disease.
    (c) Infectious disease: flu, measles.
    (d) Non- infectious disease: cancer, chronic respiratory disease.

Long Answer Type Questions

1. Treatment of an infectious disease depends on the cause. Bacterial diseases: Most bacterial infections are treated with antibiotics. These medications kill bacterial or stop them from reproducing. Antibiotics can be given orally (tablets, capsules, or liquid) or by injection, intravenous (IV) line, cream, or drops.

2. Flu is a contagious respiratory disease caused by influenza viruses that infect the nose, throat and sometimes lungs. It can cause mild to severe illness and sometimes death. The best way to prevent the flu is to get the flu vaccine every year.

   Common symptoms of the flu include:
   (a) Fever
   (b) Aching muscles
   (c) Chills and sweats
   (d) Headache
   (e) Dry, persistent cough
   (f) Shortness of breath
   (g) Tiredness and weakness
   (h) Runny or stuffy nose

   Prevention:
   (a) Avoid close contact. Avoid close contact with sick people.
   (b) Stay home when you are sick.
   (c) Cover your mouth and nose.
   (d) Clean your hands.
   (e) Avoid touching your eyes, nose and mouth.

3. **Causes of AIDS:**

   HIV is caused by a virus. It can be spread from a mother to child through sexual contact, use of illegal drugs or sharing needles, contact with infected blood, or during pregnancy, childbirth, or breastfeeding.

   Symptoms of AIDS:
   (a) Fever.
   (b) Chills.
   (c) Fatigue.
   (d) Sore throat.
   (e) Muscle aches.
   (f) Night sweats.
   (g) Rash.
   (h) Swollen lymph nodes.
   (i) Mouth sores.

   Preventive measures of AIDS:
   (a) Get tested for HIV.
   (b) Choose less risky sexual behaviors.
   (c) Use condoms every time you have sex.
   (d) Limit your number of sexual partners.
   (e) Get tested and treated for STDs.

   Treatment of AIDS: HIV treatment (antiretroviral therapy or ART) involves taking medicine as prescribed by a health care provider. HIV treatment reduces the amount of HIV in your body and helps you stay healthy. There is no cure for HIV, but you can control it with HIV treatment.

4. Refer on Page number 4.3.

5. Refer on Page number 4.12.

Case Based Questions

Case 1:

1. The disease caused due to bite of a stray dog is rabies.
2. Yes, anti-rabies vaccine is available.
3. Local authorities have planned immunization of the stray dogs against the disease.

Case 2:

1. Three conditions essential for good health are:
    - Better sanitation
    - Availability of clean drinking water
    - Availability of adequate, nutritious food.
2. We can keep our surroundings clean by:
    - Providing good sewage and rainwater disposal systems
    - Proper garbage disposal.
3. Disease can be defined as physical or functional change from the normal state that causes discomfort, of disability, or impairs the health of a living organism.

Case 3:

1. Malaria is caused by the toxins produced in human body by a malarial parasite, plasmodium; a female Anopheles mosquito.
2. Immediate spray of insecticides to kill adult mosquitoes as well as their larvae.
3. Quinine; Bark of Cinchona tree.

Case 4:

1. **AIDS:** Acquired immunodeficiency syndrome.
2. The disease gets transmitted by four ways:
    (a) Sex with multiple partners.
    (b) Transfusion of HIV contaminated blood.
    (c) Use of HIV contaminated syringe.
    (d) From infected mother to her child at the time of delivery of the baby.
3. The values shown by the colleague of the employee are awareness, helpfulness, empathy, and knowledge about their rights.

Level 2

Multiple Choice Questions

1. **(D)** All of the above.
2. **(D)** Malaria is not spread from person to person like a cold or the flu, and it cannot be sexually transmitted. You cannot get malaria from casual contact with malaria-infected people, such as sitting next to someone who has malaria.
3. **(D)** There are two types of specific defense. These include cell-mediated immunity and antibody-mediated immunity. Cell-mediated immunity occurs when T-lymphocytes (T-cells) become activated by exposure to pathogens. Activated T-cells then attack pathogens directly.
4. **(D)** Both (B) & (C)
5. **(D)** The lymphatic tissues are a part of the body's immune system. Their cellular component contains leucocytes and major immune cells like B-lymphocytes. These cells are specialized cells that destroy pathogens by engulfing them and destroying their cellular structure.
6. **(B)** A non- infectious unnatural and unusual reaction to a substance or condition is allergy.
7. **(C)** HIV (Human immunodeficiency virus) is a virus that attacks the body's immune system. If HIV is not treated, it can lead to AIDS (acquired immunodeficiency syndrome). There is currently no effective cure. Once people get HIV, they have it for life.
8. **(C)** Common cold falls under the category of acute disease as it does not last for a longer period of time.
9. **(D)** December 1st
10. **(C)** Evolutionarily, several microorganisms have developed antimicrobial defense mechanisms. Antibiotics, which have been extensively obtained from molds such as penicillin, are one of many examples. Bacteriocins are antibacterial peptides or proteins produced by lactic acid bacteria (LAB).
11. **(A)** The diseases which are degenerative are non- communicable.
12. **(D)** All of the above.
13. **(C)** Diseases occurring due to infected articles of a patient are called Fomite borne.
14. **(B)** 7th April
15. **(D)** Immune system
16. **(B)** The Pulse Polio Initiative was started with an objective of achieving hundred per cent coverage under Oral Polio Vaccine. It aimed to immunize children through improved social mobilization, plan mop-up operations in areas where poliovirus has almost disappeared and maintain high level of morale among the public.

17. **(D)** All of the above are correct.

18. **(B)** Geneva, Switzerland.

19. **(B)** Droplet infection is considered as a mode of indirect transmission.

20. **(C)** Typhoid

Higher Order Thinking Skills (HOTS)

1. (a) Viral particles (as of SARS) coming out of host cells.
   (b) A — Host cell.
   B — Virus.

2. (a) Strolling is no exercise as a person moves slowly. It is a way of relaxation where stress and strain can be relieved.
   (b) No. Dengue is caused by bite of Aedes mosquito which is active during day time only.
   (c) Yes, ORS prevents dehydration. Diarrhoea is generally cured automatically after 1-2 days because it is mostly viral infection.

3. (a) Malaria
   (b) AIDS
   (c) Polio
   (d) Diarrhoea.

4. A person is most likely to fall sick when she is on a four-day fast after recovering from malaria and is taking care of someone suffering from chickenpox. There are following reasons for this:
   (a) When a person gets a disease like malaria he has loss of appetite, vomiting and high fever. This leads to loss of body fluids and makes body very weak. Under such circumstances, if she is on a four day fast, then her defense system will get totally weak and she can even collapse.
   (b) With the weak immune system, if she is taking care of someone suffering from chickenpox, then it is more likely that she may also get the disease.

5. A doctor/nurse/health-worker take the following precautions to avoid getting sick herself. He/She:
   (i) always wear masks while diagnosing mouth or chest infections.
   (ii) always wear hand gloves even while doing minor surgeries.
   (iii) always clean hands as well as instruments after diagnosis of the patient.
   (iv) makes sure that they are immunized against all contagious diseases.
   (v) takes balanced diet (especially rich in proteins) to build their powerful immune system.
   (vi) dispose of any sputum, blood sample, urine or stool, properly

6. (a) The following symptoms will help us to find out that the baby is sick :
   (i) Repeated crying and not responding to any stimuli.
   (ii) High body temperature.
   (iii) Loose motions.
   (iv) Drooping of eyes.
   (v) Redness of eyes.
   (b) The following signs will help us to find out what is the sickness:
   (i) Yellowing of eyes, pale skin and passing of yellow urine indicate that baby is suffering from jaundice.
   (ii) Redness in the eye and persistent rubbing of eyes indicate about eye-flu.
   (iii) Gripping pain in the stomach, loose skin and repeated loose motions indicates about diarrhoea.
   (iv) High fever, headache, nausea, muscular pains and feeling very cold and shivering indicates about malaria.
   (v) If only fever is there with no other visible symptoms then laboratory tests are to be done which will reveal about the signs of any disease.

7. It is because none of the symptoms specify what the disease really is. For example, a headache may just be due to an examination stress or due to meningitis or one of a dozen different diseases. Similarly, fever may be due to different reasons.

8. Kids are more vulnerable to cold and flu because their immune systems haven't fully developed. Elderly people are also more prone to catch a cold because of their poor health.

9. The indoor climate due to air-conditioning is drier due to which the cold virus can stay longer in air infecting more people.

10. The disease is called AIDS (acquired immuno-deficiency syndrome) and the microbe which is responsible for the disease is a virus called HIV (Human immunodeficiency virus). The ways to control the disease are creating awareness among people regarding the modes of spread of the disease, use of disposable syringes in hospitals and clinics, avoiding sexual contact with multiple partners.

11. The symptoms of Rohit show that he was suffering from Jaundice. The microbe which

causes the disease is virus. The values shown by Ram are awareness, scientific temper, concern for others and helpful nature.

12. The dead or the inactivated germs in the vaccines stimulate our immune system to develop antibodies against the disease-causing microbes present in the vaccine and store the antibodies for action during any subsequent infection. In this way, the vaccines provide immunity to the person against the disease. The values shown by Dr Seema are concern for others, helpfulness and patience.

13. (i) The disease is most likely Tuberculosis caused by bacteria.
(ii) The disease gets transmitted when a healthy person inhales the droplets released into air by an infected person while coughing or sneezing.
(iii) Megha shows a helpful nature, scientific attitude, concern for others and sympathetic nature.

14. (i) The disease is Malaria caused by Plasmodium and transmitted by the vector female Anopheles mosquito.
(ii) The drops of oil or petrol in the stagnant water pools kill the larvae of the mosquito as they will not be able to breathe.
(iii) The values shown by the children are public good, helpful attitude, scientific temper and work for social good.

15. (a) Three steps taken by government are:
- Each cigarette pack has a label 'smoking is injurious to health',
- Creation of 'no smoking zones' in the cities.
- Putting up hoardings at public places and advertisement clippings in cinema halls about harmful effects of use of tobacco.

(b) Passive smoking means inhalation of tobacco smoke released by smokers, by non-smokers.
(c) Cancer (oral cancer/lung cancer).

Archive Corner

1. (C) P : a, 1, 5 Q : b, 3, 4 R : b, 1, 3 S : c, 1, 5
2. (C) Acute diseases persist for a short period of t time which generally have a relatively severe course. Acquired diseases develop after birth. AIDS and German measles can be transferred to baby from infected mothers.
3. (A) Tuberculosis is a chronic bacterial disease and is not sexually transmitted. AIDS is a chronic viral disease that is sexually transmitted.
4. (C) p-Virus, q-Cholera, r-Virus, s-Mosquito, t-Protozoan
5. (B) According to Venn diagram X could be Anthrax as it is caused by bacteria and it is communicable disease whereas Y could be Dengue as, it is a communicable disease caused by virus.
6. (C) Tuberculosis causing organism enters via air from an infected person.
7. (A) According to the given graph, X refers to a bacterial infection where Y refers to a viral infection.
8. (D) Osteomalacia is a bone disease that occurs due to deficiency of vitamin D in adults.
9. (A)

Disease	Causative organism
Mumps	*Rubela virus*
Elephantiasis	*Wuchereria bancrofti*
Anthrax	*Bacillus anthracis*
Ringworm	*Epidermophyton*

10. (D) According to the given Venn diagram P is a communicable disease caused by a protozoa, e.g., sleeping sickness, malaria, kala-azar, etc., and Q is a communicable disease caused by a virus, e.g., dengue. Sleeping sickness is caused by bite of tse-tse fly. Cholera is caused by vibrio cholerae. Cancer is characterised by uncontrolled cell divisions. Malaria could be treated by drug obtained from bark of cinchona-tree.
11. (A) Acute diseases occur very rapidly but last for only a short period of time. (i.e., few days).

12. **(D)** According to the given table, P could be typhoid as itis a communicable disease that spreads through contaminated food and water. Q could be chickenpox as it is a communicable disease that spreads through direct contact. R could be Goitre as it is non-communicable disease.

13. **(C)** P-*Helicobacter pylori*, Q-Acute, R-Grave's disease, S-Myxoedema, T-*Aedes* mosquito, U-Tsetse fly

14. **(D)** The given box contains three protozoan diseases and three bacterial diseases where all the protozoan diseases are vector borne. Out of the two hormonal disorders listed in the given box, cretinism is caused due to hyposecretion of thyroid hormone.

15. **(A)** Charulata developed active immunity whereas Ajeet's immunity is a passive immunity. Immunity of both Charulata and Ajeet will be long lasting. Immunity developed against chickenpox virus does not provide immunity to diseases like measles and polio. Ajeet's immunity does not cause any side effect in his body.

16. **(D)** The basic objectives of pulse polio immunization programme are to immunise those children who are not earlier immunized or are partially immunized, to boost the immunity of children who are already immunized and to eradicate the polio causing virus from the world.

17. **(C)** Photosynthesis is the first step of carbon cycle when atmospheric carbon gets incorporated in plant tissue with the help of chlorophyll and sunlight. Burning of fossil fuel returns carbon dioxide to the atmosphere. Ocean acts as a global sink for CO_2 as they absorb atmospheric CO_2.

18. **(B)** In the given paragraph X refers to active transport. Active transport is a rapid and uphill transport that takes place against the concentration gradient.

19. **(B)** (a) - (i) Amoebiasis, (ii) Pyorrhoea
(b) - (i) Rhizobium
(c) - (i) Thiobacillus, (ii) Pseudomonas

20. **(D)** According to the given dichotomous key, P, Q, R, S and T could be Down's syndrome or cleft palate, measles or rhinitis, sleeping sickness or elephantiasis, night blindness or scurvy, and goiter or cretinism respectively. Kala-azar is not spread by direct contact. It is a vector-transmitted disease. Similarly, haemophilia is caused due to chromosomal mutation and cretinism is caused by the hyposecretion of thyroid hormone.

21. **(D)** From the given Venn diagram, it can be inferred that P could be chikungunya or dengue transmitted by *Aedes aegypti* mosquito, whereas Q could be malaria (caused by *Plasmodium*) or dum-dum fever (caused by *Leishmania*) or sleeping sickness (caused by *Trypanosoma*).

22. **(A)** X and Y depicted in the given graph could be bacterial and viral infections respectively. Bacterial infection decreased rapidly on administration of antibiotics but had no effect on viral infection. The person's body recovered from the viral infection due to body's own immunity.

23. **(B)** The given box contains four protozoan diseases and two bacterial diseases where all protozoan diseases are vector borne.

24. **(A)** A person who has recovered from an attack of mumps, develops natural active immunity because of the exposure to antigen (disease causing pathogen) which triggers the immune system to produce antibodies.

CHAPTER 5: NATURAL RESOURCES

CHECK POINT 1

1. The atmosphere on Venus and Mars mainly consists of carbon dioxide.
2. It maintains consistency in temperature throughout the day making it a comfortable place to stay.
3. Refer to the topic-Wind.
4. Refer to the topic-Role of the atmosphere in climate control.

CHECK POINT 2

5. Carbon monoxide and nitrogen oxide.
6. Ultraviolet radiation causes **erythema, sunburn, and photodamage (photoaging)**.
7. Refer to the topic-Effect of acid rain.
8. (a) It causes respiratory problems.

   (b) It damages plants and trees.

CHECK POINT 3

9. (i) All cellular processes occur due to water.

   (ii) Transportation of substances in our body takes place by dissolving in water.
10. Groundwater and surface waters are the major sources of fresh water in India.
11. Refer to the topic-Underground water.

CHECK POINT 4

12. Refer to the topic-Structure and formation of soil.
13. Soil erosion is a gradual process that occurs when the impact of water or wind detaches and removes soil particles, causing the soil to deteriorate.
14. (a) Maintaining a healthy, perennial plant cover.
    (b) Mulching.
    (c) Planting a cover crop such as winter rye in vegetable gardens.

CHECK POINT 5

15. DNA (deoxy ribonucleic acid) and RNA (ribonucleic acid).
16. The two forms of oxygen present in the atmosphere are: ozone (O_3) and molecular oxygen (O_2).
17. (a) Refer to the topic-Carbon cycle.

    (b) Refer to the topic-Oxygen cycle.

    (c) Refer to the topic-Nitrogen cycle.

LEVEL 1

Fixed Response Type

Multiple Choice Questions

1. **(D)** Wood is considered as a renewable source of energy because if trees are cut to obtain wood, then more trees will grow in due course of time.
2. **(A)** The maximum air in which we breath is present at troposphere.
3. **(C)** When acid rain and dry acidic particles fall to earth, the nitric and sulfuric acid that make the particles acidic can land on statues, buildings, and other manmade structures, and damage their surfaces.

4. (A) Parent rock from which soil is formed.

5. (B) Most ozone (about 90%) is found in the stratosphere.

6. (A) 75%

7. (A) Biotic resources are the living thing of the biosphere. Plants and animals have life. Therefore, plants and animals are biotic resources.

8. (A) Forests and coal are exhaustible natural resources.

9. (D) It is **11-16 km** above equator.

10. (C) Biosphere is made up of living things.

11. (B) Metals are renewable resources.

12. (A) Photosynthesis balances carbon dioxide and oxygen in the atmosphere.

13. (B) The main cause of ozone layer depletion is **chlorofluorocarbons (CFCs).**

14. (D) Acid rain mainly contains nitric acid and sulphuric acid.

15. (D) It is emitted whenever coal, oil, natural gas, and other carbon-rich fossil fuels are burned. This leads to an increasing concentration of carbon dioxide in our atmosphere, which in turn causes the average temperature on earth to raise leading to global warming.

16. (B) Sulphur dioxide.

17. (B) Pollutant released by the jet planes is aerosol.

18. (D) Air

19. (A) 3% of total water.

20. (D) All of the above are consequences of water pollution.

21. (A) Sources that increase the biological oxygen demand of water are both natural and man-made. Pollution is a major contributor to increasing the bod of water.

22. (A) Mineral matter makes the maximum part of soil.

23. (C) Ozone and oxygen.

24. (D) All of the above are the causes of soil erosion.

25. (C) The **Bhopal gas tragedy** occurred on 3rd December, 1984 when methyl isocyanate reacted with water in a cooling tank. This resulted in an exothermic reaction leading to an increase in pressure which caused the safety valve to burst, and the gas leaked out.

26. (B) Soil erosion can be prevented by afforestation.

27. (B) Soil is a part of lithosphere.

28. (D) Calcium.

29. (C) Nitrosomonas convert ammonia to nitrites, which are then converted to nitrates by nitro bacteria. These bacteria play an important part in the nitrogen cycle.

30. (B) **Azospirillum** bacteria are present in the roots of c4 plants, for example, babool.

Assertion and Reason Type Questions

1. (C) Lichens cannot grow in polluted areas.

2. (A) The atmosphere of **Venus** is composed of **96.5%** carbon dioxide, **3.5%** nitrogen, and traces of other gases, most notably sulfur dioxide.

3. (D) **Carbon dioxide and carbon monoxide (CO)** gases are emitted during the combustion of various fuels. Carbon monoxide is poisonous, whereas carbon-dioxide is non-toxic in nature. Carbon monoxide is an odorless gas that causes thousands of deaths each year in north America. Breathing in carbon monoxide is very dangerous.

4. (B) Both assertion and reason are true, but the reason is not the correct explanation of assertion.

5. (A) People need plants to live. When green plants make food, they give off oxygen. This is a gas that all animals must breathe in order to stay alive. Without plants, animals would have no oxygen to breathe and would die.

6. (B) Water is a good solvent but this is not the reason for the transportation of substances from one part of the body to another.

7. (A) The plant releases the oxygen into the air, and stores energy within the glucose molecules by the process of photosynthesis.

8. (A) Soil erosion is the washing away of soil by wind or water. The roots of a plant hold the soil firmly. Because of this, soil cannot easily be washed or blown away. So, plants prevent soil erosion.

9. (A) Heavy treatment of soil with pesticides can cause populations of beneficial soil microorganisms to decline. If we lose both bacteria and fungi, then the soil degrades.

10. (A) Manure is recognized as an excellent source of the plant nutrients **nitrogen (N), phosphorus (P) and potassium (K)**. In addition, manure returns organic matter and other nutrients such as calcium, magnesium and sulphur to the soil, building soil fertility and quality.

Comprehension Type Questions

Passage 1:

1. (D) All the statements are correct.
2. (B) The molecule containing three atoms of oxygen is Ozone.
3. (C) Molecular formulae of Ozone is O_3.
4. Ozone performs an essential function where it is found. It absorbs harmful radiations from the sun. It also prevents those harmful radiations from reaching the surface of the earth where they may damage many forms of life.

Passage 2:

5. (B) 21% Oxygen is present in the Atmosphere.
6. (D) All the above statements are correct.
7. (D) All the above are correct.
8. (B) Photosynthesis helps to maintain Oxygen in the atmosphere.
9. (B) O_3 .

Passage 3:

10. (D) All the statements are correct.
11. (A) The unburnt carbon particles or substances which suspended in air are termed as Smog.
12. (B) An increase in the content of harmful substances in air is called as Air pollution
13. (B) The unburnt carbon particles or substances which suspended in air called hydrocarbons.

Free Response Type

Very Short Answer Type Questions

1. (a) Overconsumption of natural resources.
   (b) Industrial and technological development.
2. Sulfur dioxide, carbon monoxide.
3. Fog or haze intensified by smoke or other atmospheric pollutants.
4. In the process of respiration, oxygen is absorbed and carbon dioxide is released.
5. Refer to the topic-aerosol.
6. Refer on page number 5.14.
7. Sleet and snow.
8. *Rhizobium*, *Azospirillum*, *Cyanobacteria* etc.
9. The full form of CFC is "**chlorofluorocarbon**."
10. Refer to the topic-Greenhouse effect.

Short Answer Type Questions

1. Refer to the topic-Soil.
2. The greenhouse effect is a natural process that warms the Earth's surface by trapping heat from the sun.
3. Patterns of rainfall are decided primarily by wind patterns depending on the circulation of winds, the pressure of an area changes. Warm, humid winds result in low pressure that leads to heavy rainfall and thunderstorms.

   Vegetation: Greater vegetation implies a higher release of water vapour.
4. Clouds form when water vapor in the air condenses into water droplets or ice crystals.
5. Refer to the topic-ozone depletion.
6. (a) Rainfall and flooding: Higher intensity of rainstorms is the main cause of soil erosion.
   (b) Agriculture: The farming practices are the major cause of soil erosion.
   (c) Grazing
   (d) Logging and mining
   (e) Construction
7. These six pollutants are carbon monoxide, lead, nitrogen oxides, ground-level ozone, particle pollution (often referred to as particulate matter), and sulfur oxides.
8. Refer to the topic-Global warming.
9. Refer to the topic-depletion of ozone.

10. Dust is harmful because suspended particles make up dust. Dust inhalation can lead to a variety of unpleasant symptoms, such as allergic bronchitis, colds, and coughs. It lessens the light intensity. Dust particles can obstruct stomata and reduce gas exchange in plants when they settle over leaves.

Long Answer Type Questions

1. Carbon dioxide is a necessary element of photosynthesis in plants. It is used in optimum amount by plants to make their food. But a high concentration of carbon dioxide can damage the plant. High concentration of carbon dioxide is not only harmful to plants but also to environment. This is why, we consider it as a pollutant at the same time.
2. Refer to the topic-different zones of atmosphere or air.
3. Water pollution: Water pollution is the contamination of water sources by substances which make the water unusable for drinking, cooking, cleaning, swimming, and other activities.

   Causes of water pollution:
   (a) Global warming
   (b) Deforestation
   (c) Industry, agriculture and livestock farming
   (d) Rubbish and faecal water dumping

   Control of water pollution:
   (a) Dispose of toxic chemicals properly.
   (b) Shop with water pollution in mind.
   (c) Do not pour fat and grease down the drain.
   (d) Use phosphate-free detergent and dish cleaner.
4. Refer on page number 5.8.
5. Refer to the topic-Nitrogen cycle and carbon cycle.

Case Based Questions

Case 1:

1. (A) The ozone layer is in the stratosphere of the atmosphere
2. (A) Chlorofluorocarbon (CFC) is responsible for ozone layer depletion.
3. (A) Skin cancer is the main risk associated with exposure to extreme ultraviolet radiation in the atmosphere due to ozone depletion.
4. (C) The first ozone hole he discovered in 1970 in the Antarctic stratosphere.

Case 2:

1. It is a dark fog formed by condensation of water vapour, dust and smoke particles, and various gaseous. Pollutants such as oxides of nitrogen, sulphur dioxide, hydrogen sulphide etc. In the troposphere; it is a secondary pollutant.
2. • Smog reduces visibility leading to accidents.
   • It produces respiratory problems, particularly in young ones and old people.

Case 3:

1. Faecal matter of rhinoceros provides extra nutrients in the water body. As a result, there occurs excessive growth of algae (commonly called algal bloom). This process is called as eutrophication.
2. The algae die and aerobic decomposers in the benthic region become active. They rapidly consume dissolved oxygen of the water to decompose these dead algae. In the absence of dissolved oxygen, all aquatic life (including fishes) will die. In this way, eutrophication deprives us of one of our sources of food.
3. Government must take immediate steps to clean these water bodies by removing algae as well as sediment.

Level 2

Multiple Choice Questions

1. (D) Because disposable paper cups recycle easily and does not harm the environment in any way in comparison to disposable plastic cups.
2. (D) Carrying capacity can be defined as a species' average population size in a particular habitat. The species population size is limited by environmental factors like adequate food, shelter, water, and mates. If these needs are not met, the population will decrease until the resource rebounds.
3. (D) Trees
4. (A) During the oxidation of ammonium by ammonia-oxidizing bacteria, nitrite is formed as an end product that is further oxidized to nitrate by nitrite-oxidizing bacteria.

5. (B) Grass, cow, humans.

6. (A) Aluminum foil cannot be degraded by the action of micro-organisms and hence is non-biodegradable.

7. (C) Forests and the by-products of wood and paper mills represent a wealth of renewable resources that can be used to generate everyday materials.

8. (A) SO_3 is the secondary air pollutant according to origin.

9. (C) 45

10. (A) Troposphere

11. (A) Vegetables

12. (C) Reduce, reuse, recycle

13. (B) Polythene, glass, PVC

14. (C) Acid rain

15. (D) Noosphere is the part of bioshere domineted by human thoughts, culture and activities.

16. (D) Chloroflurocarbons, CO_2, CH_4, NO_2

17. (C) Acid rain is the secondary effect of air pollution. The gases like sulphur dioxide and nitrogen oxide when in very high concentration in the air, mix with the air moisture in the clouds and form sulphuric and nitric acids as a result.

18. (C) Animal waste can be easily degraded so it does not fall under the category of non-biodegradable pollutants.

19. (D) Biosphere.

20. (D) The sedimentary cycles like the phosphorus cycle, however, have their nutrient reserves in the soil, rocks, and minerals; elements are released from the rock and deposited in the sea. The phosphorus cycle does not have a gaseous phase.

Higher Order Thinking Skills (HOTS)

1. (a) Organic molecules ($C_6H_{12}O_6$)
   (b) Photosynthesis
   (c) Respiration

   (b) Identification: Oxygen cycle.

2. (a) Ammonification
   (b) Ammonia
   (c) Nitrites
   (d) Nitrates
   (e) Nitrification
   (f) Denitrification

   (b) Lack of step a: No protein degradation to release ammonia.

   (c) Absence of step f: No atmospheric nitrogen replenishment.

3. Air forms a protective blanket around the Earth due to its low thermal conductivity. Prevents sudden temperature rise during the day. At night, the release of heat into space slows down.

4. Lichen is a bio-indicator and sensitive to S02 pollution from automobiles. Delhi has maximum pollution auto mobile, hence has highly polluted environment. Due to the polluted environment, lichen do not survive in Delhi whereas they are present it the of Darjeeling.

5. The Mathura Refinery emits toxic gases (such as sulphur oxides) that cause acid rain. This causes discoloration and corrosion of Taj Mahal marble.

6. Infrared rays contained in sunlight pass through the glass and heat the interior of the car. The radiation emitted by the car's upholstery and other interior components cannot escape through the glass, so the heat trapped inside increases the temperature inside the car. This is because the glass is transparent to the sun's infrared radiation, which has a shorter wavelength than the infrared radiation emitted from the interior of the car, and the longer wavelengths at which the glass is opaque.

7. If the sun heated the earth's surface equally there would be no pressure difference and thus no movement of air. This would ultimately result in an increased surface temperature.

8. A large amount of energy is always lost to the atmosphere when moving from one level to another. This lost energy cannot be replenished from the atmosphere. Therefore, energy flow is unidirectional. Biogeochemical, on the other hand, are not lost in biogeochemical cycles. They are just recycled.

Archive Corner

1. **(D)** According to the given paragraph, l, m and n are sandy soil, loamy soil and clayey soil, respectively. Sandy soil is commonly found in those regions where xerophytes are abundant. Loamy soil is best suited for growing garden plants. Clayey soil is best suited for making pots, statues and toys.
2. **(B)** Soil x represents sandy soil which is not fit for plant growth. Soil y represents clayey soil suitable for growth of crops like paddy whereas soil z represents loamy soil, and it is best suitable soil for plant growth.
3. **(C)** Glass object is a non-biodegradable soil pollutant.
4. **(A)** DDT is a non-biodegradable compound that does not get metabolised hence gets stored in the body tissues, therefore its concentration goes on increasing from one trophic level to another as it enters a food chain.
5. **(C)** Oxygen is not an example of greenhouse gas. Acid rain results when oxides of sulphur and nitrogen react with water in the atmosphere to form H_2SO_4 and HNO_3. These oxides are mainly produced by combustion of fossil fuels.
6. **(D)** Good ozone occurs naturally in the stratosphere. Examples of suspended particulate matter (spm) are dust, smoke, soot, etc. Carbon monoxide (CO) combines with haemoglobin and affects the oxygen carrying capacity of blood.
7. **(D)** According to the given paragraph l, m and n are sandy soil, loamy soil and clayey soil respectively. Sandy. Soil is commonly found in those areas where xerophytes are abundant. Loamy soil is best suited for growing garden plants. Clayey soil is best suited for making pots, statues and toys.
8. **(B)** Capillary water should be replaced with hygroscopic water.
9. **(D)** Xinthegivenparagraphreferstowaterlogging. It damages the crop as it reduces air in the spaces between soil particles that cuts off oxygen supply for roots hence, they are not able to breathe. It also increases the amount of salt in the soil that reduces soil fertility.
10. **(C)** Some water falling on ground, forms an extremely thin, tightly held film around the soil particles called hygroscopic water while some water moves down upto the water table and is called gravitational water.
11. **(A)** Soil x, y and z in the given paragraph could be sandy soil, loamy soil and clayey soil respectively. Clayey soil is not suitable for plant growth but is ideal for making pots. Sandy soil is best suited for growth of plants like casuarina, eucalyptus and watermelon.
12. **(B)** In the given outline of nitrogen cycle, the processes x and y are denitrification and ammonification, respectively.
13. **(D)** The use of disposable paper-cups is more beneficial over disposable plastic-cups, because its recycling process has no harmful impact on environment.
14. **(D)** Population size is controlled by carrying capacity of environment.
15. **(C)** Depletion of ozone layer is mainly due to chlorofluorocarbon.
16. **(A)** The function of nitrosomonas bacteria in nitrogen cycle is to oxidizes ammonium salts into nitrites.
17. **(B)** Grass, cow, human.
18. **(A)** Aluminium foil is not a biodegradable material.
19. **(C)** Forest is a renewable resource.
20. **(A)** According to origin, identify the secondary air pollutant SO_3.
21. **(C)** 45 decibels.
22. **(C)** Carbon dioxide mainly increases global warming.
23. **(A)** Vegetable is the example of the waste biodecomposition of living beings.
24. **(C)** The three R's, which can, help us to conserve natural resources for future generation are reduce, reuse, recycle.
25. **(B)** Polythene, glass, PVC contains only non-biodegradable items.
26. **(D)** SO_2 and NO_2 gases related with acid rain.
27. **(D)** The part of biosphere dominated by human beings is known as noosphere.

CHAPTER 6: IMPROVEMENT IN FOOD RESOURCES

Check Point 1

1. Refer to the keystone.
2. The father of white revolution is Dr.Verghese Kurien.
3. Any 2 examples of rabi crops are wheat and pulses.
4. Refer to the topic-Zaid crops.

Check Point 2

5. Refer to the topic-Biofertilizers.
6. Manure is obtained naturally by the decomposition of dead plants and animals, whereas fertilisers are chemical substances and are not typically natural. It is not very rich in nutrients. It is rich in nutrients like N, P, K, etc.
7. Refer to the topic-advantages of manure.
8. Carbon, Hydrogen and Oxygen are called the framework elements as they are most essential for plant life.

Check Point 3

9. Fertigation is the injection of fertilizers, used for soil amendments, water amendments and other water-soluble products into an irrigation system.
10. Refer to the topic-irrigation.
11. The supply of a controlled restricted flow of water to a number of points in a cultivated area is called 'Trickle Irrigation.'

Check Point 4

12. Refer to pg. no. 13 under the topic 'type of intercropping'.
13. Refer to the topic-Crop protection management.
14. Refer to the topic-Advantage of mixed cropping.
15. They increase the soil fertility. Those crops which require high fertility level, maybe grown after growing legumes. They also replenish the soil with nitrogen content.

Check Point 5

16. Karen Swiss and Holstein Friesian.
17. Refer to the topic-Poultry diseases.
18. 'Layers' are the hens raised specifically to lay eggs, whereas chicken that are raised for meat are called 'Broilers'. These chickens are typically white and are bred specifically for optimal health and size to produce a quality product for the consumer.
19. Refer to the topic-Characteristics of healthy cattle.

Check Point 6

20. Refer to the topic-Apiculture.
21. The products obtained from apiculture are – wax pollen, bee wax, honey, royal jelly, bee venom etc.
22. Refer to the topic-Pisciculture.
23. The rearing of honeybee to obtain honey and other commercially important products is known

as Apiculture. On the other hand, production of useful aquatic animals such as fishes, prawns, shrimps, lobsters, crabs and molluscs by proper utilisation of small and large bodies of water is known as Aquaculture.

Level 1

Fixed Response Type

Multiple Choice Questions

1. **(D)** Sunflower is an oilseed crop.
2. **(A)** Transplantation is done in paddy.
3. **(C)** Beet sugar is made using a process that involves thinly slicing sugar beets to extract the natural sugar juice. The juice is purified and heated to create a concentrated syrup, which is crystallized to form granulated sugar.
4. **(A)** **Wheat** is the principal cereal crop of India.
5. **(D)** **Cereal** is the most important source of food and fodder. After harvesting cereals from the crops, such as rice, wheat, sorghum, etc., the remaining stalk or hay is used as fodder for the cattle.
6. **(A)** **C, N and Ca** are the macronutrients among the following.
7. **(B)** Sunflower
8. **(B)** Interspecific hybridization is the crossing of two species from the same genus. This allows the exploitation of useful genes from wild, unimproved species for the benefit of the cultivated species.
9. **(A)** It enhances soil fertility as Green Revolution increased crop production because of the use of new varieties of seeds, the use of pesticides and new agricultural techniques.
10. **(C)** **Colchicine** is a type of drug used to make plants resistant of drought.
11. **(B)** Plants can be disease resistant by breeding with a plant that naturally have a resistance gene. Generally, wild varieties of plants have resistance gene for disease so breed important crop with their wild varieties to get disease-resistant plants.
12. **(C)** Phosphorus as a macronutrients is required by plants in large amounts.
13. **(B)** Nodules with N-fixing bacteria are present in wheat.
14. **(D)** Application of nitrogenous manure to a plant causes growth retardation due to toxicity of NH_3.
15. **(C)** Rotation of crops is essential for increasing quality of protein in crops.
16. **(C)** The unwanted plants are known as weeds.
17. **(D)** Growth of moulds take place where there is high moisture content and it destroys the crop gradually.
18. **(C)** Green manuring refers to adding decomposed organic matter to soil.
19. **(D)** Earthworms.
20. **(D)** Gram
21. **(B)** Concentrates is the term that is used for cattle feed that is less in fibre but rich in nutrient content.
22. **(D)** None of the above.
23. **(B)** Broilers.
24. **(C)** *Apis dorsata* produces maximum amount of honey.
25. **(B)** Macro-nutrients
26. **(B)** These all are indigenous breeds of buffalo.
27. **(A)** It refers to culturing fishes in fresh water.
28. **(D)** All of the above are correct.
29. **(B)** Dairy farming
30. **(B)** Compost manure is produced from both farm refuse and household refuse.

Comprehension Type Questions

Passage 1:

1. **(D)** Rearing of bee is done for Honey and Wax.
2. **(C)** Honeybee is kept in Beehive.
3. **(C)** *A. Florae*, and *A. dorsata*, both are useful honeybees.

Passage 2:

4. **(A)** Aseel is an Indian poultry breed.
5. **(A)** Poultry breeds which are produce eggs are termed as Layers.

6. (B) Poultry breeds which are produce for meat are termed as Broilers.

Passage 3:

7. (B) Kharif season period from June to October.
8. (A) Rabi season period from November to April.
9. (A) Plants manufacture their food in sunlight by the process called Photosynthesis.

Assertion and Reason Type Questions

1. (A) The amount and the time of rains changes every year. Sometimes, there may be excess of rain and sometimes there may be very less or no rain at all. So, we cannot depend on such uncertain rains as the crops may get damaged due to excess or less rain.
2. (B) All living organisms require food. Plants can synthesise food for themselves but animals including humans cannot. They get it from plants or animals that eat plants. Thus, humans and animals are directly or indirectly dependent on plants.
3. (C) Manure is the decomposed form of dead plants and animals, which is applied to the soil to increase production. It is a natural form of fertilizer and is cost-effective. The human and animal excreta are also used as manure. The livestock manure is rich in nitrogen, phosphorus, and potassium.
4. (A) Presentation of clean cattle for slaughter and good slaughter hygiene are fundamental prerequisites for reducing carcass contamination and ensuring food safety in retail products.
5. (C) The hazards associated with fungicides are minuscule because our exposure to these chemicals is very low, most of the fungicides do not accumulate in the environment, and most fungicides are not very toxic to humans.
6. (A) Earthworms make their way through the soil, by loosening the soil and allowing more air to get in. Earthworms improve the quality of the soil as it recycles the organic waste into humus. This makes the soil fertile and helps the crops to grow. That is why earthworms are regarded as farmer's friends.
7. (B) Intercropping can reduce insect pest infestation and crop damage by disrupting visual or olfactory host plant location, reducing host plant quality or increasing natural enemy activity. Pests can also be controlled by their natural pesticides and pathogens.
8. (A) Vaccinating animals help in stimulating an immune response without causing the disease itself. This creates early exposure to disease-causing organisms, where the animals' immune system is able to recall the infectious agent to which the animal is vaccinated.
9. (A) Modern chemical fertilizers include one or more of the three elements that are most important in plant nutrition: nitrogen, phosphorus, and potassium. The elements which are of secondary importance are sulphur, magnesium, and calcium.
10. (B) 2,4-D is a chemical used to destroy weeds and it is prepared in factories synthetically, but this is not the reason for it's being a chemical.

Free Response Type

Very Short Answer Type Questions

1. Refer to keystone on page 2.
2. Refer to keystone on page 2.
3. Kharif-June-Early days of November-Paddy, Maize, Jute, Sugarcane, Cotton, Millet.
   Rabi-November-March-Wheat, Tobacco.
4. Eutrophication is a process that occurs when a body of water becomes enriched with nutrients, leading to an increase in aquatic plant growth.
5. Two main components of cattle feed are roughage and concentrate.
6. Refer to the topic-Crop rotation confers following benefits.
7. Refer on page number 6.7.
8. The two viral diseases of chickens are fowl pox and fowl cholera.
9. Refer to the topic-Fertilizers.
10. Refer to Exemplification.

Short Answer Type Questions

1. Refer to the topic-Fertilizers.
2.

Aquaculture	Pisciculture
Done in both freshwater and saltwater.	It mostly involves farming in ponds or reservoirs or tanks. Rice fields can also be used as water sources for fish farming
It helps restore endangered species and habitats and prevents the escape of species not in that habitat.	Species raised on the farm include salmon, catfish, carp and tilapia. It also improves overfishing in fisheries.

3. Refer to the topic-Organic farming.
4. Diseases that affect cattle:
   (a) Bluetongue
   (b) Botulism

   Diseases that affect poultry:

   (a) avian influenza (highly pathogenic)
   (b) duck virus enteritis (duck plague)

   Diseases of fishes:

   (a) Columnaris
   (a) Dropsy
5. Refer on page number 6.26.
6. Refer on page number 6.20.
7. Abiotic factors: moisture (found in grains), humidity (in the air), and temperature are abiotic variables that are responsible for losses of grain during storage. Biotic factors: insects, rats, birds, mites, bacteria, and fungi are biotic forces that are responsible for the losses of grain during storage.
8. The method of cross-breeding is widely used to improve cattle breeds. Cross-breeding two good cattle varieties will lead to a new, improved variety.
9. (A) **Roughage:** This part of cattle feed contains mostly fibres that come from hay (straw of cereals or Bhusa), green fodder (cowpea, berseem etc.
   (B) **Concentrates:** These are mixtures of substances containing fewer fibres and relatively excessive amounts of protein, fat, carbohydrates, vitamins, minerals etc.
10. Compost is made up of all types of waste products. Vermicompost is made up of only organic waste products.

Long Answer Type Questions

1. Refer to Exemplifications.
2.

Manures	Fertilizers
A. Fertilizer is an organic matter made by decomposing vegetables and animal excrement.	A. Fertilizers are inorganic substances manufactured in factories.
B. They enrich the soil with humus by providing organic matter and nutrients	B. Ensures healthy growth and development of plants by supplying nutrients but lacking humus deficiency in the soil
C. The addition of manure to soil does not require any special guideline.	C. The addition of fertilizer to soil requires special guidelines like dose time and post addition precautions should be followed to avoid mineral toxicity.

3. Cover crops help prevent the spread of pests and diseases in the field. Crop rotation also prevents soil depletion, increases soil fertility and reduces soil erosion, but also increases soil fertility. Both methods reduce the need for fertilizer.
4. Refer on page number 6.5.
5. Refer on page number 6.15.

Case Based Questions

Case 1:

1. **(D)** Rearing of honeybees is done for getting all of the above, i.e. honey, wax and furfural etc.
2. **(C)** Honey bees are kept in beehives.
3. **(C)** Both of the above are the useful honeybees.

Case 2:

1. **(A)** Layers are the egg laying hens.
2. **(B)** broilers are the chicken used for meat purposes.
3. **(D)** **Leghorn** is the best exotic breed for the production of eggs.

Case 3:

1. **(A)** There exists a great variety of agro climatic conditions and different varieties are suitable for preparing different food items. A variety

of a crop plant generally gives good yield in a particularly set of agro climatic conditions. Therefore, different varieties with varying traits are produced keeping in view the agro climatic conditions and market demands.

2. **(B)** Plant Breeding

3. **(C)** These are: Introduction → Selection → Hybridization → Recombinant DNA Technology or Genetic Engineering.

4. **(D)** It is a technique in which the two plants having the desired characters are made to cross and develop seeds.

LEVEL 2

Multiple Choice Questions

1. **(A)** Wheat, rice and maize contribute maximum to global food grain production.
2. **(D)** All of the above diseases can be controlled by chemical control.
3. **(B)** To reduce the period of life span of plants.
4. **(D)** Mustard, as it comes in oilseed crops.
5. **(B)** **Sonalika** is a variety of wheat.
6. **(C)** High cost production
7. **(A)** Gram
8. **(A)** Radish, as the bulged-out roots of these plants are known as **tuberous** roots. Storing food in the roots help them to use it during scarcity of food and survive.
9. **(A)** It bears buds and nodes.
10. **(C)** Weed
11. **(D)** Baking soda, as it is basic in nature so, it will neutralise the acidity.
12. **(A)** **Penicillium**, as it obtains its nutrition from dead organisms.
13. **(B)** Milk, soyabean and eggs are related to body building group.
14. **(D)** Organic farming needs all of the above for producing quality food material.
15. **(D)** **Ethylene** is the growth hormone which helps in fruit ripening.
16. **(A)** Wings of house fly and wings of sparrow are the examples of Analogous Organs.
17. **(B)** Rice.
18. **(A)** Pea is not a weed.
19. **(A)** Mexican varieties.
20. **(C)** Pulses are rich in protein because they contain Rhizobium bacteria.

Higher Order Thinking Skills (HOTS)

1. Most agriculture in India is rain-fed and the success of crops in most areas is dependent on timely monsoons and sufficient rainfall. Poor monsoons can cause crop failure. Irrigation systems have been put into practice in India to irrigate agricultural lands to ensure a timely supply of water during the growing season of plants.
2. (B) → (C) → (A) → (D)
3. Insects have a negative impact on crop yield. Some insects cut off parts of plants to stunt their growth, while others suck cell sap, so bees cannot help with pollination. Some insects are even considered borers that damage whole crops.
4. Legumes have root nodules that harbour nitrogen-fixing bacteria such as Rhizobium. These bacteria convert atmospheric nitrogen to nitrates for plants to use. Therefore, legumes usually do not require nitrogen fertilizers.
5. (i) When we chemical fertlizers there will be sudden increase in the yield as nutrients are released abundantly. But with time crop yield decrease because excess usage of chemical fertilizers kills the useful micro-organisms present in the soil and also reduces the organic material present in the soil.

   (ii) Manure release the nutrients slowly as they are rich in organic matter. But manure enriches the soil by providing nutrients and necessary environment for the growth of useful micro-organisms.

   (iii) Different pattern in the graph is due to the release of nutrients into soil by two different methods. Graph shows that excessive usage of chemical fertilizers is detrimental and using manure is beneficial for long time. Yield remain high when quantity of the manure increases.

6. **Guar Crop** is mulched by tillage, so crops like kuar are grown by farmers before the crop seeds are sown. It becomes green manure and enriches the soil with nitrogen and phosphorus.

7.
- **Energy yielding** — wheat, rice, maize
- **Protein yielding** — gram, pigeon gram, lentil, soyabean
- **Oil yielding** — groundnut, castor, mustard, soyabean
- **Fodder crops** — berseem, oat, sudan grass

Archive Corner

1. (B) **Mycorrhiza** is a symbiotic association between a green plant and a fungus. Red Sindhi is an indigenous milch breed of cow.
2. (D) **Red sindhi and Sahiwal** are indigenous breeds of cattle whereas **Jersey and Brown Swiss** are exotic breeds of cattle.
3. (C) **Sahiwal** is the indigenous breed of cow. **Australorp** is the exotic breed of chicken (poultry). **A. dorsata** is the indigenous breed of honey bee.
4. (B) According to the given table X is a kharif and Y is a rabi crop.
   Rabi crops–Wheat, green gram, linseed
   Kharif crops–Cotton, groundnut, jute, rice, soybean.
5. (B) Substance that is applied in field X increases humus content of the soil whereas substance that is applied in field Y decreases humus content of the soil. Therefore, substance applied in field X will be manure and substance applied in field Y will be fertiliser. Absorption of manure by plant is slow as it is less soluble in water whereas absorption of fertiliser by plants is rapid as it is easily soluble in water.
6. (C) Bee wax obtained from beehive is secreted by wax glands of worker bees to make compartments in beehive. **Sahiwal and Murrah** are indigenous breeds used in cattle farming. Sahiwal is the indigenous breed of cow while Murrah is the indigenous breed of buffalo.
7. (B) Carbon, oxygen, nitrogen, sulphur and potassium are macronutrients whereas iron, manganese, copper, molybdenum, zinc, chlorine and nickel are micronutrients.
8. (A) Jersey is an exotic breed of cow, Aseel is an indigenous breed of poultry and A. mellifera is the exotic breed of honeybee.
9. (A) Three crops that contribute maximum to global food grain production are Wheat, Rice and Maize.
10. (D) All of the options are correct.
11. (B) To reduce the period of life span of plants.
12. (D) Mustard is not a cereal crop.
13. (B) **'Sonalika'** is a variety of Wheat.
14. (D) Epis meliphera of Italian honeybee is useful for honey production.
15. (B) Honeybee culture is known as **Apiculture**.
16. (A) Radish plant store food in their root.
17. (A) **Potato Tuber** is an underground stem because it bears Buds and nodes.
18. (C) Weeding is not a method to maintain the fertility of the soil.
19. (D) Reena has a burning sensation in her stomach due to acidity, she needs to eat baking soda.
20. (A) Penicillium fungi is a saprophyte.
21. (B) Milk, soyabean, eggs are related to body building foods.
22. (D) All of the options are correct.
23. (D) Ethylene Phytohormone helps in fruit ripening.
24. (A) The wings of house fly and the wings of a sparrow are an example of Analogous organs.
25. (B) Jaya and Ratna are varieties of Rice.
26. (B) Sargam in not an ancient water harvesting structure.
27. (A) High yielding varieties of wheat were initially developed by an Indian scientist by cross breeding the traditional varieties with Mexican Varieties.

HINTS AND EXPLANATIONS

Photo Credits

Chapter 1

Page 1.4—**Fig. 1.3**—Pearson Education Ltd; **Page 1.4**—**Fig. 1.4**—PDQ Digital Media Solutions Ltd / Pearson Education Ltd; **Page 1.5**—**Testing Room 1**—Blueringmedia / 123RF; **Page 1.6**—**Competition Corner**—PAN XUNBIN / 123RF; **Page 1.7**—**Fig. 1.5**—Alila Medical Media / Shutterstock; **Page 1.7**—**Fig. 1.6**—BigBearCamera / Shutterstock; **Page 1.8**—**Fig. 1.7**—Roberto Biasini / 123RF; **Page 1.9**—**Testing Room 2**—Achiichiii / Shutterstock; **Page 1.12**—**Fig. 1.9**—Gritsalak Karalak / 123RF; **Page 1.13**—**Fig. 1.10**—Oxford Designers & Illustrators Ltd / Pearson Education Ltd; **Page 1.14**—**Fig. 1.12**—Pearson Education Ltd; **Page 1.15**—**Testing Room 4**—Pri-Rew / Shutterstock; **Page 1.15**—**Fig. 1.13**—Fancy Tapis / Shutterstock; **Page 1.16**—**Fig. 1.14**—Fancy Tapis / Shutterstock; **Page 1.21**—**Fig. 1.16**—Designua / 123RF; **Page 1.21**—**Fig. 1.17**—Snapgalleria / 123RF; **Page 1.22**—**Fig. 1.18**—Tefi / Shutterstock; **Page 1.23**—**Fig. 1.19**—Tefi / Shutterstock; **Page 1.25**—**Fig. 1.23**—Designua / Shutterstock

Chapter 2

Page 2.5—**Fig. 2.4**—normaals / 123RF; **Page 2.6**—**Fig. 2.5**—designua / 123RF; **Page 2.7**—**Fig. 2.6**—VectorMine / Shutterstock; **Page 2.8**—**Testing Room 2**—Jubal Harshaw / Shutterstock; **Page 2.14**—**Fig. 2.12**—Ramazangm / Shutterstock; **Page 2.17**—**Fig. 2.15**—Timonina / Shutterstock; **Page 2.19**—**Fig. 2.18**—Choksawatdikorn / Shutterstock; **Page 2.21**—**Fig. 2.24**—Tefi / Shutterstock; **Page 2.27**—**NCERT Compendium Q6**—Tefi / Shutterstock; **Page 2.28**—**NCERT Compendium Q9**—Tefi / Shutterstock; **Page 2.37**—**Archive Corner Q3**—Tefi / Shutterstock

Chapter 3

Page 3.4—**Fig. 3.1**—Alila Medical Media / Shutterstock; **Page 3.5**—**Fig. 3.2(a)**—Vecton / Shutterstock; **Page 3.5**—**Fig. 3.2(b)**—Designua / Shutterstock; **Page 3.9**—**Fig. 3.7(a)**—Dariusz Leszczynski / Shutterstock; **Page 3.9**—**Fig. 3.7(b)**—Peter Etchells / Shutterstock; **Page 3.10**—**Fig. 3.9**—Morphart Creation / Shutterstock; **Page 3.13**—**Fig. 3.13(a)**—Designua / Shutterstock; **Page 3.13**—**Fig. 3.13(b)**—snapgalleria / 123RF; **Page 3.39**—**HOTs Q1**—Monkik / Shutterstock

Chapter 4

Page 4.3—**Fig. 4.1**—Viaceslav Chapkevich / 123RF; **Page 4.8**—**Fig. 4.3**—Designua / Shutterstock; **Page 4.9**—**Fig. 4.6**—Designua / Shutterstock

Chapter 5

Page 5.4—**Fig. 5.1**—Designua / Shutterstock; **Page 5.9**—**Fig. 5.3**—siberianart / 123RF; **Page 5.10**—**Fig. 5.4**—HL Studios / Pearson Education Ltd; **Page 5.11**—**Fig. 5.5**—Inna Bigun / Shutterstock; **Page 5.20**—**Fig. 5.7**—Artisticco / Shutterstock; **Page 5.20**—**Fig. 5.8**—Oxford Designers & Illustrators Ltd / Pearson Education Ltd; **Page 5.21**—**Fig. 5.9**—Oxford Designers & Illustrators Ltd / Pearson Education Ltd

Chapter 6

Page 6.11—**Fig. 6.5**—Aleksandra Duda / Shutterstock; **Page 6.11**—**Fig. 6.6**—Sirichai Chinprayoon/123RF; **Page 6.13**—**Fig. 6.7**—Pixeljoy / Shutterstock; **Page 6.25**—**Fig. 6.11**—angelshot / Shutterstock